THERMODYNAMICS

JOHN WILEY & SONS, INC.

New York · London · Sydney

THERMODYNAMICS

an introduction to the
physical theories of equilibrium thermostatics
and irreversible thermodynamics

HERBERT B. CALLEN

Professor of Physics
University of Pennsylvania

Library of Congress Catalog Card Number: 60–5597

Printed in the United States of America

ISBN 0 471 13035 4

To my wife
Sara
and to
Jill and Jed

Preface

In writing this book I have forsaken the conventional inductive development of thermodynamics in favor of a postulational approach, which I believe to be more direct and logically simple. I have not sought to formulate the most logically economical or minimum set of postulates, but rather I have chosen postulates that can be made plausible and intuitive. In order to motivate the postulates, an elementary qualitative statistical discussion is given in an appendix and some appeal is made to experimental observations, but the spirit of the development is that the postulates are best justified by a posteriori success of the theory rather than by a priori proof.

The postulational approach I have adopted was conceived by Professor Laszlo Tisza of the Massachusetts Institute of Technology, and the influence of his teaching is reflected throughout this work. Responsibility for the specific form of development and presentation is, of course, entirely mine.

Each of the classical subjects of physics was developed originally by direct induction from experimental observation. The inductive developments of mechanics and of electromagnetic theory subsequently led to postulatory reformulations that were more elegant, abstract, and concise. The Newtonian formulation of mechanics led to the Lagrangian and Hamiltonian formulations, and Coulomb's law and Ampère's rule yielded to Maxwell's equations.

The purposes of these shifts to abstract formulations have been several. First, the concise postulates exhibit more explicitly the internal consistency of the logical structure. Furthermore, after sufficient experience with the abstract postulates, it actually becomes possible to develop a deeper insight and intuition than on the basis of the elementary theory. And, finally, important extensions and generalizations of the theory frequently are suggested and made practical by the abstract formulations, just as the development of quantum mechanics was expedited by the Hamiltonian formulation of classical mechanics.

It is a striking fact that thermodynamics is the last of the major classical theories to undergo a postulatory reformulation. The reasons for this delay lie in the scientific tenor of the period during which thermodynamics underwent its major development. At the turn of the century the molecular theory of matter was highly suspect, and its ultimate truth was seriously doubted. It therefore was felt to be safest to keep the foundations of thermodynamics as close as possible to macroscopic experimental observations. The molecular theory has now blossomed into quantum theory, and we no longer view it with distrust. Statistical mechanics has been rid of the self-contradictions and artificialities that necessarily resulted from an attempt to fit atomic dynamics into a classical mold. The situation has, in fact, so far reversed that we now consider quantum mechanics and quantum statistical mechanics to be more trustworthy than our macroscopic sciences. And although it remains desirable to preserve thermodynamics as a self-contained macroscopic discipline, autonomous and distinct from statistical mechanics, it is nevertheless desirable to recast thermodynamics so that its basic postulates are those which are most directly related to its ultimate statistical mechanical foundation.

The postulatory formulation of thermodynamics features states, rather than processes, as fundamental constructs. Statements about Carnot cycles and about the impossibility of perpetual motion of various kinds do not appear in the postulates, but state functions, energy, and entropy become the fundamental concepts. An enormous simplification in the mathematics is obtained, for processes then enter simply as differentials of the state functions. The conventional method proceeds inversely from processes to state functions by the relatively difficult procedure of integration of partial differential equations.

The mathematical equipment required in this book is the standard elementary calculus, plus a few special topics (such as Legendre transformations and the simplest aspects of the theory of quadratic forms), which are treated either in the text or in the appendices. Senior students in the Departments of Physics, Chemistry, and Engineering at the University of Pennsylvania have taken the course successfully without experiencing any special mathematical or conceptual difficulty.

I have written this textbook as an introduction to thermodynamics for advanced undergraduate or first-year graduate students. I believe that the first ten chapters on the principles of thermodynamics could also be used to advantage in an elementary course at the junior level. In that case, the eighth chapter and the last two sections of the ninth chapter on stability considerations should be omitted, and one of the several excellent books on thermodynamic applications should be used jointly.

The graduate curriculum is continually under pressure for the inclusion of new modern topics, and classical topics such as thermodynamics eventually will have to be treated fully in undergraduate courses. Such a course must provide the student with a thorough mastery both of the fundamentals and of significant contemporary research developments. These goals are attempted in this book by strict concentration upon theoretical principles, to the exclusion of descriptions of apparatus and of experimental detail.

Finally, as statistical mechanics, the kinetic theory of gases, and the quantum theory of solids and liquids are closely related to thermodynamics, a brief comment on their interrelationships may prove helpful to the reader.

A fundamental approach to the theory of the properties of macroscopic matter has three aspects. First, there is the detailed characterization of the atomic states and structure in terms of the formalism of quantum mechanics. Second, there is the application of statistical considerations to these states; this is the subject matter of statistical mechanics. And, third, there is the development of the macroscopic consequences of the statistical theory, constituting the subject matter of thermodynamics.

The theories of statistical mechanics and of thermodynamics are not restricted to particular models of matter—they are general and model-independent. The theory of the solid state, the theory of liquids, and the kinetic theory of gases result if these general considerations are applied to definite models. The specific theories are more detailed in their predictions than are statistical mechanics and thermodynamics but are also subject to the oversimplifications inevitable in any analytically tractable model of the structure of matter. Statistical mechanics and thermodynamics provide a rigorous general framework for the development of the specific theories of matter, and they assume a new importance in relation to the rapidly developing and highly practical theory of the solid state.

Each of the foregoing subjects is concerned with the properties of systems in equilibrium. Within the last few years important extensions of the thermodynamic method have been made outside the domain of equilibrium. The associated theory is generally referred to as irreversible thermodynamics or the theory of irreversible processes. It seems probable that this new extension of the theory will provide some of the most significant rewards of the thermodynamic method. Some results of the theory of irreversible thermodynamics are presented in the final chapters of this book.

HERBERT B. CALLEN

Philadelphia, Pennsylvania
November 1959

Contents

PART II

REPRESENTATIVE APPLICATIONS

PART III

FLUCTUATIONS AND IRREVERSIBLE THERMODYNAMICS

APPENDICES

PART I

Chapters 1–11

General Principles
of Classical
Thermodynamics

CHAPTER 1

Basic Concepts
and Postulates

1.1 The Nature of Thermodynamics

Mechanics, electricity and magnetism, and thermodynamics are three parallel divisions of classical macroscopic physics. The manner in which this natural division arises can be appreciated by considering the nature of macroscopic observations and their relation to the underlying atomic structure of matter.

From the atomic point of view a macroscopic sample of matter is an agglomerate of an enormous number of electrons and nuclei. A complete mathematical description of the sample accordingly consists of the specification of suitable coordinates for each electron and nucleus. Some 10^{24} or 10^{25} coordinates are thereby required to describe the state of a pint of alcohol! Now this type of description is undoubtedly valid in a certain sense, but it is clearly not what would be considered an appropriate description by the man who writes the label on the bottle. Only a very few parameters are required to describe a system macroscopically in contrast to a relatively enormous number required for an atomistic description. In the transition from the atomic to the macroscopic level of description there is a tremendous simplification and a drastic reduction in the number of pertinent variables.

The clue to the simplicity of the macroscopic specification is the slowness of macroscopic measurements in comparison to the speed of atomic motions. During the very time that a macroscopic measurement is being made the atoms of the system go through enormously rapid and complex motions.

A macroscopic measurement of length may be made by placing a meter stick beside a sample and snapping a photograph. The time of measurement is determined by the speed of the camera shutter and typically is of the order of one hundredth of a second. But a characteristic period of atomic motion is 10^{-15} second!

Even during a "rapid" measurement, completed in a single microsecond, the atoms of a typical solid go through ten million vibrations. Consequently, *macroscopic measurements sense only averages of the atomic coordinates.* The mathematical process of averaging over a coordinate obviously eliminates it from the mathematical formulation, so that we can see, in principle, how the number of relevant coordinates is reduced in going from the atomic to the macroscopic level of description.

Although statistical averaging drastically reduces the number of pertinent variables, it does not eliminate all. Of the original 10^{24} atomic parameters, a few very special parameters survive the averaging process and remain as the appropriate parameters for a description of a macroscopic system. Or, stated differently, of the multitude of atomic coordinates, there are a few with the unique property that they are macroscopically observable. The formal criterion* for these few coordinates is rather subtle, but the general idea can be represented by a simple analogy.

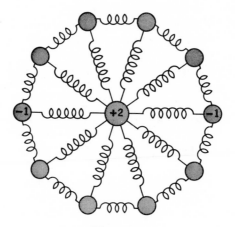

Figure 1.1

Suppose that our macroscopic system is that represented in Figure 1.1, consisting not of 10^{24} atoms but of only eleven. The system contains one central heavy atom and ten symmetrically placed light atoms of equal mass. The central atom has a positive charge of two units, and each of two of the light atoms, on opposite sides of the central atom, carries a

---

* M. J. Klein and L. Tisza, MIT. R.L.E. Rept. 111, 1949.

negative charge of one unit. Each atom is bound to its neighbors by simple linear forces, represented by springs in Figure 1.1.

The motions of the individual atoms are strongly coupled so that the atoms tend to move in organized patterns, called *normal modes*. Three such normal modes of motion are indicated schematically in Figure 1.2. In Figure 1.2*a* the two charged light atoms remain fixed while the uncharged

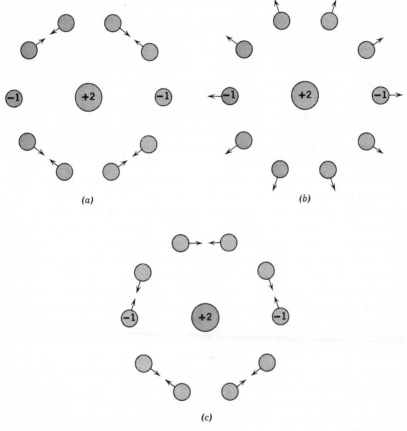

(a)   (b)

(c)

Figure 1.2

light atoms vibrate out of phase in pairs along the tangential direction. In Figure 1.2*b* all of the light atoms vibrate in phase along the radial directions. In Figure 1.2*c* neighboring light atoms vibrate out of phase along the tangential direction. There are many other simple normal modes of motion, but the three particular normal modes that we have described will suffice for our discussion.

Rather than describe the atomic state of the system by specifying the position of each atom, it is more convenient (and mathematically equivalent) to specify the instantaneous amplitude of each normal mode. These amplitudes are called *normal coordinates*, and the number of normal coordinates is exactly equal to the number of atomic coordinates. We are interested here in understanding qualitatively how most of these normal coordinates are lost in the statistical averaging, whereas a certain few unique normal coordinates survive.

In a macroscopic system composed of eleven atoms there is no precise distinction between *macroscopic* and *atomic* observations. For the purposes of illustration, however, we think of a macroscopic observation as a kind of "hazy" observation which discerns gross features but not fine detail. A macroscopic mechanical observation is made by looking at the system through a smoked glass, and a macroscopic electrical observation is made by probing the electric fields around the system with a very coarse probe. In each case the insensitivity to fine details is meant to represent in a qualitative way the statistical averaging that is implicit in true macroscopic observations.

When viewed through a smoked glass the mode of motion in Figure 1.2*a* becomes unobservable; this represents the type of normal mode that is eliminated by the statistical averaging. The mode of motion of Figure 1.2*b*, however, is associated with a gross change in the size of the system—it is basically a volume dilatation. Such a mode is observable even through a smoked glass and is correspondingly preserved through the statistical averaging. Because of the survival of this type of mode, the volume is a valid parameter in the description of a macroscopic system. Finally, although the mode of motion of Figure 1.2*c* is unobservable through a smoked glass, we note that it is associated with a gross electric dipole moment. The negative charges suffer a net displacement relative to the positive charge. In Figure 1.2*c* this relative displacement is shown as upward; half a cycle later the relative displacement would be downward and the dipole moment would be reversed. To an electrically sensitive "hazy" observation the mode of Figure 1.2*c* is observable. The mode of Figure 1.2*c*, therefore, will survive the statistical averaging, whence the electric dipole moment becomes a valid parameter for the description of a macroscopic system. Of our three modes of atomic motion, one is lost in the averaging process, one survives as a mechanical parameter (the volume), and one survives as an electrical parameter (the dipole moment) of the macroscopic system.

The example we have discussed illustrates a very general result. Of the enormous number of atomic coordinates, a very few, with unique symmetric properties, survive the statistical averaging associated with a transition to a macroscopic description. Certain of these surviving coordinates are mechanical in nature—they are volume, parameters descriptive of the shape, components of elastic strain, etc. Other surviving coordinates are electrical in nature—they are electric dipole moments, magnetic dipole moments, various multipole moments, etc. *The subject of mechanics (including elasticity, hydrodynamics, and rheology) is the study of one set of surviving coordinates. The subject of electricity (including electrostatics, magnetostatics, and ferromagnetism) is the study of another set of surviving coordinates.* In this perspective we are now prepared to confront the question of "What is thermodynamics?"

Thermodynamics is the study of the macroscopic consequences of myriads of atomic coordinates, which, by virtue of the statistical averaging, do not appear explicitly in a macroscopic description of a system.

Now what are the chief consequences of the existence of the "hidden" atomic modes of motion with which thermodynamics is concerned? There is one main consequence we can immediately perceive qualitatively and which illustrates the nature of the problems with which we shall deal henceforth. We first recall that in both the sciences of mechanics and electricity we are much concerned with the concept of energy. Energy can be transferred to a mechanical mode of a system, such a flux of energy being called *mechanical work.* Similarly, energy can be transferred to an electrical mode of a system. Mechanical work is typified by the term $-P \, dV$ (P is pressure, V is volume), and *electrical work* is typified by the term $-E \, d\mathscr{P}$ (E is electric field, $\mathscr{P}$ is electric dipole moment). These energy terms and various other mechanical and electrical work terms are treated fully in the standard mechanics and electricity references. *But it is equally possible to transfer energy to the hidden atomic modes of motion as well as to those which happen to be macroscopically observable.* An energy transfer to the hidden atomic modes is called *heat.* The existence of a heat term in addition to the mechanical and electrical work terms is the outstanding consequence of the existence of the hidden atomic coordinates. Thus much of thermodynamics is concerned with processes of heat transfer.

With this qualitative preview we proceed to certain definitions and conventions necessary to the theoretical development.

1.2 The Composition of Thermodynamic Systems

Thermodynamics is a subject of great generality, applicable to systems of elaborate structure with all manner of complex mechanical, electrical, and thermal properties. It is the thermal properties on which we wish to focus our chief attention. Therefore it is convenient to idealize and simplify the mechanical and electrical properties of the systems that we shall study initially. Similarly, in mechanics we consider uncharged and unpolarized systems, whereas in electricity we consider systems with no elastic compressibility or other mechanical attributes. The generality of either subject is not essentially reduced by this idealization, and after the separate content of each subject has been studied it is a simple matter to combine the theories to treat systems of simultaneously complicated electrical and mechanical properties. Similarly, in our study of thermo-dynamics we idealize our systems so that their mechanical and electrical properties are almost trivially simple. When the essential content of thermodynamics has thus been developed, it again is a simple matter to extend the analysis to systems with relatively complex mechanical and electrical structure. The essential point we wish to stress is that the restrictions on the types of systems considered in the following several chapters are *not* basic limitations on the generality of thermodynamic theory but are adopted merely for simplicity of exposition.

We restrict our attention to *simple systems, defined as systems that are macroscopically homogeneous, isotropic, uncharged, and chemically inert, that are sufficiently large that surface effects can be neglected, and that are not acted on by electric, magnetic, or gravitational fields.*

For such a simple system there are no macroscopic electric coordinates whatsoever. The system is uncharged and has neither electric nor magnetic dipole, quadrupole, or higher-order moments. All elastic shear components and other such mechanical parameters are zero.

Although the various parameters mentioned do not apply to a simple system, the *volume V* is a relevant mechanical parameter. Furthermore, a simple system has a definite *chemical composition* which must be described by an appropriate set of parameters. One reasonable set of composition parameters would be the numbers of molecules in each of the chemically pure components of which the system is a mixture. Alternatively, to obtain numbers of more convenient size, we adopt the *mole numbers*, defined as the actual number of each type of molecule divided by Avogadro's number (6.024×10^{23}).

The mole number N_k of the kth chemical component of a system can be computed conveniently as the ratio of the mass of that component to its *molar mass*. The molar mass is the mass of 6.024×10^{23} molecules.

In describing the composition of a thermodynamic system by the mole numbers of its chemical components, we implicitly adopt the view that the pure chemical components are permanent and indivisible. We shall subsequently consider chemical reactions, in which the molecular species do change. But even chemical reactions maintain the integrity of the individual *atomic* species. It is clear that such treatments are inadequate to describe the interior of a hot star, where the individual neutrons, protons, and electrons are the fundamental components that may enter into transitory combinations to form atomic ions. In such a case we would take the "mole numbers" N_k as proportional to the numbers of neutrons, protons, and electrons. However, for our present purposes we ignore the possibility of either molecular or atomic disruption and we describe the composition of a system by the mole numbers of its *chemical* components.

The macroscopic parameters $V, N_1, N_2 \cdots N_r$ have a common property that will prove to be quite significant. Suppose that we are given two identical systems and that we now regard these two systems taken together as a single system. The value of the volume for the composite system is then just twice the value of the volume for a single subsystem. Similarly, each of the mole numbers of the composite system is twice that for a single subsystem. Parameters that have values in a composite system equal to the sum of the values in each of the subsystems are called *extensive* parameters. Extensive parameters play a key role throughout thermodynamic theory.

Various ratios of the extensive parameters find frequent use in our later discussions. If a system is a mixture of r chemical components, the r ratios $N_k \Big/ \left(\sum_{j=1}^{r} N_j \right)$ $(k = 1, 2 \cdots r)$ are called the *mole fractions*. The sum of all r mole fractions is unity. The quantity $V \Big/ \left(\sum_{j=1}^{r} N_j \right)$ is called the *molar volume*.

Problems—Section 1.2

1.2-1. Ten grams of NaCl and 15 grams of sugar ($C_{12}H_{22}O_{11}$) are dissolved in 50 grams of pure water. The volume of the resultant thermodynamic system is 55 cm^3. What are the mole numbers of the three components of the system? What are the mole fractions? What is the molar volume of the system?

1.2-2. Twenty cubic centimeters each of ethyl alcohol (C_2H_5OH; density $= 0.79$ gram/cm^3), methyl alcohol (CH_3OH; density $= 0.81$ gram/cm^3), and water (H_2O; density $= 1$ gram/cm^3) are mixed together. What are the mole numbers of the three components of the system?

1.2-3. Most naturally occurring elements are mixtures of several isotopes, and the atomic weights given in chemical tables represent the average atomic weight of the mixture. If the thermodynamic analysis is not to be applied to problems of isotopic separation, the isotopic mixture may be considered a single substance, and the average atomic weight may be used to compute the mole number. If isotopic separation is of interest, however, each isotope must be considered a separate, independent component, with its own unique atomic weight.

The composition of naturally occurring lithium is 7.5 atomic per cent Li^6

(atomic mass $= 6.01697$) and 92.5 atomic per cent Li^7 (atomic mass $= 7.01822$). Find the mole numbers of each of the isotopes in a 1-kg sample.

Answer: $N(Li^6) = 10.8$.

1.2–4.   A ten-gram sample is composed of 70 molecular per cent H_2, 20 molecular per cent HD (hydrogen deuteride), and 10 molecular per cent D_2. What additional mass of D_2 must be added if the mole fraction of D_2 in the final mixture is to be 0.2?

1.3   The Internal Energy

The development of the principle of conservation of energy has been one of the most significant achievements in the evolution of physics. The present form of the principle was not discovered in one magnificent stroke of insight but has been slowly and laboriously developed over two and a half centuries. The first recognition of a conservation principle, by Leibnitz in 1693, referred only to the sum of the kinetic energy ($\frac{1}{2} mv^2$) and the potential energy (mgh) of a simple mechanical mass point in the terrestrial gravitational field. As additional types of systems were considered, the established form of the conservation principle repeatedly failed, but in each case it was found possible to revive it by the addition of a new mathematical term—a "new kind of energy." Thus consideration of charged systems necessitated the addition of the *Coulomb interaction energy* (Q_1Q_2/r) and eventually of the energy of the electromagnetic field. In 1905 Einstein extended the principle to the relativistic region, adding such terms as the relativistic rest-mass energy. In the 1930's Enrico Fermi postulated the existence of a new particle, called the *neutrino*, solely for the purpose of retaining the energy conservation principle in nuclear reactions. Contemporary research in nuclear physics seeks the form of interaction between nucleons within a nucleus in order that the conservation principle may be formulated explicitly at the subnuclear level. Despite the fact that unsolved problems of this type remain, the energy conservation principle is now accepted as one of the most fundamental, general, and significant principles of physical theory.

Viewing a macroscopic system as an agglomerate of an enormous number of electrons and nuclei, interacting with complex but definite forces to which the energy conservation principle applies, we conclude that *macroscopic systems have definite and precise energies, subject to a definite conservation principle.* That is, we now accept the existence of a well-defined energy of a thermodynamic system as a macroscopic manifestation of a conservation law, highly developed, tested to an extreme precision, and apparently of complete generality at the atomic level.

The foregoing justification of the existence of a thermodynamic energy function is quite different from the historical thermodynamic method. Because thermodynamics was developed largely before the atomic hypothesis was accepted, the existence of a conservative macroscopic energy function had to be demonstrated by purely macroscopic means. A significant step in that direction was taken by Count Rumford in 1798, as he observed certain thermal effects associated with the boring of brass cannons. Sir Humphry Davy, Sadi Carnot, Robert Mayer, and, finally (between 1840 and 1850), James Joule carried Rumford's initial efforts to their logical fruition. The history of the concept of heat as a form of energy transfer is unsurpassed as a case study in the tortuous development of scientific theory, as an illustration of the almost insuperable inertia presented by accepted physical doctrine, and as a superb tale of human ingenuity applied to a subtle and abstract problem. The interested reader is referred to *The Early Development of the Concepts of Temperature and Heat* by D. Roller (Harvard University Press, 1950), to "The Caloric Theory of Heat" by S. C. Brown [*Am. J. Phys.* **18**, 319 (1950)], or to any standard work on the history of physics.

Although we shall not have recourse explicitly to the experiments of Rumford and Joule in order to justify our postulate of the *existence* of an energy function, we make reference to them in section 1.6 in our discussion of the *measurability* of the thermodynamic energy.

Only differences of energy, rather than absolute values of the energy, have physical significance, either at the atomic level or in macroscopic systems. It is conventional therefore to adopt some particular state of a system as a fiducial state, the energy of which is arbitrarily taken as zero. The energy of a system in any other state, relative to the energy of the system in the fiducial state, is then called the thermodynamic *internal energy* of the system in that state and is denoted by the symbol U.

Like the volume and the mole numbers, the internal energy is an extensive parameter.

1.4 Thermodynamic Equilibrium

It is purely as a matter of convenience that we have chosen temporarily to restrict our theory to simple systems. Of a much more fundamental nature is a further restriction of the theory to certain simple states of any given system. The particular simple states to which thermodynamics applies are called *equilibrium states.*

Even a cursory consideration of various states of a given system makes it apparent that some states are relatively simple and others are relatively complicated. Thus a fluid at rest clearly is in a simpler state than a fluid in laminar flow. And a fluid in laminar flow, in turn, is in a simpler state than a fluid in turbulent flow. Moreover, it is experimentally observed that isolated systems generally tend to evolve spontaneously toward simple terminal states. Turbulences in fluid systems eventually damp out, concentration inhomogeneities ultimately are destroyed by diffusion currents, and plastic deformations yield to inhomogeneous internal strains. It is natural that a physical theory should first attempt to treat the properties associated with the simplest states of a system rather than to attack all possible complicated states in a completely general way. A limited theory of the relatively complicated nonequilibrium states has been developed under the name *irreversible thermodynamics*, but thermostatics treats only the properties of systems in equilibrium.

The foregoing discussion is qualitative and suggestive rather than formal or precise. Consequently we seek to rephrase the description of equilibrium in a manner that will provide a basis for further theoretical development. Now, a formal criterion of simplicity is the possibility of description in terms of a small number of variables. It therefore seems plausible to adopt the following postulate, suggested by experimental observation and formal simplicity, and to be verified ultimately by the success of the derived theory:

✳   **Postulate I.** *There exist particular states* (*called equilibrium states*) *of simple systems that, macroscopically, are characterized completely by the internal energy U, the volume V, and the mole numbers N_1, $N_2 \cdots N_r$ of the chemical components.*

As we expand the generality of the systems to be considered, eventually permitting more complicated mechanical and electrical properties, the number of parameters required to characterize an equilibrium state is increased to include such parameters as the electric dipole moment and certain elastic strain parameters. These new variables play roles in the formalism which are completely analogous to the role of the volume V for a simple system.

A persistent problem of the experimentalist is to determine somehow whether a given system actually is in an equilibrium state, to which thermodynamic analysis may be applied. He can, of course, observe whether it is static and quiescent and reject it if it is not so. But quiescence is not sufficient. As the state is assumed to be characterized completely by the extensive parameters U, V, N_1, $N_2 \cdots N_r$, it follows that the properties of the system must be independent of the past history. This is hardly an operational prescription for the recognition of an equilibrium state, but in certain cases this independence of the past history is obviously *not* satisfied, and these cases give some insight into the significance of equilibrium. Thus two pieces of chemically identical commercial steel may have very different properties imparted by cold-working, heat treatment, quenching, and annealing in the manufacturing process. Such systems are clearly not in equilibrium. Similarly, the physical characteristics of glass depend upon the cooling rate and other details of its manufacture, so that glass is not in equilibrium.

If a system that is not in equilibrium is analyzed on the basis of a thermodynamic formalism predicated on the supposition of equilibrium, inconsistencies appear in the formalism, and predicted results are at variance with experimental observations. This failure of the theory is used by the experimentalist as an a posteriori criterion for the detection of nonequilibrium states.

In those cases in which an unexpected inconsistency arises in the thermodynamic formalism a more incisive quantum-statistical theory usually provides valid reasons for the failure of the system to attain equilibrium. The occasional theoretical discrepancies that arise are therefore of great heuristic value by calling attention to some unsuspected complication in the molecular mechanisms of the system. Such circumstances led to the discovery of ortho- and parahydrogen,* and to the understanding of the molecular mechanism of conversion between the two forms.

From the atomic point of view, the macroscopic equilibrium state is associated with incessant and rapid transitions among all the atomic states consistent with the given boundary conditions. If the transition mechanism among the atomic states is sufficiently effective, the system passes rapidly through all representative atomic states in the course of a macroscopic observation; such a system is in equilibrium. However, under certain unique conditions, the mechanism of atomic transition may be ineffective and the system may be trapped in a small subset of atypical atomic states. Or even if the system is not completely trapped the rate of transition may be so slow that a macroscopic measurement does not yield a proper average over all possible atomic states. In these cases the system is not in equilibrium. It is readily apparent that such situations are most likely to occur in solid rather than in fluid systems, for the comparatively high atomic mobility in fluid systems and the random nature of the interatomic collisions militate strongly against any restrictions of the atomic transition probabilities.

---

* If the two nuclei in a H_2 molecule have parallel angular momentum, the molecule is called ortho-H_2; if antiparallel, para-H_2. The ratio of ortho-H_2 to para-H_2 in a gaseous H_2 system should have a definite value in equilibrium, but this ratio may not be obtained under certain conditions. The resultant failure of H_2 to satisfy certain thermodynamic equations motivated the investigations of the ortho- and para- forms of H_2.

In actuality, few systems are in absolute and true equilibrium, but many are in *metastable equilibrium*. In absolute equilibrium all radioactive materials would have completely decayed, all nuclear reactions would have come to completion, and the system would bear little similarity to earthly systems. These reactions, which would take cosmic times, are ignored when we say the system is in metastable equilibrium. We return to the criterion, admittedly circular, that a system is *effectively* in equilibrium (i.e., in metastable equilibrium) if its properties are consistent with thermodynamic theory.

1.5 Walls and Constraints

A description of a thermodynamic system requires the specification of the "walls" that separate it from the surroundings and that provide its boundary conditions. It is by means of manipulations of the walls that the extensive parameters of the system are altered and the processes are initiated.

The processes arising by manipulations of the walls generally are associated with a redistribution of some quantity among various systems or among various portions of a single system. A formal classification of thermodynamic walls can be based accordingly on the property of the walls in permitting or preventing such redistributions. As a particular illustration, consider two systems contained within a closed, rigid cylinder but separated by an internal piston. If the position of the piston is rigidly fixed, the wall prevents the redistribution of volume between the two systems, but if the piston is left free such a redistribution is permitted. The cylinder and the rigidly fixed piston may be said to constitute a wall *restrictive* with respect to the volume, whereas the cylinder and the movable piston may be said to constitute a wall *nonrestrictive* with respect to the volume. In general, a wall that constrains an extensive parameter of a system to have a definite and particular value is said to be restrictive with respect to that parameter, whereas a wall that permits the parameter to change freely is said to be nonrestrictive with respect to that parameter.

A wall that is impermeable to a particular chemical component is restrictive with respect to the corresponding mole number, whereas a permeable membrane is nonrestrictive with respect to the mole number. Semipermeable membranes are restrictive with respect to certain mole numbers and nonrestrictive with respect to others. A wall with holes in it is nonrestrictive with respect to all mole numbers.

The existence of walls that are restrictive with respect to the energy is associated with the larger problem of measurability of the energy to which we now turn our attention.

1.6 Measurability of the Energy

On the basis of atomic considerations, we have been led to postulate the existence of a macroscopic conservative energy function. In order that this energy function may be meaningful in a practical sense, however, we must convince ourselves that it is macroscopically *controllable* and *measurable*. We shall now show that practical methods of measurement of the energy do exist; and in doing so we shall also be led to a quantitative operational definition of heat.

An essential feature in our demonstration of measurability of the energy is the recognition of the existence of walls that do not permit the transfer of energy in the form of heat. We shall briefly examine a simple experimental situation that suggests that such walls do indeed exist.

Consider a system of ice and water enclosed in a container. We find that the ice can be caused to melt rapidly by stirring the system vigorously. By stirring the system we are clearly transferring energy to it mechanically, so that we infer that the melting of the ice is associated with an input of energy to the system. If we now allow the system to sit out on the table on a summer day, we observe that the ice spontaneously melts despite the fact that no work is done on the system. It therefore seems plausible that energy is being transferred to the system in the form of heat. Now we further observe that by changing the wall surrounding the system from thin metal sheet, to thick glass, and thence to a Dewar wall (consisting of two silvered glass sheets separated by an evacuated interspace) the rate of melting of the ice is progressively decreased. This observation strongly suggests that the metal, glass, and Dewar walls are progressively less permeable to the flow of heat. The ingenuity of experimentalists has produced walls which are able to reduce the melting rate of the ice to a negligible value, and such walls are correspondingly excellent approximations to the limiting idealization of a wall which is truly impermeable to the flow of heat.

It is conventional to refer to a wall which is impermeable to the flow of heat as *adiabatic*, whereas a wall that permits the flow of heat is termed *diathermal*. If a wall allows the flux of neither work nor heat, it is *restrictive with respect to the energy*. A system enclosed by a wall that is restrictive with respect to the energy, volume, and all the mole numbers is said to be *closed*.

The existence of these several types of walls resolves the first of our concerns with the thermodynamic energy. That is, these walls demonstrate that the energy is macroscopically *controllable*. It can be trapped by restrictive walls and manipulated by diathermal walls. If the energy of a system is measured today, and if the system is enclosed by a wall restrictive with respect to the energy, we can be certain of the energy of the system tomorrow. Without such a wall, the concept of a macroscopic thermodynamic energy would be purely academic.

We can now proceed to our second concern—that of *measurability* of the energy. More accurately, we are concerned with the measurability of energy differences, which alone have physical significance. Again we invoke the existence of adiabatic walls, and we note that for a simple system enclosed by an impermeable adiabatic wall the only type of permissible energy transfer is in the form of work. The theory of mechanics provides us with quantitative formulas for its measurement. If the work is done by compression, displacing a piston in a cylinder, the work is the product of force times displacement, or, if the work is done by stirring, it is the product of the torque times the angular rotation of the stirrer shaft. In any case, the work is well defined and measurable by the theory of mechanics. We conclude that we are able to measure the energy difference of two states *provided that one state may be reached from the other by some mechanical process while the system is enclosed by an adiabatic impermeable wall.*

The entire matter of controllability and measurability of the energy can be succinctly stated as follows: *There exist walls, called adiabatic, with the property that the work done in taking an adiabatically enclosed system between two given states is determined entirely by the states, independent of all external conditions. The work done is the difference in the internal energy of the two states.*

In subsequent discussion we shall determine how serious a limitation is imposed on the choice of the two states by the foregoing condition. But however limited our choice of two states may be, we now recognize that at least for such pairs of states the energy difference is measurable, and we consider a specific example. Suppose we are given a system composed of ice and water in a definite state. We enclose the system in a rigid adiabatic impermeable wall. Through a small hole in this wall we pass a thin shaft carrying a propellor blade at the inner end and a crank handle at the outer end. By turning the crank handle we can do work on the system. The work done is equal to the angular rotation of the shaft multiplied by the viscous torque. After turning the shaft for a definite time the system is allowed to come to a new equilibrium state in which some definite amount of the ice is observed to have been melted. The difference in energy of the final and initial states is equal to the work that we have done in turning the crank.

We now inquire as to the possibility of starting with some arbitrary given state of a system, of enclosing the system in an adiabatic impermeable wall, and of then being able to contrive some mechanical process that will take the system to another arbitrarily specified state. To determine the existence of such processes, we must have recourse to experimental observation, and it is here that the great classical experiments of Joule are relevant. His work can be interpreted as demonstrating that _for a system enclosed by an adiabatic impermeable wall any two equilibrium states with the same set of mole numbers $N_1, N_2 \cdots N_r$ can be joined by some possible mechanical process_. Joule discovered that if two states (say A and B) are specified it may _not_ be possible to find a mechanical process (consistent with an adiabatic impermeable wall) to take the system _from A to B_ but that it is always possible to find _either_ a process to take the system from A to B _or_ a process to take the system from B to A. That is, for any states A and B with equal mole numbers either the adiabatic mechanical process $A \rightarrow B$ or $B \rightarrow A$ exists. For our purposes either of these processes is equally satisfactory. Experiment thus shows that _the methods of mechanics permit us to measure the energy difference of any two states with equal mole numbers_.

Joule's observation that only one of the processes $A \rightarrow B$ or $B \rightarrow A$ may exist is of profound significance. This asymmetry of two given states is associated with the concept of _irreversibility_, with which we shall subsequently be much concerned.

The only remaining limitation to the measurability of the energy difference of any two states is the requirement that the states must have equal mole numbers. This restriction is easily eliminated by the following observation. Consider two simple subsystems separated by an impermeable wall and assume that the energy of each subsystem is known (relative to appropriate fiducial states, of course). If the impermeable wall is removed, the subsystems will intermix, but the total energy of the composite system will remain constant. Therefore the energy of the final mixed system is known to be the sum of the energies of the original subsystems. This technique enables us to relate the energies of states with different mole numbers.

In summary, we have seen that _by employing adiabatic walls and by measuring only mechanical work the energy of any thermodynamic system, relative to an appropriate fiducial state, can be measured_.

1.7 Quantitative Definition of Heat—Units

The fact that the energy difference of any two states is measurable provides us directly with a quantitative definition of the heat. To wit, _the heat flux to a system in any process_ (_at constant mole numbers_) _is_ *simply the difference in internal energy between the final and initial states, diminished by the work done in that process.*

Consider some specified process that takes a system from the initial state A to the final state B. We wish to know the amount of energy transferred to the system in the form of work and the amount transferred in the form of heat in that particular process. The work is easily measured by the methods of mechanics. Furthermore, the total energy difference $U_B - U_A$ is measurable by the procedures discussed in section 1.6. Subtracting the work from the total energy difference gives us the heat flux in the specified process.

It should be noted that the amount of work associated with different processes may be different, even though each of the processes initiates in the same state A and each terminates in the same state B. Similarly, the heat flux may be different for each of the processes. But the sum of the work and heat fluxes is just the total energy difference $U_B - U_A$ and is the same for each of the processes. In referring to the total energy flux we therefore need specify only the initial and terminal states, but in referring to heat or work fluxes we must specify in detail the process considered.

Restricting our attention to thermodynamic simple systems, the quasi-static work is associated with a change in volume and is given quantitatively by

$$dW_M = -P\,dV \tag{1.1}$$

where P is the pressure. In recalling this equation from mechanics, we stress that the equation applies only to *quasi-static processes*. We give a precise definition of quasi-static processes in section 4.1, but now we merely indicate the essential qualitative idea of such processes. Let us suppose that we are discussing, as a particular system, a gas enclosed in a cylinder fitted with a moving piston. If the piston is pushed in very rapidly, the gas immediately behind the piston acquires kinetic energy and is set into turbulent motion and the pressure is not well defined. In such a case the work done on the system is not quasi-static and is not given by equation 1.1. If, however, the piston is pushed in at a vanishingly slow rate (quasi-statically), the system is, at every moment, in a quiescent equilibrium state, and equation 1.1 then applies. The "infinite slowness" of the process is, roughly, the essential feature of a quasi-static process, although we again refer to section 4.1 for a more precise statement.

A second noteworthy feature of equation 1.1 is the sign convention. The work is taken positive if it increases the energy of the system. If the volume of the system is decreased, work is done on the system, increasing its energy; hence the negative sign in equation 1.1.

With the quantitative expression $dW_M = -P\,dV$ for the quasi-static work, we can now give a quantitative expression for the heat flux. In an infinitesimal quasi-static process at constant mole numbers the *quasi-static heat dQ* is defined by the equation

$$dQ = dU - dW_M \qquad \text{at constant mole numbers} \qquad (1.2)$$

or

$$dQ = dU + P\, dV \qquad \text{at constant mole numbers} \qquad (1.3)$$

It will be noted that we use the terms *heat* and *heat flux* interchangeably. Heat, like work, is only a form of energy *transfer*. Once energy is transferred to a system, either as heat or as work, it is indistinguishable from energy which might have been transferred differently. Thus, although dQ and dW_M add together to give dU, there are no quantities W_M nor Q which have any separate meanings. The infinitesimal quantity dW_M is *not* a differential of some hypothetical function W_M, and to avoid this implication we have put a stroke through the symbol d. This is true also of the quantity dQ. Mathematically, infinitesimals such as dW_M and dQ are called *imperfect differentials*.

The concepts of heat, work, and energy may possibly be clarified in terms of a simple analogy. A certain gentleman owns a little pond, fed by one stream and drained by another. The pond also receives water from an occasional rainfall and loses it by evaporation, which we shall consider as "negative rain." In the analogy we wish to pursue the pond is our system, the water within it is the internal energy, water transferred by the streams is work, and water transferred as rain is heat.

The first thing to be noted is that no examination of the pond at any time can indicate how much of the water within it came by way of the stream and how much came by way of rain. The term rain refers only to a method of water *transfer*.

Let us suppose that the owner of the pond wishes to measure the amount of water in the pond. He can purchase flow meters to be inserted in the streams, and with these flow meters he can measure the amount of stream water entering and leaving the pond. But he cannot purchase a rain meter. However, he can throw a tarpaulin over the pond, enclosing the pond in a wall impermeable to rain (an *adiabatic wall*). The pond owner consequently puts a vertical pole into the pond, covers the pond with his tarpaulin, and inserts his flow meters into the streams. By damming one stream and then the other, he varies the level in the pond at will, and by consulting his flow meters he is able to calibrate the pond level, as read on his vertical stick, with total water content (U). Thus, by carrying out processes on the system enclosed by an adiabatic wall, he is able to measure the total water content of any state of his pond.

Our obliging pond owner now removes his tarpaulin to permit rain as well as stream water to enter and leave the pond. He is then asked to ascertain the amount of rain entering his pond during a particular day. He proceeds simply: he reads the difference in water content from his vertical stick, and from this he deducts the total flux of stream water, as registered by his flow meters. The difference is a quantitative measure of the rain. The strict analogy of each of these procedures with the thermodynamic counterparts is evident.

Since work and heat refer to particular modes of energy transfer, each is measured in energy units. In the cgs system the unit of energy, hence

Table 1.1

ENERGY UNITS AND CONVERSION FACTORS

	Ergs	Joules (Absolute)	Calories (Mean)	Btu	Liter-Atmospheres	Foot-Pounds	Watt-Hours	Horse-power-Hours
1 erg =	1	10^{-7}	2.389×10^{-8}	9.480×10^{-11}	9.869×10^{-10}	7.376×10^{-8}	2.778×10^{-11}	3.724×10^{-14}
1 joule (absolute) =	10^7	1	0.2389	9.480×10^{-4}	0.009869	0.7376	2.778×10^{-4}	3.724×10^{-7}
1 calorie (mean) =	4.186×10^7	4.186	1	0.003968	0.04131	3.087	0.001163	1.559×10^{-6}
1 British thermal unit =	1.055×10^{10}	1055	252.0	1	10.41	778.0	0.2930	3.929×10^{-4}
1 liter-atmosphere =	1.013×10^9	101.3	24.21	0.09607	1	74.73	0.02815	3.775×10^{-5}
1 foot-pound =	1.356×10^7	1.356	0.3239	0.001285	0.01338	1	3.766×10^{-4}	5.050×10^{-7}
1 watt-hour =	3.600×10^{10}	3600	860.0	3.413	35.53	2655	1	0.001341
1 horsepower-hour =	2.686×10^{13}	2.686×10^6	0.6413×10^6	0.2545×10^4	2.649×10^4	1.980×10^6	0.7457×10^4	1

of work and heat, is the erg. In the mks system the unit of energy is the joule, or 10^7 ergs. A practical unit of energy is the calorie, or 4.1858 joules. Historically, the calorie was introduced for the measurement of heat flux before the relationship of heat and work was clear, and the prejudice toward the use of the calorie for heat and of the joule for work still persists. From our point of view, however, the calorie and the joule are simply alternative units of energy, to be employed as convenient, independent of whether the energy flux is work, heat, or some inseparable combination of both. Other common units of energy are the *British thermal unit* (Btu), the liter-atmosphere, the foot-pound, and the watt-hour. When one is concerned with high precision, there are actually several slightly different definitions of the calorie; the *mean calorie*, the *15° calorie*, and the *IT calorie* (or international steam table calorie).

There are also two definitions of the joule; the *absolute joule* and the *international joule*. Without recounting the devious and complex development of standards and definitions and the elaborate experimental measurements of conversion factors among units, we give a partial listing of energy units in Table 1.1.

Problems—Section 1.7

1.7–1. A cylinder and piston contain a gas at a pressure P. The cross section of the piston is 10 cm². The piston is pushed inward 1 mm. The work required to displace the piston is 0.025 cal. Find the pressure P in atmospheres.

1.7–2. What is the price of the energy required to raise 1 ton of material to the top of the Empire State Building (1250 ft high) if the energy is purchased from the electric company at the rate of 2.5¢/kw-hr?

1.7–3. A given system is such that quasi-static adiabatic change in the volume at constant mole numbers is found to change the pressure in accordance with the equation.

$$P = \text{constant } V^{-5/3}$$

Find the quasi-static work done on the system and the net heat flux to the system in each of the three processes indicated in the figure. Each process is initiated in the state A, with a pressure of 32 atm and a volume of 1 liter, and each process terminates in the state B, with a pressure of 1 atm and a volume of 8 liters.

Process a: The system is expanded from its original to its final volume, heat being added to maintain the pressure constant. The volume is then kept constant and heat is extracted to reduce the pressure to 1 atm.

Process b: The volume is increased and heat is supplied to cause the pressure to decrease linearly with the volume.

Process c: The two steps of process a are interchanged in order.

Answer for process a: $W = -224$ liter-atm
$Q = 188$ liter-atm.

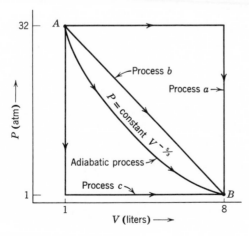

1.7–4. A small paddle wheel is installed in the system of problem 1.7–3. The shaft of the paddle wheel extends through the walls of the system and can be driven at 240 rps by an external motor. The viscous torque on the paddle wheel is then 10^4 cm-dynes. If the motor is thus permitted to do work on the system while the volume is kept constant and the system is adiabatically enclosed, the pressure is found to increase at a rate

$$\frac{dP}{dt} = \frac{2}{3V} T\omega$$

where T is the viscous torque and ω is the angular velocity of the paddle wheel.

Using the foregoing process and the process of adiabatic expansion described in problem 1.7–3, find the internal energy of any equilibrium state with arbitrary pressure P and volume V. Choose the state A ($P = 32$ atm, $V = 1$ liter) as the fiducial state.

What are the heat fluxes in each separate step of process a in problem 1.7–3? In each step of process c?

Answer: Heat flux in the first step of process a = 560 liter-atm.

1.7–5. Two moles of a particular single-component system are found to have a dependence of internal energy U on pressure and volume given by

$$U = APV^2 \qquad \text{(for } N = 2\text{)}$$

where $A = 10$ cm^{-3}. Note that doubling the system doubles the volume, energy, and mole number but leaves the pressure unaltered, and write the complete dependence of U on P, V, and N for arbitrary mole number.

Answer: $U = BPV^2/N$, $\qquad B = 20/$cm^3.

1.7–6. Assuming the system of problems 1.7–3 and 1.7–4 to have been a single-component system, show that the complete functional dependence of U on P, V, and N is, in fact, independent of N.

1.7–7. A particular single-component system of one mole has adiabats of the form $PV^{5/3} = $ constant. It is fitted with a stirrer, as in problem 1.7–4. When the stirrer does an amount of work, dW, the pressure increase dP (at constant volume) is given by

$$dW = (\tfrac{3}{2}V + V^{5/3})\, dP$$

Find the internal energy as a function of P, V, and N.

1.7–8. Show that if a single-component system is such that PV^k is constant in an adiabatic process (k is a positive constant) the energy is

$$U = \frac{1}{k-1} PV + Nf(PV^k/N^k)$$

where f is an arbitrary function.

Hint: First show that $U - \dfrac{1}{k-1} PV$ is constant on each adiabat.

1.8   The Basic Problem of Thermodynamics

In terms of the definitions and discussions of the preceding sections we are now able to formulate the basic problem of thermodynamics. We shall find that the mere statement of the problem suggests the postulates which provide its solution.

Let us suppose that two simple systems are contained within a closed cylinder, separated from each other by an internal piston. Assume that the cylinder walls and the piston are rigid, impermeable to matter, and adiabatic and that the position of the piston is firmly fixed. Each of the systems is closed. If we now free the piston, it will, in general, seek some new position. Similarly, if the adiabatic coating is stripped from the piston so that heat can flow between the two systems, there will be a redistribution of energy between the two systems. Again, if holes are punched in

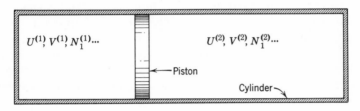

$U^{(1)}, V^{(1)}, N_1^{(1)}...$ $U^{(2)}, V^{(2)}, N_1^{(2)}...$

←—— Piston

Cylinder

Figure 1.3

the piston, there will be a redistribution of matter (and also of energy) between the two systems. Thus the removal of a constraint in each case results in the onset of some spontaneous process, and when the systems finally settle into new equilibrium states they do so with new values of the parameters $U^{(1)}$, $V^{(1)}$, $N_1^{(1)} \cdots$ and $U^{(2)}$, $V^{(2)}$, $N_1^{(2)} \cdots$. The basic problem of thermodynamics is the calculation of the equilibrium values of these parameters.

Before formulating the postulate that provides the means of solution of this problem, we rephrase the problem in a slightly more general form without reference to such special devices as cylinders and pistons.

Given two or more simple systems, they may be considered as constituting a single *composite* system. The composite system is termed closed if it is surrounded by a wall that is restrictive with respect to the total energy, the total volume, and the total mole numbers of each component of the composite system. The individual simple systems within a closed composite system need not themselves be closed. Thus, in the particular example referred to, the composite system is closed even if the internal piston is free to move or has holes in it. Constraints that prevent the flow of energy, volume, or matter among the simple systems constituting the composite system are known as *internal* constraints. If a closed composite system is in equilibrium with respect to certain internal constraints and if some of these constraints are then removed, the system eventually comes into a new equilibrium state. That is, certain processes which were previously disallowed become allowed or, in the terminology of mechanics, become *virtual* processes. *The basic problem of thermodynamics is the determination of the equilibrium state that eventually results after the removal of internal constraints in a closed composite system.*

1.9 The Entropy Maximum Postulates

The induction from experimental observation of the central principle that provides the solution of our basic problem is by no means straight-forward. The logical deviousness of the historical method is matched by the subtlety of the elegant modern quantum statistical approach. Rather than attempting to induce the solution from experiment or deriving it from quantum statistical theory, we therefore merely adopt it as a postulate, depending upon a posteriori rather than a priori justification. But even by this method we shall see that our postulate is not unmotivated; it appears as the most natural and plausible guess that we might make. That is, the postulates that we now adopt provide the *simplest conceivable formal solution* to our basic problem. On this basis alone the problem *might* have been solved; the tentative postulation of the simplest formal solution of a problem is a conventional and frequently successful mode of procedure in theoretical physics.

What then is the simplest criterion that can reasonably be imagined for the determination of the final equilibrium state? From our experience with many physical theories we might expect that the most economical form for the equilibrium criterion is in terms of an extremum principle. That is, we might hope that the values of the extensive parameters in the final equilibrium state are simply those that maximize* some function. And, straining our optimism to the limit, we might hope that this hypothetical function has several particular simple mathematical properties, designed to guarantee simplicity of the derived theory. We develop this proposed solution in a series of postulates.

✳   **Postulate II.** *There exists a function (called the entropy S) of the extensive parameters of any composite system, defined for all equilibrium states and having the following property. The values assumed by the extensive parameters in the absence of an internal constraint are those that maximize the entropy over the manifold of constrained equilibrium states.*

---

* Or minimize the function, this being purely a matter of convention in the choice of the sign of the function, having no consequence whatever in the logical structure of the theory.

It must be stressed that we postulate the existence of the entropy only for equilibrium states, and that our postulate makes no reference whatsoever to nonequilibrium states. In the absence of a constraint the system is free to select any one of a number of states, *each of which might also be realized in the presence of a suitable constraint.* The entropy of each of these constrained equilibrium states is definite, and the entropy is largest in some particular state of the set. In the absence of the constraint it is this state of maximum entropy that is selected by the system.

In the case of two systems separated by a diathermal wall we may wish to predict the manner in which the total energy U distributes between the two systems. We then consider the composite system with the internal diathermal wall replaced by an adiabatic wall and with particular values of $U^{(1)}$ and $U^{(2)}$ (consistent, of course, with the restriction that $U^{(1)} + U^{(2)} = U$). For each such constrained equilibrium state there is an entropy of the composite system, and for some particular values of $U^{(1)}$ and $U^{(2)}$ this entropy is maximum. These, then, are the values of $U^{(1)}$ and $U^{(2)}$ that obtain in the presence of the diathermal wall, or in the absence of the adiabatic constraint.

All problems in thermodynamics are essentially equivalent to the basic problem we formulated in section 1.8. But the basic problem can be completely solved with the aid of the extremum principle if the entropy of the system is known as a function of the extensive parameters. The relation that gives the entropy as a function of the extensive parameters is known as a *fundamental relation.* It therefore follows that *if the fundamental relation of a particular system is known all conceivable thermodynamic information about the system is ascertainable therefrom.*

The importance of the foregoing statement cannot be overemphasized. The information contained in a fundamental relation is all-inclusive—it is equivalent to all conceivable numerical data, to all charts, and to all imaginable types of descriptions of thermodynamic properties. If the fundamental relation of a system is known, there remains not a single thermodynamic attribute that is not completely and precisely determined.

 Postulate III. *The entropy of a composite system is additive over the constituent subsystems. The entropy is continuous and differentiable and is a monotonically increasing function of the energy.*

Several mathematical consequences follow immediately. The additivity property states that the entropy S of the composite system is merely the sum of the entropies $S^{(\alpha)}$ of the constituent subsystems:

$$S = \sum_{\alpha} S^{(\alpha)} \qquad (1.4)$$

The entropy of each subsystem is a function of the extensive parameters of that subsystem alone

$$S^{(\alpha)} = S^{(\alpha)}(U^{(\alpha)}, V^{(\alpha)}, N_1^{(\alpha)} \cdots N_r^{(\alpha)}) \qquad (1.5)$$

The additivity property when applied to conceptually distinct (rather than actually physically distinct) subsystems requires the following property. _The entropy of a simple system is a homogeneous first-order function of the extensive parameters._ That is, if all the extensive parameters of a system are multiplied by a constant λ, the entropy is multiplied by this same constant. Or, omitting the superscript (α),

$$S(\lambda U, \lambda V, \lambda N_1 \cdots \lambda N_r) = \lambda S(U, V, N_1 \cdots N_r) \qquad (1.6)$$

The monotonic property postulated implies that _the partial derivative_ $(\partial S/\partial U)_{V, N_1 \cdots N_r}$ _is a positive quantity_,

$$\left(\frac{\partial S}{\partial U}\right)_{V, N_1 \cdots N_r} > 0 \qquad (1.7)$$

As the theory develops in subsequent sections, we shall see that the reciprocal of this partial derivative is taken as the definition of the temperature. Thus the temperature is postulated to be nonnegative.[*]

The continuity, differentiability, and monotonic property imply that the entropy function can be inverted with respect to the energy and that _the energy is a single-valued, continuous, and differentiable function of_ _S, V, N_1 \cdots N_r_. The function

$$S = S(U, V, N_1 \cdots N_r) \qquad (1.8)$$

can be solved uniquely for U in the form

$$U = U(S, V, N_1 \cdots N_r) \qquad (1.9)$$

Equations 1.8 and 1.9 are alternative forms of the fundamental relation, and each contains _all_ thermodynamic information about the system.

We note that the extensivity of the entropy permits us to scale the properties of a system of N moles from the properties of a system of 1 mole. The fundamental equation is subject to the identity

$$S(U, V, N_1, N_2 \cdots N_r) = NS(U/N, V/N, N_1/N \cdots N_r/N) \qquad (1.10)$$

in which we have taken the scale factor λ equal to $1/N \equiv 1/\sum_k N_k$. For a single-component simple system, in particular,

$$S(U, V, N) = NS(U/N, V/N, 1) \qquad (1.11)$$

---

[*] The possibility of negative values of this derivative (that is, of negative temperatures) has been discussed by N. F. Ramsey, _Phys. Rev._ **103**, 20 (1956). Such states can be produced and maintained for short times in certain unique systems. To accommodate their existence requires subtler and more abstract postulates, and in the interest of simplicity we exclude consideration of these very specialized states.

But U/N is the energy per mole, which we denote by u.

$$u \equiv U/N \tag{1.12}$$

Also, V/N is the volume per mole, which we denote by v.

$$v \equiv V/N \tag{1.13}$$

Thus $S(U/N, V/N, 1) \equiv S(u, v, 1)$ is the entropy of a system of a single mole, to be denoted by $s(u, v)$.

$$s(u, v) \equiv S(u, v, 1) \tag{1.14}$$

Equation 1.11 now becomes

$$S(U, V, N) = Ns(u, v) \tag{1.15}$$

Postulate IV. *The entropy of any system vanishes in the state for which*

$(\partial U/\partial S)_{V,N_1 \cdots N_r} = 0$ *(that is, at the zero of temperature)*

This postulate is an extension, due to Planck, of the so-called *Nernst postulate or third law of thermodynamics.* Historically, it was the latest of the postulates to be developed, being inconsistent with classical statistical mechanics and requiring the prior establishment of quantum statistics in order that it could be properly appreciated. The bulk of thermodynamics does not require this postulate, and we make no further reference to it until Chapter 10. Nevertheless, we have chosen to present the postulate at this point to close the postulatory basis.

The foregoing postulates are the logical bases of our development of thermodynamics. In the light of these postulates, then, it may be well to reiterate briefly the method of solution of the standard type of thermo-dynamic problem, as formulated in section 1.8. We are given a composite system and we assume the fundamental equation of each of the constituent systems to be known in principle. These fundamental equations determine the individual entropies of the subsystems when these systems are in equilibrium. If the total composite system is in a constrained equilibrium state, with particular values of the extensive parameters of each con-stituent system, the total entropy is obtained by addition of the individual entropies. This total entropy is known as a function of the various extensive parameters of the subsystems. By straightforward differentia-tion, we compute the extrema of the total entropy function, and then, on the basis of the sign of the second derivative, we classify these extrema as minima, maxima, or as horizontal inflections. In an appropriate physical terminology we first find the *equilibrium states* and we then classify them on the basis of *stability.* It should be noted that in the adoption of this conventional terminology we augment our previous definition of equilibrium; that which was previously termed equilibrium is now termed *stable equilibrium*, whereas *unstable equilibrium* states are newly defined in terms of extrema other than maxima.

It is perhaps appropriate at this point to acknowledge that although all applications of thermodynamics are equivalent in principle to the procedure outlined there are several alternative procedures that frequently prove more convenient. These alternate procedures are developed in subsequent chapters. Thus we shall show that under appropriate conditions the energy $U(S, V, N_1 \cdots)$ may be minimized rather than the entropy $S(U, V, N_1 \cdots)$ maximized. That these two procedures determine the same final state is analogous to the fact that a circle may be characterized either as the closed curve of minimum perimeter for a given area or as the closed curve of maximum area for a given perimeter. In later chapters we also introduce several new functions, the minimization of which is logically equivalent to the minimization of the energy or to the maximization of the entropy.

The inversion of the fundamental equation and the alternative statement of the basic extremum principle in terms of a minimum of the energy rather than a maximum of the entropy suggests another viewpoint from which the extremum postulate perhaps may appear plausible. In the theories of electricity and mechanics, ignoring thermal effects, the energy is a function of various mechanical parameters, and the condition of equilibrium is that the energy shall be a minimum. Thus a cone is stable lying on its side, rather than standing on its point, because the first position is of lower energy. If thermal effects are to be included, the energy ceases to be a function simply of the mechanical parameters. According to the inverted fundamental equation, however, the energy is a function of the mechanical parameters and of one additional parameter (the entropy). By the introduction of this additional parameter the form of the energy-minimum principle is extended to the domain of thermal effects as well as to pure mechanical phenomena. In this manner we obtain a · sort of correspondence principle between thermodynamics and mechanics—insuring that the thermodynamic equilibrium principle reduces to the mechanical equilibrium principle when thermal effects can be neglected.

We shall see that the mathematical condition that a maximum of $S(U, V, N_1 \cdots)$ implies a minimum of $U(S, V, N_1 \cdots)$ is that the derivative $(\partial S / \partial U)_{V, N_1 \ldots}$ be positive. The motivation for the introduction of this statement in postulate III may be understood in terms of our desire to insure that the entropy maximum principle will go over into an energy minimum principle on inversion of the fundamental equation.

The attention of the reader is called to Appendix B, in which the entropy is given an atomistic significance in terms of statistical mechanical concepts. Our further considerations do not depend in any way on the material in the Appendix. However, the reader who is plagued by the question "But what is the entropy?" may wish to allay this curiosity by reading Appendix B at this point.

Problems—Section 1.9

1.9–1. The following ten equations are purported to be fundamental equations of various thermodynamic systems. However, five are inconsistent with one or more of postulates II, III, and IV and consequently are not physically acceptable. Find the five that are not physically permissible and indicate the postulate violated by each.

The quantities v_0, θ, and R are positive constants, and in all cases in which fractional exponents appear only the real positive root is to be taken.

(a) $\quad S = \left(\dfrac{R^2}{v_0\theta}\right)^{1/3} [NVU]^{1/3}$

(b) $\quad S = \left(\dfrac{R}{\theta^2}\right)^{1/3} \left[\dfrac{NU}{V}\right]^{2/3}$

(c) $\quad S = \left(\dfrac{R}{\theta}\right)^{1/2} \left[NU - \dfrac{R\theta V^2}{v_0^2}\right]^{1/2}$

(d) $\quad S = \left(\dfrac{R^2\theta}{v_0^3}\right) V^3/NU$

(e) $\quad S = \left(\dfrac{R^3}{v_0\theta^2}\right)^{1/5} [N^2VU^2]^{1/5}$

(f) $\quad S = NR \ln (UV/N^2R\theta v_0)$

(g) $\quad S = \left(\dfrac{R}{\theta}\right)^{1/2} [NU]^{1/2} \exp (-V^2/2N^2v_0^2)$

(h) $\quad S = \left(\dfrac{R}{\theta}\right)^{1/2} [NU]^{1/2} \exp \left(-\dfrac{UV}{NR\theta v_0}\right)$

(i) $\quad U = \left(\dfrac{v_0\theta}{R}\right) \dfrac{S^2}{V} \exp (S/NR)$

(j) $\quad U = \left(\dfrac{R\theta}{v_0}\right) NV \left(1 + \dfrac{S}{NR}\right) \exp (-S/NR)$

1.9–2. For each of the five physically acceptable fundamental equations in problem 1.9–1 find U as a function of S, V, and N.

1.9–3. The fundamental equation of system A is

$$S_A = \left(\frac{R^2}{v_0\theta}\right)^{\frac{1}{3}}[N_A V_A U_A]^{\frac{1}{3}}$$

and that of system B is

$$S_B = \left(\frac{R^2}{v_0\theta}\right)^{\frac{1}{3}}[N_B V_B U_B]^{\frac{1}{3}}$$

What is the fundamental equation of the composite system $A + B$?

1.9–4. Assume that the internal wall between subsystems A and B in problem 1.9–3 is restrictive with respect to both volume and mole number but non-restrictive with respect to energy; that is, it is rigid, impermeable, and diathermal. Assume that system A has a volume of 9 cm^3 and a mole number of 3 moles. System B has a volume of 4 cm^3 and a mole number of 2 moles. The total energy in the composite system is 20 cal. Plot the entropy against the fraction $U_A/(U_A + U_B)$ of the energy in subsystem A. When the system has come to equilibrium, what are the internal energies of each of the individual subsystems?

CHAPTER 2

The Conditions
of Equilibrium

2.1 Intensive Parameters

By virtue of our interest in processes and in the associated changes of the extensive parameters, we anticipate that we shall be concerned with the differential form of the fundamental equation. Writing the fundamental equation in the form

$$U = U(S, V, N_1, N_2 \cdots N_r) \tag{2.1}$$

we compute the first differential:

$$dU = \left(\frac{\partial U}{\partial S}\right)_{V, N_1 \cdots N_r} dS + \left(\frac{\partial U}{\partial V}\right)_{S, N_1 \cdots N_r} dV + \sum_{j=1}^{r} \left(\frac{\partial U}{\partial N_j}\right)_{S, V \cdots N_k} dN_j \tag{2.2}$$

The various partial derivatives appearing in the foregoing equation recur so frequently that it is convenient to introduce special symbols for them. They are called *intensive parameters*, and the following notation is conventional:

$$\left(\frac{\partial U}{\partial S}\right)_{V, N_1 \cdots N_r} \equiv T, \quad \text{the } \textit{temperature} \tag{2.3}$$

$$-\left(\frac{\partial U}{\partial V}\right)_{S, N_1 \cdots N_r} \equiv P, \quad \text{the } \textit{pressure} \tag{2.4}$$

$$\left(\frac{\partial U}{\partial N_j}\right)_{S, V \cdots N_k \cdots} \equiv \mu_j, \quad \begin{array}{l}\text{the } \textit{electrochemical potential of}\\ \textit{the jth component}\end{array} \tag{2.5}$$

31

With this notation, equation 2.2 becomes

$$dU = T\,dS - P\,dV + \mu_1\,dN_1 + \cdots + \mu_r\,dN_r \qquad (2.6)$$

The formal definition of the temperature soon will be shown to agree with our intuitive qualitative concept, based on the physiological notion of "hot" and "cold." We certainly would be reluctant to adopt a definition of the temperature that would contradict such strongly entrenched although qualitative notions. For the moment, however, we merely introduce the concept of temperature by the formal definition (2.3).

Similarly, we shall soon corroborate that the pressure defined by equation 2.4 agrees in every respect with the pressure defined in mechanics. With respect to the several electrochemical potentials, we have no prior definitions or concepts and we are free to adopt the definition (equation 2.5) forthwith.

For brevity, the electrochemical potential is often referred to simply as the *chemical potential*, and we shall use these two terms interchangeably. However it should be noted that occasionally, and particularly in the theory of solids, the chemical potential is defined as μ minus the molar electrostatic energy.

The term $-P\,dV$ in equation 2.6 is identified as the quasi-static work dW_M, as given by equation 1.1.

In the special case of constant mole numbers equation 2.6 can then be written as

$$T\,dS = dU - dW_M \qquad \text{if} \quad dN_1 = dN_2 = dN_r = 0 \qquad (2.7)$$

Recalling our definition of the quasi-static heat, or comparing equation 2.7 with equation 1.2, we now recognize $T\,dS$ as the quasi-static heat flux.

$$dQ = T\,dS \qquad (2.8)$$

A quasi-static flux of heat into a system is associated with an increase of entropy of that system.

The remaining terms in equation 2.6 represent an increase of internal energy associated with the addition of matter to a system. This type of energy flux, although intuitively meaningful, is not frequently discussed outside thermodynamics and does not have a familiar distinctive name. We shall call $\sum_j \mu_j\,dN_j$ the *quasi-static chemical work*.

$$dW_c \equiv \sum_{j=1}^{r} \mu_j\,dN_j \qquad (2.9)$$

Therefore

$$dU = dQ + dW_M + dW_c \qquad (2.10)$$

2.2 Equations of State

The temperature, pressure, and the electrochemical potentials are partial derivatives of a function of $S, V, N_1 \cdots N_r$ and consequently are also functions of $S, V, N_1 \cdots N_r$. We thus have a set of functional relationships,

$$T = T(S, V, N_1 \cdots N_r) \tag{2.11}$$

$$P = P(S, V, N_1 \cdots N_r) \tag{2.12}$$

$$\mu_j = \mu_j(S, V, N_1 \cdots N_r) \tag{2.13}$$

Such relationships, expressing intensive parameters in terms of the independent extensive parameters, are called _equations of state._

Knowledge of a single equation of state does _not_ constitute complete knowledge of the thermodynamic properties of a system. We shall see, subsequently, that knowledge of _all_ the equations of state of a system is equivalent to knowledge of the fundamental equation and consequently is thermodynamically complete.

The fact that the fundamental equation of a system is homogeneous first-order has direct implications for the functional form of the equations of state. It follows immediately that the equations of state are _homogeneous zero-order_. That is, multiplication of each of the independent extensive parameters by a scalar λ leaves the function unchanged.

$$T(\lambda S, \lambda V, \lambda N_1 \cdots \lambda N_r) = T(S, V, N_1 \cdots N_r) \tag{2.14}$$

It therefore follows that the temperature of a composite system composed of two identical subsystems is equal to the temperature of either subsystem. This is certainly in agreement with our intuitive concept of temperature. The pressure and the electrochemical potentials also have the property (2.14).

To summarize the foregoing considerations, it is convenient to adopt a condensed notation. We denote the extensive parameters $V, N_1 \cdots N_r$ by the symbols $X_1, X_2 \cdots X_t$, so that the fundamental relation takes the form

$$U = U(S, X_1, X_2 \cdots X_t) \tag{2.15}$$

The intensive parameters are denoted by

$$\left(\frac{\partial U}{\partial S}\right)_{X_1, X_2 \cdots} \equiv T = T(S, X_1, X_2 \cdots X_t) \tag{2.16}$$

$$\left(\frac{\partial U}{\partial X_j}\right)_{S \cdots X_k \cdots} \equiv P_j = P_j(S, X_1, X_2 \cdots X_t) \quad j = 1, 2 \cdots t \tag{2.17}$$

whence

$$dU = T\, dS + \sum_{j=1}^{t} P_j\, dX_j \tag{2.18}$$

The negative sign which appears in equation 2.4, but which does not appear in equation 2.17, should be noted. The formalism of thermodynamics is uniform if the *negative pressure*, $-P$, is considered an intensive parameter, analogous to T and $\mu_1, \mu_2 \cdots$. Correspondingly one of the general intensive parameters P_j of equation 2.17 is $-P$.

For single-component simple systems the energy differential is frequently written in terms of molar quantities, and we briefly indicate this form for completeness. Analogous to equations 1.11–1.15 the fundamental equation per mole is

$$u = u(s, v) \tag{2.19}$$

where

$$s = S/N, \qquad v = V/N \tag{2.20}$$

and

$$u(s, v) = \frac{1}{N} U(S, V, N) \tag{2.21}$$

Taking an infinitesimal variation of equation 2.19,

$$du = \frac{\partial u}{\partial s} ds + \frac{\partial u}{\partial v} \partial v \tag{2.22}$$

However,

$$\left(\frac{\partial u}{\partial s}\right)_v = \left(\frac{\partial u}{\partial s}\right)_{V,N} = \left(\frac{\partial U}{\partial S}\right)_{V,N} = T \tag{2.23}$$

and similarly

$$\left(\frac{\partial u}{\partial v}\right)_s = -P \tag{2.24}$$

Thus

$$du = T\, ds - P\, dv \tag{2.25}$$

Problems—Section 2.2

2.2-1.   Find the three equations of state for a system with the fundamental equation

$$U = \left(\frac{v_0\theta}{R^2}\right)\frac{S^3}{NV}$$

2.2-2.   For the system of problem 2.2-1 find μ as a function of T, V, and N.

2.2-3.   Show by a diagram (drawn to arbitrary scale) the dependence of pressure on volume for fixed temperature for the system of problem 2.2-1. Draw two such "isotherms," corresponding to two values of the temperature, and indicate which isotherm corresponds to the higher temperature.

2.2-4.   Find the three equations of state for a system with the fundamental equation

$$u = \left(\frac{\theta}{R}\right)s^2 + \left(\frac{R\theta}{v_0{}^2}\right)v^2$$

2.2–5. Express μ as a function of T and P for the system of problem 2.2–4.

2.2–6. Find the three equations of state for a system with the fundamental equation

$$u = \left(\frac{v_0\theta}{R}\right)\frac{s^2}{v}\, e^{s/R}$$

2.2–7. Indicate schematically the dependence of temperature on volume in an adiabatic quasi-static expansion ($dS = 0$) for the system of problem 2.2–6.

2.2–8. By substituting equations 2.20 and 2.21 into equation 2.25, show that the appropriate form of equation 2.6 is regained.

2.3 Entropic Intensive Parameters

If, instead of considering the fundamental equation in the form $U = U(S \cdots X_j \cdots)$ with U as dependent, we had considered S as dependent, we could have carried out all the foregoing formalism in an inverted but equivalent fashion. Adopting the notation X_0 for U, we write

$$S = S(X_0, X_1 \cdots X_t) \tag{2.26}$$

We take an infinitesimal variation to obtain

$$dS = \sum_{k=0}^{t} \frac{\partial S}{\partial X_k} dX_k \tag{2.27}$$

The quantities $\partial S/\partial X_k$ are denoted by F_k.

$$F_k \equiv \frac{\partial S}{\partial X_k} \tag{2.28}$$

By carefully noting which variables are kept constant in the various partial derivatives and by using the calculus of partial derivatives as reviewed in Appendix A, the reader can demonstrate that

$$F_0 = \frac{1}{T}, \qquad F_k = \frac{-P_k}{T}, \qquad k = 1, 2, 3 \cdots \tag{2.29}$$

These equations also follow from solving equation 2.18 for dS and comparing with equation 2.27.

Despite the close relationship between the F_k and the P_k, there is a very important difference in principle. Namely, the P_k are obtained by differentiating a function of $S \cdots X_j \cdots$ and are considered as functions of these variables, whereas the F_k are obtained by differentiating a function of $U \cdots X_j \cdots$ and are considered as functions of these variables. That is, in one case the entropy is a member of the set of independent parameters, and in the second case the energy is such a member. In performing formal manipulations in thermodynamics, it is extremely important to make a definite commitment to one or the other of these choices and to adhere rigorously to that choice. A great deal of confusion results from a vacillation between these two alternatives within a single problem.

If the entropy is considered dependent and the energy, independent, as in $S = S(U \cdots X_k \cdots)$, we shall refer to the analysis as being in the _entropy representation._ If the energy is dependent and the entropy is independent, as in $U = U(S \cdots X_k \cdots)$, we shall refer to the analysis as being in the _energy representation._

The formal development of thermodynamics can be carried out in either the energy or entropy representations alone, but for the solution of a particular problem either one or the other representation may prove to be by far the more convenient. Accordingly, we shall develop the two representations in parallel, although a discussion presented in one representation generally requires only a brief outline in the alternate representation.

The relation $S = S(X_0 \cdots X_j \cdots)$ is said to be the _entropic fundamental relation_, the set of variables $X_0 \cdots X_j \cdots$ is called the _entropic extensive parameters_, and the set of variables $F_0 \cdots F_j \cdots$ is called the _entropic intensive parameters._ Similarly, the relation $U = U(S, X_1 \cdots X_j \cdots)$ is said to be the _energetic fundamental relation_, the set of variables $S, X_1 \cdots X_j \cdots$ is called the _energetic extensive parameters_, and the set of variables $P_1 \cdots P_j \cdots$ is called the _energetic intensive parameters._

Problems—Section 2.3

2.3–1.   Find the three equations of state in the entropy representation for a system with the fundamental equation

$$u = \left(\frac{v_0^{1/2}\theta}{R^{3/2}}\right)\frac{s^{5/2}}{v^{1/2}}$$

2.3–2.   Show by a diagram (drawn to arbitrary scale) the dependence of temperature on volume for fixed pressure for the system of problem 2.3–1. Draw two such "isobars," corresponding to two values of the pressure, and indicate which isobar corresponds to the higher pressure.

2.3–3.   Find the three equations of state in the entropy representation for a system with the fundamental equation

$$u = \left(\frac{\theta}{R}\right)s^2 e^{v^2/v_0^2}$$

2.4 Thermal Equilibrium—Temperature

We are now in a position to illustrate several interesting implications of the extremum principle which we have postulated for the entropy. Consider a closed composite system consisting of two simple systems separated by a wall that is rigid and impermeable to matter but that does allow the flow of heat. The volumes and mole numbers of each of the simple systems are fixed, but the energies $U^{(1)}$ and $U^{(2)}$ are free to change, subject to the conservation restriction

$$U^{(1)} + U^{(2)} = \text{constant} \qquad (2.30)$$

imposed by the closure of the composite system as a whole. Assuming that the system has come to equilibrium, we wish to find the values of $U^{(1)}$ and $U^{(2)}$. Now, by our fundamental postulate, the values of $U^{(1)}$ and $U^{(2)}$ are such as to maximize the entropy. Therefore, by the usual mathematical condition for an extremum, we conclude that in the equilibrium state a virtual infinitesimal transfer of energy from system 1 to system 2 will produce no change in the entropy of the whole system. That is,

$$dS = 0 \qquad (2.31)$$

The additivity of the entropy for the two subsystems gives the relation

$$S = S^{(1)}(U^{(1)}, V^{(1)} \cdots N_j^{(1)} \cdots) + S^{(2)}(U^{(2)}, V^{(2)} \cdots N_j^{(2)} \cdots). \qquad (2.32)$$

As $U^{(1)}$ and $U^{(2)}$ are changed by the virtual energy transfer, the entropy change is

$$dS = \left(\frac{\partial S^{(1)}}{\partial U^{(1)}}\right)_{V^{(1)} \cdots N_j^{(1)} \cdots} dU^{(1)} + \left(\frac{\partial S^{(2)}}{\partial U^{(2)}}\right)_{V^{(2)} \cdots N_j^{(2)} \cdots} dU^{(2)} \qquad (2.33)$$

or, employing our definition of the temperature,

$$dS = \frac{1}{T^{(1)}} dU^{(1)} + \frac{1}{T^{(2)}} dU^{(2)} \qquad (2.34)$$

By the conservation condition (equation 2.30), we have

$$dU^{(2)} = -dU^{(1)} \qquad (2.35)$$

whence

$$dS = \left(\frac{1}{T^{(1)}} - \frac{1}{T^{(2)}}\right) dU^{(1)} \qquad (2.36)$$

The condition of equilibrium (equation 2.31) demands that dS vanish for arbitrary values of $dU^{(1)}$, whence

$$\boxed{\frac{1}{T^{(1)}} = \frac{1}{T^{(2)}}} \qquad \text{entropy representation} \qquad (2.37)$$

This is the condition of equilibrium. If the fundamental equations of each of the subsystems were known, then $1/T^{(1)}$ would be a known function of $U^{(1)}$ (and also of $V^{(1)}$ and $N_k^{(1)} \cdots$, which, however, are merely constants). Similarly, $1/T^{(2)}$ would be a known function of $U^{(2)}$, and the equation $1/T^{(1)} = 1/T^{(2)}$ would be one equation in $U^{(1)}$ and $U^{(2)}$. The conservation condition $U^{(1)} + U^{(2)} = \text{constant}$ provides a second equation, and these two equations completely determine, in principle, the values of $U^{(1)}$ and of $U^{(2)}$. To proceed further and actually to obtain the values of $U^{(1)}$ and of $U^{(2)}$ would require knowledge of the explicit forms of the fundamental equations of the systems. In thermodynamic theory, however, we accept the existence of the fundamental equations, but we do not assume explicit forms for them, and we therefore do not obtain explicit answers. In practical applications of thermodynamics the fundamental equations may be known, either by empirical observations (in terms of measurements to be described later) or on the basis of statistical mechanical calculations based on simple models. In this way applied thermodynamics is able to lead to explicit numerical answers.

Equation 2.37 could also be written as $T^{(1)} = T^{(2)}$. We write it in the form $1/T^{(1)} = 1/T^{(2)}$ to stress the fact that our analysis is couched in the entropy representation. By writing $1/T^{(1)}$, we indicate a function of $U^{(1)}$, $V^{(1)} \cdots$, whereas $T^{(1)}$ would imply a function of $S^{(1)}$, $V^{(1)} \cdots$. The *physical* significance of equation 2.37, however, remains the equality of the temperatures of the two subsystems.

A second phase of the problem is the investigation of the stability of the predicted final state. In the solution given we have not exploited fully the basic postulate that the entropy is a maximum in equilibrium, but we merely have investigated the consequences of the fact that it is an extremum. The condition that it be a maximum requires, in addition to the condition $dS = 0$, that

$$d^2S < 0 \qquad\qquad (2.38)$$

The consequences of this condition lead to considerations of stability, to which we shall give explicit attention in Chapter 8.

2.5 Agreement with Intuitive Concept of Temperature

In the foregoing example we have seen that if two systems are separated by a diathermal wall heat will flow until each of the systems attains the same temperature. This prediction is in agreement with our intuitive notion of temperature, and it is the first of several observations that corroborate the plausibility of our formal definition of the temperature.

Inquiring into our example in slightly more detail, we suppose that the two subsystems are initially separated by an adiabatic wall and that the temperatures of the two subsystems are almost, but not quite, equal. In particular let us assume that

$$T^{(1)} > T^{(2)} \qquad (2.39)$$

The system is considered to be in equilibrium with respect to the internal adiabatic constraint. If, now, the internal adiabatic constraint is removed, the system is no longer in equilibrium, heat flows across the wall, and the entropy of the composite system *increases*. Finally the system comes to a new equilibrium state, determined by the condition that the final values of $T^{(1)}$ and $T^{(2)}$ are equal and with the maximum possible value of the entropy that is consistent with the remaining constraints. Let us now compare the initial and the final states. If ΔS denotes the entropy difference between the final and initial states, we have

$$\Delta S > 0 \qquad (2.40)$$

But, as in equation 2.34, we find

$$\Delta S \simeq \left(\frac{1}{T^{(1)}} - \frac{1}{T^{(2)}} \right) \Delta U^{(1)} \qquad (2.41)$$

where $T^{(1)}$ and $T^{(2)}$ are the initial values of the temperatures. By the condition that $T^{(1)} > T^{(2)}$, we now find that

$$\Delta U^{(1)} < 0 \qquad (2.42)$$

This means that the spontaneous process that occurred was one in which heat flowed *from* subsystem 1 *to* subsystem 2. We conclude therefore that heat tends to flow *from* a system with a *high* value of T *to* a system with a *low* value of T. This is again in agreement with our intuitive notion of the temperature. It should be noted that these conclusions do not depend on our assumption that $T^{(1)}$ is approximately equal to $T^{(2)}$; this assumption was made merely for the purpose of obtaining mathematical simplicity in equation 2.41, which otherwise would require a formulation in terms of integrals.

If we now take stock of our intuitive notion of temperature, based on the physiological sensations of hot and cold, we realize that it is based upon two essential properties. First, we expect temperature to be an intensive parameter, having the same value in a part of a system as it has in the entire system. Second, we expect that heat should tend to flow from regions of high temperature toward regions of low temperature. These properties imply that thermal equilibrium is associated with equality and homogeneity of the temperature. We have demonstrated that our formal definition of the temperature possesses each of these properties, so that we have now corroborated that our definition is intuitively satisfactory.

2.6 Temperature Units

The physical dimensions of temperature are those of energy divided by those of entropy. But we have not yet committed ourselves on the dimensions of entropy; in fact its dimensions can be selected quite arbitrarily. For if the entropy is multiplied by any dimensional constant, we obtain a new function of different dimensions but with exactly the same extremum properties and therefore also quite acceptable as the entropy. The only restriction we must maintain is that the product of temperature and entropy have the dimensions of energy. We summarily resolve the arbitrariness simply by adopting the convention that the entropy is dimensionless; from the more incisive viewpoint of statistical mechanics, this is a physically reasonable choice. Consequently the dimensions of temperature are identical to those of energy. However, just as torque and work have the same dimensions, but are very different types of quantities and are measured in different units (the cm-dyne and the erg, respectively), so the temperature and the energy must be carefully distinguished. The *dimensions* of both energy and temperature are [mass · (length)^2/(time)^2]. The *units* of energy are joules, ergs, calories, etc. The units of temperature remain to be discussed.

In our later discussion of thermodynamic engines and of the Carnot cycle we show that the ratio of the temperatures of two given systems can be measured directly and unambiguously. The measurability of the ratio of temperatures determines the scale of temperature, except for an arbitrary multiplicative constant. The temperature of some arbitrarily chosen standard system may be assigned at will, and the temperatures of all other systems are then uniquely determined, with values directly proportional to the chosen temperature of the fiducial system.

Various choices of a fiducial system, and various assignments of its temperature, lead to different scales of temperature. The *absolute Kelvin* scale of temperature is obtained by assigning the number 273.16 to the temperature of a mixture of pure ice, water, and water vapor in mutual equilibrium; a state which we show in our later discussion of "triple points" to determine a unique temperature. The corresponding unit of temperature is called a *degree Kelvin*, designated by the notation °K. The temperature of the ice-water vapor system then is 273.16°K.

The *absolute Fahrenheit* scale is obtained by assigning the temperature $9/5(273.16) = 491.688°R$ to the ice-water-vapor system referred to. The unit, denoted by °R, is called the *absolute Fahrenheit degree*, or the *degree Rankine*. Absolute Fahrenheit temperatures are merely $\frac{9}{5}$ times the corresponding absolute Kelvin temperature.

The definitions cited are those adopted by the Tenth General Conference of Weights and Measures in 1954, and by universal acceptance they supplant the earlier definitions in terms of two fixed points.

Closely related to the absolute Kelvin scale of temperature is the *international Kelvin* scale, which is a "practical" scale, defined in terms of the properties of particular systems in various temperature ranges and contrived to coincide as closely as possible with the absolute Kelvin scale. The practical advantage of the international Kelvin scale is that it provides reproducible laboratory standards for temperature measurement throughout the temperature range. However, from the thermodynamic point of view it is not a true temperature scale at all, and to the extent that it deviates from the absolute scale it will not yield temperature ratios that are consistent with those demanded by the thermodynamic formalism.

Still another scale of temperature is the *thermodynamic Celsius* scale. The unit of temperature is the *degree Celsius*, denoted by °C, and this unit is identical in size with the absolute degree Kelvin. The thermodynamic Celsius temperatures are defined (by the 1954 agreement) as 273.15 less than Kelvin temperatures. The temperature of ice, water, and water-vapor in equilibrium is 0.01°C. However, the temperature of a mixture of ice and water at 1 atm pressure is very nearly 0°C, with the error appearing only in the third decimal place, and the temperature of boiling water at 1 atm pressure is approximately 100°C. Consequently, the Celsius scale provides convenient numbers for general use.

Clearly the Celsius scale yields different temperature ratios than the Kelvin scale, and consequently the Celsius scale is *not* an acceptable scale for thermodynamic use. Celsius temperatures must be converted into Kelvin temperatures (merely by the addition of 273.15) before substitution in thermodynamic formulas.

Prior to the 1954 international agreement, the Celsius scale was referred to in many countries, including the United States, as the *Centigrade scale*.

An international Celsius scale is defined as bearing the same relationship to the international Kelvin scale as the thermodynamic Celsius scale bears to the absolute Kelvin scale. To the accuracy that will generally concern us, we need make no distinction between the two Kelvin scales nor between the two Celsius scales, but the difference in principle should be kept in mind.

Finally, a Fahrenheit scale is defined in terms of the absolute Fahrenheit scale by subtraction of 459.67. This number is exactly $9/5(273.15) - 32$.

It follows that conversion of a Celsius temperature to a Fahrenheit temperature involves multiplication by $\frac{9}{5}$ and addition of 32. The temperature of ice and water at 1 atm pressure is about 32°F, the temperature of boiling water at 1 atm pressure is about 212°F, and room temperatures are in the vicinity of 70°F.

Although we have defined the temperature formally in terms of a partial derivative of the fundamental relation, we note briefly, in conclusion, the conventional method of introduction of the temperature concept, as developed by Kelvin and Caratheodory. The heat flux dQ is first defined very much as we have introduced it in connection with the energy conservation principle. From the consideration of certain cyclic processes it is then inferred that there exists an integrating factor $(1/T)$ such that the product of this integrating factor with the imperfect differential dQ is a perfect differential (dS).

$$dS = \frac{1}{T} dQ \qquad (2.43)$$

The temperature and the entropy thereby are introduced by analysis of the existence of integrating factors in particular types of differential equations called *Pfaffian forms*.

Problems—Section 2.6

2.6–1. The temperature of a system composed of ice, water, and water-vapor in mutual equilibrium has a temperature of *exactly* 273.16°K, by definition. The temperature of a system of ice and water at 1 atm of pressure is then measured as 273.15°K, with the third and later decimal places uncertain. The temperature of a system of water and water-vapor (i.e. boiling water) at 1 atm is measured as 373.15°K $\pm$ 0.01°K. Compute the temperature of water–water-vapor at 1 atm, with its probable error, on the Celsius, absolute Fahrenheit, and Fahrenheit scales.

2.6–2. The "gas constant" R is a constant having the value $R = 1.986$ cal/mole°K. Since the size of the Celsius degree is the same as the Kelvin degree, it also has the value 1.986 cal/mole°C. Express R in units of joules/mole°F.

2.6–3. Two particular systems have the following equations of state:

$$\frac{1}{T^{(1)}} = \frac{3}{2} R \frac{N^{(1)}}{U^{(1)}}$$

and

$$\frac{1}{T^{(2)}} = \frac{5}{2} R \frac{N^{(2)}}{U^{(2)}}$$

where R is a constant having the value 1.986 cal/mole°K. The mole number of the first system is $N^{(1)} = 2$, and that of the second is $N^{(2)} = 3$. The two systems are separated by a diathermal wall, and the total energy in the composite system is 6000 cal. What is the internal energy of each system in equilibrium?

2.6–4. Two systems with the equations of state given in problem 2.6–3 are separated by a diathermal wall. The respective mole numbers are $N^{(1)} = 2$ and $N^{(2)} = 3$. The initial temperatures are $T^{(1)} = 250°K$ and $T^{(2)} = 350°K$. What are the values of $U^{(1)}$ and $U^{(2)}$ after equilibrium has been established? What is the equilibrium temperature?

2.7 Mechanical Equilibrium

A second application of the extremum principle for the entropy yields an even simpler result and therefore is useful in making the procedure clear. We consider a closed composite system consisting of two simple systems separated by a movable diathermal wall that is impervious to the flow of matter. The values of the mole numbers are fixed and constant, but the values of $U^{(1)}$ and $U^{(2)}$ may change, subject only to the closure condition

$$U^{(1)} + U^{(2)} = \text{constant} \tag{2.44}$$

and the values of $V^{(1)}$ and $V^{(2)}$ may change, subject only to the closure condition

$$V^{(1)} + V^{(2)} = \text{constant} \tag{2.45}$$

The extremum principle requires that no change in entropy result from infinitesimal virtual processes consisting of transfer of heat across the wall and displacement of the wall.

Then

$$dS = 0 \tag{2.46}$$

where

$$dS = \left(\frac{\partial S^{(1)}}{\partial U^{(1)}}\right)_{V^{(1)} \cdots N_k^{(1)} \cdots} dU^{(1)} + \left(\frac{\partial S^{(1)}}{\partial V^{(1)}}\right)_{U^{(1)} \cdots N_k^{(1)} \cdots} dV^{(1)}$$

$$+ \left(\frac{\partial S^{(2)}}{\partial U^{(2)}}\right)_{V^{(2)} \cdots N_k^{(2)} \cdots} dU^{(2)} + \left(\frac{\partial S^{(2)}}{\partial V^{(2)}}\right)_{U^{(2)} \cdots N_k^{(2)} \cdots} dV^{(2)} \tag{2.47}$$

By the closure conditions

$$dU^{(2)} = -dU^{(1)} \tag{2.48}$$

and

$$dV^{(2)} = -dV^{(1)} \tag{2.49}$$

whence

$$dS = \left(\frac{1}{T^{(1)}} - \frac{1}{T^{(2)}}\right) dU^{(1)} + \left(\frac{P^{(1)}}{T^{(1)}} - \frac{P^{(2)}}{T^{(2)}}\right) dV^{(1)} = 0 \tag{2.50}$$

As this expression must vanish for arbitrary and independent values of $dU^{(1)}$ and $dV^{(1)}$, we must have

and

$$\frac{1}{T^{(1)}} - \frac{1}{T^{(2)}} = 0 \qquad \text{(2.51)}$$

entropy representation (2.51)

$$\frac{P^{(1)}}{T^{(1)}} - \frac{P^{(2)}}{T^{(2)}} = 0 \qquad \text{(2.52)}$$

Although these two equations are the equilibrium conditions in the proper form, appropriate to the entropy representation, we note that they imply the physical conditions of equality of both temperature and pressure.

$$T^{(1)} = T^{(2)} \qquad \text{(2.53)}$$

$$P^{(1)} = P^{(2)} \qquad \text{(2.54)}$$

The equality of the temperatures is just our previous result for equilibrium with a diathermal wall. The equality of the pressures is the new feature introduced by the fact that the wall is movable. Of course, the equality of the pressures is precisely the result that we would expect on the basis of mechanics, and this result corroborates our identification of the function P as the mechanical pressure.

The reader may ask why we have considered the problem of a movable diathermal wall rather than the ostensibly simpler case of a movable adiabatic wall. The latter, unfortunately, is a subtle problem lacking a unique physical answer. As the difficulties of this problem are quite specialized, we shall not consider it here, but a discussion is given in Appendix C for the interested reader.

Problems—Section 2.7

2.7–1. Two particular systems have the following equations of state:

$$\frac{1}{T^{(1)}} = \frac{3}{2} R \frac{N^{(1)}}{U^{(1)}}, \qquad \frac{P^{(1)}}{T^{(1)}} = R \frac{N^{(1)}}{V^{(1)}}$$

and

$$\frac{1}{T^{(2)}} = \frac{5}{2} R \frac{N^{(2)}}{U^{(2)}}, \qquad \frac{P^{(2)}}{T^{(2)}} = R \frac{N^{(2)}}{V^{(2)}}$$

where $R = 1.986$ cal/mole°K. The mole number of the first system is $N^{(1)} = 0.5$, and that of the second is $N^{(2)} = 0.75$. The two systems are contained in a closed cylinder, separated by a movable diathermal piston. The initial temperatures are $T^{(1)} = 200$°K and $T^{(2)} = 300$°K, and the total volume is 20 liters. What is the energy and the volume of each system in equilibrium? What is the pressure and the temperature?

2.8 Equilibrium with Respect to Matter Flow

A final example employing the entropy maximum principle gives some insight into the nature of the chemical potential. We consider the equilibrium state of <u>two simple systems connected by a rigid and dia-thermal wall, permeable to one type of material (N_1) and impermeable to all others ($N_2, N_3 \cdots N_r$).</u> We thus seek the equilibrium values of $U^{(1)}$ and $U^{(2)}$ and of $N_1^{(1)}$ and $N_1^{(2)}$. The virtual change in entropy in the appropriate virtual process is

$$dS = \frac{1}{T^{(1)}} dU^{(1)} - \frac{\mu_1^{(1)}}{T^{(1)}} dN_1^{(1)} + \frac{1}{T^{(2)}} dU^{(2)} - \frac{\mu_1^{(2)}}{T^{(2)}} dN_1^{(2)} \qquad (2.55)$$

and the closure conditions demand

$$dU^{(2)} = -dU^{(1)} \qquad (2.56)$$

and

$$dN_1^{(2)} = -dN_1^{(1)} \qquad (2.57)$$

whence

$$dS = \left(\frac{1}{T^{(1)}} - \frac{1}{T^{(2)}} \right) dU^{(1)} - \left(\frac{\mu_1^{(1)}}{T^{(1)}} - \frac{\mu_1^{(2)}}{T^{(2)}} \right) dN_1^{(1)} \qquad (2.58)$$

As dS must vanish for arbitrary values of both $dU^{(1)}$ and $dN_1^{(1)}$, we find as the conditions of equilibrium

$$\boxed{\frac{1}{T^{(1)}} = \frac{1}{T^{(2)}}} \qquad (2.59)$$

and

$$\boxed{\frac{\mu_1^{(1)}}{T^{(1)}} = \frac{\mu_1^{(2)}}{T^{(2)}}} \quad \text{(whence also } \mu_1^{(1)} = \mu_1^{(2)}) \qquad (2.60)$$

Thus, just as the temperature can be looked upon as a sort of "potential" for heat flux and the pressure can be looked upon as a sort of "potential" for volume changes, so the chemical potential can be looked upon as a sort of "potential" for matter flux. A difference in chemical potential provides a "generalized force" for matter flow.

The direction of the matter flow can be analyzed by the same method used in section 2.5 to analyze the direction of the heat flow. If we assume that the temperatures $T^{(1)}$ and $T^{(2)}$ are equal, equation 2.58 becomes

$$dS = \frac{\mu_1^{(2)} - \mu_1^{(1)}}{T} dN_1^{(1)} \qquad (2.61)$$

If $\mu_1^{(1)}$ is greater than $\mu_1^{(2)}$, $dN_1^{(1)}$ will be negative, since dS must be positive. Thus matter tends to flow from regions of high chemical potential to regions of low chemical potential.

In later chapters we shall see that the chemical potential provides the generalized force not only for the flow of matter from point to point but also for its changes of phase and for chemical reactions. The chemical potential thus plays a dominant role in theoretical chemistry.

The units of electrochemical potential are calories per mole, joules per mole, or any desired energy unit per mole.

Problems—Section 2.8

2.8–1. The fundamental equation of a particular type of two-component system is

$$S = NA + NR \ln \frac{U^{3/2}V}{N^{5/2}} - N_1 R \ln \frac{N_1}{N} - N_2 R \ln \frac{N_2}{N}$$

$$N \equiv N_1 + N_2$$

where $R = 1.986$ cal/mole°K and where A is an unspecified constant. A closed rigid cylinder of total volume 10 liters is divided into two chambers of equal volume by a diathermal rigid membrane, permeable to the first component but impermeable to the second. In one chamber is placed a sample of the system with original parameters $N_1^{(1)} = 0.5$, $N_2^{(1)} = 0.75$, $V^{(1)} = 5$ liters, and $T^{(1)} = 300°K$. In the second chamber is placed a sample with original parameters $N_1^{(2)} = 1$, $N_2^{(2)} = 0.5$, $V^{(2)} = 5$ liters, and $T^{(2)} = 250°K$. After equilibrium is established, what are the values of $N_1^{(1)}$, $N_1^{(2)}$, T, $P^{(1)}$ and $P^{(2)}$?

CHAPTER 3

Some Formal Relationships

3.1 The Euler Equation

Having seen how the fundamental postulates lead to a solution of the equilibrium problem, we now pause to examine in somewhat greater detail the mathematical properties of fundamental equations.

The homogeneous first-order property of the fundamental relation permits that equation to be written in a particularly convenient form, called the Euler form.

From the definition of the homogeneous first-order property we have, for any λ,

$$U(\lambda S, \lambda X_1 \cdots \lambda X_t) = \lambda U(S, X_1 \cdots X_t) \tag{3.1}$$

Differentiating with respect to λ,

$$\frac{\partial U(\cdots \lambda X_k \cdots)}{\partial(\lambda S)} \frac{\partial(\lambda S)}{\partial \lambda} + \frac{\partial U(\cdots \lambda X_k \cdots)}{\partial(\lambda X_j)} \frac{\partial(\lambda X_j)}{\partial \lambda} + \cdots = U(S, X_1 \cdots X_t) \tag{3.2}$$

or

$$\frac{\partial U(\cdots \lambda X_k \cdots)}{\partial(\lambda S)} S + \cdots \frac{\partial U(\cdots \lambda X_k)}{\partial(\lambda X_j)} X_j + \cdots = U(S, X_1 \cdots X_t) \tag{3.3}$$

This equation is true for any λ and in particular for $\lambda = 1$, in which case it takes the form

$$\frac{\partial U}{\partial S} S + \cdots \frac{\partial U}{\partial X_j} X_j + \cdots = U \tag{3.4}$$

$$\boxed{U = TS + \sum_{j=1}^{t} P_j X_j} \tag{3.5}$$

For a simple system in particular we have

$$U = TS - PV + \mu_1 N_1 + \cdots + \mu_r N_r \qquad (3.6)$$

The relation 3.5 or 3.6 is the particularization to thermodynamics of the Euler theorem on homogeneous first-order forms. The foregoing development merely reproduces the standard mathematical derivation. We refer to equation 3.5 or 3.6 as the Euler relation.

In the entropy representation the Euler relation takes the form

$$\boxed{S = \sum_{j=0}^{t} F_j X_j} \qquad (3.7)$$

or

$$S = \left(\frac{1}{T}\right) U + \left(\frac{P}{T}\right) V - \sum_{k=1}^{r} \left(\frac{\mu_k}{T}\right) N_k \qquad (3.8)$$

Problems—Section 3.1

3.1-1. Write each of the five physically acceptable fundamental equations of problem 1.9–1 in the Euler form.

3.2 The Gibbs–Duhem Relation

In Chapter 2 we arrived at equilibrium criteria involving the temperature, pressure, and the chemical potentials. Each of the intensive parameters entered the theory in a similar way, and the formalism is, in fact, symmetric in the several intensive parameters. In spite of this symmetry, however, the reader is apt to feel that he has an intuitive response to the concepts of temperatures and pressure, which is lacking, at least to some degree, in the case of the chemical potential. It is of some interest, then, to note that the intensive parameters are not all independent. There is a relation among the intensive parameters, and for a single-component system μ is a function of T and P.

The existence of a relationship among the various intensive parameters is a consequence of the homogeneous first-order property of the fundamental relation. For a single component system this property permits the fundamental relation to be written in the form $u = u(s, v)$, as in equation 2.19. Each of the three intensive parameters is then also a function of s and v. Elimination of s and v from among the three equations of state yields a relation among T, P, and μ.

The argument can easily be extended to the more general case and again consists of a straightforward counting of variables. Suppose we have a fundamental equation in $(t + 1)$ extensive variables

$$U = U(S, X_1, X_2 \cdots X_t) \qquad (3.9)$$

yielding, in turn, $t + 1$ equations of state

$$P_k = P_k(S, X_1, X_2 \cdots X_t) \tag{3.10}$$

If we choose the parameter λ of equation 2.14 as $\lambda = 1/X_t$, we then have

$$P_k = P_k(S/X_t, X_1/X_t \cdots X_{t-1}/X_t, 1) \tag{3.11}$$

Thus each of the $(t + 1)$ intensive parameters is a function of just t variables. Elimination of these t variables among the $(t + 1)$ equations yields the desired relation among the intensive parameters.

To find the explicit functional relationship that exists among the set of intensive parameters would require knowledge of the explicit fundamental equation of the system. That is, the analytic form of the relationship varies from system to system. Given the fundamental relation, the procedure is evident and follows the sequence of steps indicated by equations 3.9–3.11.

A differential form of the relation among the intensive parameters can be obtained directly from the Euler relation and is known as the Gibbs–Duhem relation. Taking the infinitesimal variation of equation 3.5, we find

$$dU = T \, dS + S \, dT + \sum_{j=1}^{t} P_j \, dX_j + \sum_{j=1}^{t} X_j \, dP_j \tag{3.12}$$

But, in accordance with equation 2.6, we certainly know that

$$dU = T \, dS + \sum_{j=1}^{t} P_j \, dX_j \tag{3.13}$$

whence, by subtraction we find <u>the Gibbs–Duhem relation</u>

$$\boxed{S \, dT + \sum_{j=1}^{t} X_j \, dP_j = 0} \quad \text{energy representation} \tag{3.14}$$

For a single-component simple system, in particular, we have

$$S \, dT - V \, dP + N \, d\mu = 0 \tag{3.15}$$

or

$$d\mu = -s \, dT + v \, dP \tag{3.16}$$

The variation in chemical potential is not independent of the variations of temperature and pressure, but the variation of any one can be computed in terms of the variations of the other two.

The Gibbs–Duhem relation presents the relationship among the intensive parameters in differential form. Integration of this equation yields the relation in explicit form, and this is a procedure alternative to that presented in equations 3.9–3.11. In order to integrate the Gibbs–Duhem relation, one must know the equations of state which enable one to write the X_j's in terms of the P_j's, or vice versa.

The number of intensive parameters capable of independent variation is called the number of *thermodynamic degrees of freedom* of a given system. *A simple system of r components has r + 1 thermodynamic degrees of freedom.*

In the entropy representation the Gibbs–Duhem relation again states that the sum of products of the extensive parameters and the differentials of the corresponding intensive parameters vanishes.

$$\boxed{\sum_{j=0}^{t} X_j \, dF_j = 0} \quad \text{entropy representation} \tag{3.17}$$

or

$$U d\left(\frac{1}{T}\right) + V d\left(\frac{P}{T}\right) - \sum_{k=1}^{r} N_k d\left(\frac{\mu_k}{T}\right) = 0 \tag{3.18}$$

Problems—Section 3.2

3.2–1.   Find the relation among T, P, and μ for the system with the fundamental equation

$$U = \left(\frac{v_0 \theta}{R^2}\right)\frac{S^3}{NV}$$

3.3   Summary of Formal Structure

Let us now summarize the structure of the thermodynamic formalism in the energy representation.   For the sake of clarity, and in order to be explicit, we consider a single-component simple system.   The fundamental equation

$$U = U(S, V, N) \tag{3.19}$$

contains *all* thermodynamic information about a system.   With the definitions $T = \partial U/\partial S$, etc., the fundamental equation implies three equations of state:

$$T = T(S, V, N) = T(s, v) \tag{3.20}$$

$$P = P(S, V, N) = P(s, v) \tag{3.21}$$

$$\mu = \mu(S, V, N) = \mu(s, v) \tag{3.22}$$

If *all three* equations of state are known, they may be substituted into the Euler relation, thereby recovering the fundamental equation. *Thus the totality of all three equations of state is equivalent to the fundamental equation* and contains all thermodynamic information about a system. Any single equation of state contains less thermodynamic information than the fundamental equation.

If two equations of state are known, the Gibbs–Duhem relation may be integrated to obtain the third. The equation of state so obtained will contain an undetermined integration constant. Thus two equations of state suffice to determine the fundamental equation, except for an undetermined constant.

An alternative procedure for obtaining the fundamental equation when only two equations of state are given is by direct integration of the molar relation

$$du = T\,ds - P\,dv \qquad (3.23)$$

Clearly, knowledge of $T = T(s, v)$ and $P = P(s, v)$ yields a differential equation in the three variables u, s, and v, and integration gives

$$u = u(s, v) \qquad (3.24)$$

which is a fundamental equation. Again, of course, we have an undetermined constant of integration.

It is always possible to express the internal energy as a function of parameters other than S, V, and N. Thus we could eliminate S from $U = U(S, V, N)$ and $T = T(S, V, N)$ to obtain an equation of the form $U = U(T, V, N)$. However, we wish to stress that such an equation is *not* a fundamental relation and does not contain all possible thermodynamic information about the system. In fact, recalling the definition of T as $\partial U/\partial S$, we see that $U = U(T, V, N)$ actually is a partial differential equation. Even if this equation were integrable, it would yield a fundamental equation with undetermined functions Thus knowledge of the relation $U = U(S, V, N)$ allows one to compute the relation $U = U(T, V, N)$, but knowledge of $U = U(T, V, N)$ does not permit one inversely to compute $U = U(S, V, N)$. Associated with every equation there is both a truth-value and an informational content. Each of the equations $U = U(S, V, N)$ and $U = U(T, V, N)$ may be true, but only the former has the optimum informational content.

3.4 An Example—The Ideal Monatomic Gas

An *ideal monatomic gas* is characterized by the two equations

$$PV = NRT \qquad (3.25)$$

and

$$U = \tfrac{3}{2}NRT \qquad (3.26)$$

in which R is a constant with the value 1.986 cal/mole °K.

The ideal monatomic gas is a special case of a more general class of systems known as *general ideal gases*. General ideal gases, and various real gases, are discussed in detail in Appendix D.

Returning to the ideal monatomic gas, we proceed to find its fundamental equation. As the two given equations involve intensive parameters, neither is a fundamental equation, but both are, rather, equations of state. The extensive parameters appearing in the equations are U, V, and N, whence we see that the equations are in the entropy representation. The equations may therefore be written in the more natural form

$$\frac{1}{T} = \frac{3}{2} R \frac{N}{U} = \frac{3}{2} \frac{R}{u} \tag{3.27}$$

$$\frac{P}{T} = R \frac{N}{V} = \frac{R}{v} \tag{3.28}$$

The third equation of state would be in the form

$$\frac{\mu}{T} = \frac{\mu}{T}(U, V, N) = \frac{\mu}{T}(u, v) \tag{3.29}$$

If this equation of state were known, we could simply substitute the three equations of state into the Euler relation,

$$S = \left(\frac{1}{T}\right) U + \left(\frac{P}{T}\right) V - \left(\frac{\mu}{T}\right) N \tag{3.30}$$

and we would have the fundamental equation. Our essential problem, then, is to find the third equation of state. The relationship among the three intensive parameters is given by the Gibbs–Duhem equation:

$$d\left(\frac{\mu}{T}\right) = ud\left(\frac{1}{T}\right) + vd\left(\frac{P}{T}\right) \tag{3.31}$$

and the third equation of state can be computed by integration of this equation. Computing $d(1/T)$ and $d(P/T)$ from equations 3.27 and 3.28, we find

$$d\left(\frac{\mu}{T}\right) = u\left(-\frac{3}{2}\frac{R}{u^2}\right) du + v\left(-\frac{R}{v^2}\right) dv = -\frac{3}{2}\frac{R}{u} du - \frac{R}{v} dv \tag{3.32}$$

whence

$$\frac{\mu}{T} - \left(\frac{\mu}{T}\right)_0 = -\tfrac{3}{2} R \ln\frac{u}{u_0} - R \ln\frac{v}{v_0} \tag{3.33}$$

Here u_0 and v_0 are the parameters of a fiducial state, and $(\mu/T)_0$ arises as an undetermined constant of integration. By inserting our three equations of state into the Euler relation (equation 3.8), we find directly that

$$S = \frac{N}{N_0} S_0 + NR \ln \left[\left(\frac{U}{U_0} \right)^{3/2} \left(\frac{V}{V_0} \right) \left(\frac{N}{N_0} \right)^{-5/2} \right] \qquad (3.34)$$

where

$$S_0 = \tfrac{5}{2} N_0 R - N_0 \left(\frac{\mu}{T} \right)_0 \qquad (3.35)$$

Equation 3.34 is the desired fundamental equation, and, if the integration constant S_0 were known, it would contain all possible thermodynamic information about an ideal monatomic gas.

It may be noted that this analysis might have been shortened somewhat by a direct integration of the equation

$$ds = \frac{1}{T} du + \frac{P}{T} dv \qquad (3.36)$$

rather than by first computing the third equation of state. The essential logic is identical to that employed in the foregoing method. In this case we would obtain directly from equations 3.36, 3.27, and 3.28 that

$$ds = \frac{3}{2} \frac{R}{u} du + \frac{R}{v} dv \qquad (3.37)$$

whence, by direct integration,

$$s = s_0 + \tfrac{3}{2} R \ln \frac{u}{u_0} + R \ln \frac{v}{v_0} \qquad (3.38)$$

which is equivalent to equation 3.34.

It should be noted that the fundamental equation (3.34 or 3.38) violates postulate IV of section 1.9. This is because equations 3.25 and 3.26 actually are only approximations to the true equations of state and are valid only in the high-temperature region. Consequently, the fundamental equation derived therefrom is also only an approximation to the true fundamental equation and is valid only in the high-temperature region. If the approximate fundamental equation is applied only at high temperatures, we need not be concerned with the apparent violation of the Nernst postulate.

Problems—Section 3.4

3.4–1. Show that the relation between the volume and the pressure of an ideal monatomic gas undergoing a quasi-static adiabatic compression ($dQ = T \, dS = 0$, $S =$ constant) is

$$Pv^{5/3} = \left(P_0 v_0^{5/3} e^{-\frac{2s_0}{3R}} \right) e^{\frac{2s}{3R}} = \text{constant}$$

Sketch a family of such "adiabats" in a graph of P versus V.

3.4–2. Two moles of an ideal monatomic gas are at a temperature of 0°C and a pressure of 1 atm. The gas is expanded adiabatically and quasi-statically until its temperature falls to −50°C. What is its final pressure? What were its initial and final volumes?

3.4–3. By carrying out the integral $\int P\, dV$, compute the work done by the gas in problem 3.4–2. Also compute the initial and final energies, and corroborate that the difference in these energies is the work done.

3.4–4. A tank of He gas has a volume of 1000 liters. The gas has a pressure of $\frac{1}{2}$ atm and a temperature of 20°C. A second tank of the same volume contains He at a pressure of 1 atm and a temperature of 80°C. A valve connecting the two tanks is opened. Assuming the gas to be a monatomic ideal gas and assuming the walls of the tanks to be rigid and adiabatic, find the final temperature and pressure of the system.

Hint: Note that the total internal energy is constant.

Answer: Final pressure $\cong 0.75$ atm.

3.4–5. If a monatomic ideal gas is permitted to expand into an evacuated region, increasing its volume from V_0 to λV_0, and if the walls are rigid and adiabatic, what is the ratio of its initial and final pressures? What is the ratio of its initial and final temperatures? What is the difference of its initial and final entropies?

3.5 Specific Heats and Other Derivatives

The various first derivatives of the fundamental equation have been seen to have important physical significance. The various second derivatives also prove to be of physical interest. In Chapter 7 we consider all such second derivatives exhaustively and investigate the detailed relationships among them. At the moment we simply recognize a few particularly useful prototype derivatives. Throughout this section *all mole numbers are considered constant*, but for economy of notation we shall not explicitly indicate this in each separate partial differentiation.

The *coefficient of thermal expansion* is defined by

$$\alpha \equiv \frac{1}{v}\left(\frac{\partial v}{\partial T}\right)_P = \frac{1}{V}\left(\frac{\partial V}{\partial T}\right)_P \tag{3.39}$$

The coefficient of thermal expansion is the fractional increase in the volume per unit increase in the temperature of a system maintained at constant pressure (and constant mole numbers).

The *isothermal compressibility* is defined by

$$\kappa_T \equiv -\frac{1}{v}\left(\frac{\partial v}{\partial P}\right)_T = -\frac{1}{V}\left(\frac{\partial V}{\partial P}\right)_T \tag{3.40}$$

The isothermal compressibility is the fractional decrease in volume per unit increase in pressure at constant temperature.

The *specific heat at constant pressure* is defined by

$$c_P \equiv T\left(\frac{\partial s}{\partial T}\right)_P = \frac{T}{N}\left(\frac{\partial S}{\partial T}\right)_P = \frac{1}{N}\left(\frac{dQ}{dT}\right)_P \qquad (3.41)$$

The specific heat at constant pressure is the quasi-static heat flux per mole required to produce unit increase in the temperature of a system maintained at constant pressure.

The *specific heat at constant volume* is defined by

$$c_v \equiv T\left(\frac{\partial s}{\partial T}\right)_v = \frac{T}{N}\left(\frac{\partial S}{\partial T}\right)_V = \frac{1}{N}\left(\frac{dQ}{dT}\right)_V \qquad (3.42)$$

The specific heat at constant volume is the quasi-static heat flux per mole required to produce unit increase in the temperature of a system maintained at constant volume.

Two other partial derivatives, which do not quite possess the practical usefulness of the four listed but which most conveniently illustrate a matter of formal structure we wish to demonstrate, are the following. The quantity $(\partial T/\partial V)_S$ represents the increase in temperature per unit increase in volume in a quasi-static adiabatic process. And the quantity $(\partial P/\partial S)_V$, when written in the form $T(dP/dQ)_V$, is seen to be related to the change in pressure required to induce unit flux of heat at constant volume and mole number.

The Gibbs–Duhem relation expresses the existence of a relationship among the first derivatives of the fundamental equation. Similarly, there are relationships among the second derivatives, and this is the matter of formal structure to which we alluded in the preceding paragraph. The simplest example of a relationship among second derivatives is the identity

$$\left(\frac{\partial T}{\partial V}\right)_{S,N} = -\left(\frac{\partial P}{\partial S}\right)_{V,N} \qquad (3.43)$$

The proof of this identity follows from the observation that in accordance with an elementary theorem of calculus the two mixed second partial derivatives of U with respect to V and S are equal:

$$\frac{\partial^2 U}{\partial V\,\partial S} = \frac{\partial^2 U}{\partial S\,\partial V}$$

But

$$\frac{\partial^2 U}{\partial V\,\partial S} = \frac{\partial}{\partial V}\left(\frac{\partial U}{\partial S}\right) = \left(\frac{\partial T}{\partial V}\right)_{S,N} \qquad (3.45)$$

and

$$\frac{\partial^2 U}{\partial S\,\partial V} = \frac{\partial}{\partial S}\left(\frac{\partial U}{\partial V}\right) = -\left(\frac{\partial P}{\partial S}\right)_{V,N} \qquad (3.46)$$

whence the identity (equation 3.43) immediately follows. Because of the physical interpretations we have given to each of the partial derivatives, it is clear that equation 3.43 is subject to direct empirical corroboration and constitutes a clear prediction of a nontrivial physical fact. It is perhaps the most immediate physically significant consequence of our fundamental postulates.

The identity we have derived involves just two partial derivatives. However, as we shall see subsequently, in general there must exist at least one such identity among any *four* derivatives. The foregoing identity which involved only two is simply a special case, consistent with but not required by our general claim. A less special example, which we merely cite prior to subsequent proof, is

$$c_P = c_v + \frac{TV\alpha^2}{N\kappa_T} \tag{3.47}$$

For convenience and reference we cite three other particularly useful identities to be proved in Chapter 7. These are

$$\left(\frac{\partial V}{\partial S}\right)_{P,N} = \left(\frac{\partial T}{\partial P}\right)_{S,N} \tag{3.48}$$

$$\left(\frac{\partial S}{\partial V}\right)_{T,N} = \left(\frac{\partial P}{\partial T}\right)_{V,N} \tag{3.49}$$

and

$$\left(\frac{\partial S}{\partial P}\right)_{T,N} = -\left(\frac{\partial V}{\partial T}\right)_{P,N} \tag{3.50}$$

All such relationships are associated with the equality of the various mixed second derivatives of the fundamental equation, and the class of such identities is known as *Maxwell relations*. We investigate them in detail in Chapter 7. In actuality, our purpose in mentioning the Maxwell relations at this juncture is mainly to introduce definitions of c_P, c_v, α, and κ_T and to call attention to the fact that all such derivatives are not independent.

Problems—Section 3.5

3.5–1. Show that for an ideal monatomic gas

$$c_v = \tfrac{3}{2}R$$
$$\alpha = 1/T$$
$$\kappa_T = 1/P$$

and

$$c_P = \tfrac{5}{2}R$$

Using these values corroborate equation 3.47.

3.5-2. Corroborate equation 3.43 for an ideal monatomic gas, showing that both the right- and left-hand members of the equation equal $-2T/3V$.

3.5-3. Compute the coefficient of expansion α and the isothermal compressibility κ_T, in terms of P and V, for a system with the van der Waals equation of state

$$P = \frac{NRT}{V - bN} - \frac{N^2a}{V^2}$$

where a and b are constants.

3.5-4. Compute c_P, c_v, α, and κ_T for the system in problem 1.9–1a. With these values corroborate the validity of equation 3.47.

3.5-5. The density of mercury at various temperatures is given below in grams/cm^3.

13.6202 ($-10°$C); 13.5955 (0°C); 13.5708 (10°C); 13.5462 (20°C)
13.5217 (30°C); 13.4973 (40°C); 13.4729 (50°C); 13.3522 (100°C);
13.3283 (110°C); 13.1148 (200°C); 12.8806 (300°C); 12.8572 (310°C)

Calculate α at 0°C, at 45°C, at 105°C, and at 305°C.

Should the stem of a mercury-in-glass thermometer be marked off in equal divisions for equal temperature intervals if the coefficient of thermal expansion of glass is assumed to be strictly constant?

Properties of ideal and real gases are described in Appendix D. The student for whom this is an introduction to thermodynamics is strongly advised to read Appendix D at this point. Appendix E, on the properties of simple solids and liquids, should then be interposed at some later point, according to the individual taste of the reader.

CHAPTER 4

Processes
and Thermodynamic
Engines

4.1 Quasi-Static Processes

Despite the fact that thermodynamics is fundamentally a study of equilibrium states, it is used frequently as the basis of inferences concerning processes. Essentially this is done by studying the two equilibrium states in which the process initiates and terminates. We now examine in some detail the exact relationship that can be established between thermodynamic theory and real physical processes.

The fundamental equation of a simple system can be considered as defining a surface in a *thermodynamic configuration space*. The coordinates in this space are the extensive parameters U, V, N_1, $N_2 \cdots N_r$; and S. The fundamental equation $S = S(U, V, N_1 \cdots N_r)$ then defines a surface such as that shown schematically in Figure 4.1. It should be noted that the surface of Figure 4.1 conforms to the requirements that $(\partial S/\partial U)_{\ldots X_j \ldots} \equiv 1/T$ is positive, and that U is a single valued function of $S \cdots X_j \cdots$. By definition, each point in the configuration space represents an *equilibrium* state; representation of a nonequilibrium state would require a space with *many* more dimensions.

The fundamental equation of a *composite* system can also be represented by a surface in a thermodynamic configuration space of correspondingly higher dimensionality. For a composite system composed of two simple subsystems a possible choice of coordinate axes would be S, $U^{(1)}$, $V^{(1)}$, $N_1^{(1)} \cdots U^{(2)}$, $V^{(2)}$, $N_1^{(2)} \cdots$. A more convenient choice is S, $U^{(1)}$, $V^{(1)}$, $N_1^{(1)} \cdots U$, V, $N_1 \cdots$ where $U = U^{(1)} + U^{(2)}$, and similarly for V, $N_1 \cdots$.

59

An appropriate section of the thermodynamic configuration space of a composite system is sketched in Figure 4.2.

Consider an arbitrary curve drawn from an initial state to a terminal state on the hyper-surface that represents the fundamental equation of a system in configuration space. Such a curve, shown in Figure 4.3, is known as a *quasi-static locus* or a *quasi-static process*. A quasi-static

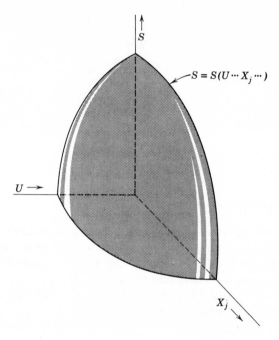

Figure 4.1   The hyper-surface $S = S(U \cdots X_j \cdots)$ in the thermodynamic configuration space of a simple system.

process is defined as a succession of *equilibrium* states. It is to be stressed that a quasi-static process therefore is an idealized concept, quite distinct from a real physical process, for a real process always involves non-equilibrium intermediate states, having no representation in the thermo-dynamic configuration space. Furthermore, a quasi-static process, in contrast to a real process, does not involve considerations of rates, velocities, or time. The quasi-static process simply is an ordered succession of (equilibrium) states, whereas a real process is a *temporal* succession of (equilibrium and nonequilibrium) states.

Now, although no real process is identical to a quasi-static process, it is possible to contrive real processes that have a certain close relationship to quasi-static processes. In particular, it is possible to lead a system

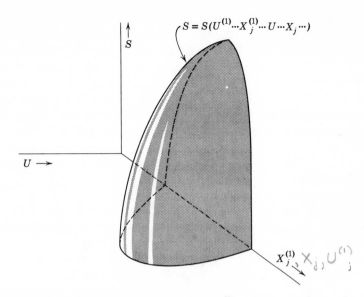

Figure 4.2   The hyper-surface $S = S(U^{(1)} \cdots X_j^{(1)} \cdots U \cdots X_j \cdots)$ in the thermodynamic configuration space of a composite system.

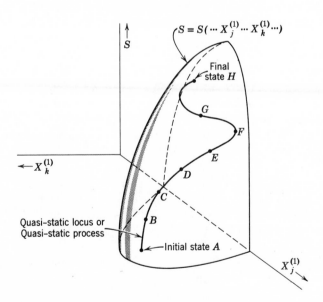

Figure 4.3   Representation of a quasi-static process in the thermodynamic configuration space.

through a succession of states that coincides at any desired number of points with a given quasi-static locus. Thus consider a system originally in the state A of Figure 4.3. There are real processes that take the system from this initial state to the final state H through a succession of intermediate nonequilibrium states. In the course of such a process the system "disappears" from point A and subsequently reappears at point H; the intermediate states have no representation in the thermodynamic configuration space. The real process we have described is a poor approximation to the quasi-static process. A much better approximation can be obtained by proceeding in several steps. We first start with the system at A, and we then arrange a real process that terminates in the equilibrium state B. The system disappears from point A and subsequently appears at point B. We then arrange another real process that takes it in a similar way from B to C, thence by another real process from C to D and by similar steps eventually to H. By this succession of real processes, we have now obtained a closer approximation to the quasi-static locus than our original process, which simply went directly from A to H. It is clear that by spacing the points A, B, $C \cdots$ arbitrarily closely along the quasi-static locus a real process can be contrived to approximate arbitrarily closely a given quasi-static locus.

The differentials dS, dU, etc., of the preceding chapters refer to changes along quasi-static loci. These differentials can be interpreted in terms of real processes only insofar as particular real processes approximate quasi-static loci.

In a quasi-static process the increase in entropy is given by $dS = dQ/T$. In a real physical process the entropy can increase even if the system is adiabatically enclosed ($dQ = 0$), and in any case $dS > dQ/T$.

Consider a system that is to be led along the quasi-static locus of Figure 4.3. The constraints on the system are to be removed step-by-step, at each step permitting the system to come to a new state lying on the locus. In principle, these constraints should be lifted infinitely slowly. In practice, the rate at which they can be lifted is characterized by the *relaxation time* τ of the system. *For a given system, with a given relaxation time* τ, *processes that occur in times short compared to* τ *are not quasi-static, whereas processes that occur in times long compared to* τ *are approximately quasi-static.* For such slow processes we can write, approximately, that $dS = dQ/T$.

As an example of the concept of relaxation time, consider a cylinder filled with a gas and fitted with a piston. The cylinder and piston walls are assumed to be adiabatic. If the piston is pushed inward quasistatically, the increase in entropy is zero. But, if the piston is pushed in rapidly, inducing all sorts of complicated hydrodynamic flows in the gas, the increase in entropy is positivé, despite the fact that $dQ = 0$. We can estimate the relaxation time of this system as follows. We know that a slight motion of the piston tends to compress the gas adjacent to the piston. In order for the process to be quasi-static, this compression must be dissipated throughout the entire volume of the gas before the next appreciable compression occurs. The time required for a localized compression to equalize through the gas must be of the order of L/c, where L is some average dimension of the system and c is the velocity of sound in the gas. The relaxation time of the system for compression processes consequently is of the order of $V^{1/3}/c$.

4.2   Reversible and Irreversible Processes

A second important classification of processes is suggested by the basic extremum principle. Let us suppose that a closed system is in a state A and that the lifting of a constraint initiates a spontaneous process terminating in a state B. The very fact that the process is assumed to proceed implies that the entropy in state B is greater than that in state A. If, now, it is desired to reverse the process and to restore the system to the state A, it is impossible to accomplish this simply by the manipulation of constraints within the closed system. For if such a reverse process were to proceed, it would involve a decrease in the entropy in violation of the basic extremum principle and contrary to experience. For this reason a real physical process, such as that leading from A to B, is said to be an *irreversible process*.

Although all real processes are irreversible and are accompanied by a positive increase of the entropy, we may consider the limiting case in which the entropy increase becomes arbitrarily small. The idealized type of process in which the entropy increase vanishes is called a *reversible process*.

A reversible process is initiated in a system by removal of a constraint, the remaining constraints permitting the system to traverse a locus of constant entropy in the thermodynamic configuration space. A system in any state along this locus is in equilibrium and finds no available states of larger entropy. Thus a reversible process is constituted of a succession of equilibrium states and consequently coincides with a quasi-static locus as shown in Figure 4.4. *Every reversible process coincides with a quasi-static process.*

The inverse of the foregoing statement is not true. It is quite possible to have quasi-static processes that are not coincident with loci of constant entropy, that is, that are not reversible processes. The quasi-static locus of Figure 4.3 is this type.

The fact that a system has a smaller entropy in a state A than in a state B implies that the *closed* system will not spontaneously proceed from B to A under any arrangement of its internal constraints. It is nevertheless possible to restore the system from the state B to the state A if the system is appropriately coupled with another system, that is, if the restriction of closure is removed. Let us denote the excess of entropy in state B over

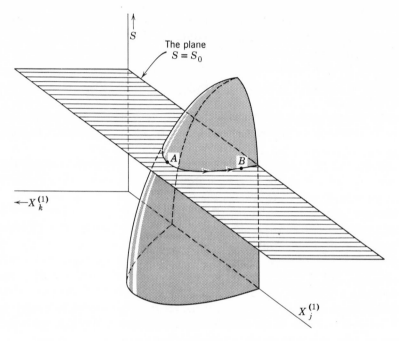

Figure 4.4 A reversible process, along a quasi-static isentropic locus.

that in state A by ΔS. Suppose we now couple the system to a second system and arrange constraints so that some process is permitted in the second system but so that this process is necessarily associated with the return of the primary system to its initial state. This complete process will occur if the total entropy of the *complete* system thereby is increased. That is, the process will occur if the increase in entropy of the secondary system is at least able to compensate for the decrease in entropy of the primary system.

A process is said to be irreversible if it is associated with an increase in the entropy; all real processes fall within this category. *To invert such a process and to decrease the entropy of a system, a corresponding (or larger) increase in entropy must occur in some coupled system.* The increase in entropy thus provides a quantitative measure of the irreversibility of a physical process.

4.3 The Reversible Work Source and Reservoirs

The tendency of a system to drift spontaneously toward equilibrium can be channeled in such a way that the system delivers work to some external agent. This ability to deliver work is exploited for useful purposes in many engineering applications. The spontaneous motion of a piston from the high toward the low pressure region within a cylinder supplies the motive power of a mechanical engine. Similarly, the tendency of heat to flow from the hot interior of a steam boiler to the cool ambient atmosphere propels a steam locomotive. Some of the most significant predictions of thermodynamics relate to the manner in which a system can act as a thermodynamic engine and can deliver work to an external agent. It is to these considerations that we now turn our attention.

An immediate question which arises as we consider thermodynamic engines is, "What is meant by the 'external agents' to which work is to be delivered?" These external agents are, of course, thermodynamic systems. However, as they are introduced solely as recipients of the delivered work, it is desirable to idealize and to simplify their thermodynamic properties as much as possible.

We now define several specifically useful types of systems. First, and most evidently useful, is the _reversible work source._ *A reversible work source is defined as a system enclosed by an adiabatic impermeable wall and characterized by relaxation times sufficiently short that all processes of interest within it are essentially quasi-static.* As the relationship between quasi-static heat flux and entropy change is $dQ = T\,dS$, the adiabatic wall insures a constant value of the entropy. When coupled to another system, a reversible work source acts as a quasi-static source or sink of work.

From the thermodynamic point of view *all the systems considered in the theory of mechanics are reversible work sources.* A simple weight suspended by a rope running over a pulley can absorb or deliver work, and $dQ = dS = 0$; it is a prototype of a reversible work source.

A reversible heat source is defined as a system enclosed by a rigid impermeable wall and characterized by relaxation times sufficiently short that all processes of interest within it are essentially quasi-static. The only possible flux of energy to or from a reversible heat source is in the form of heat, so that $dU = dQ = T\,dS$. The reversible heat source acts as a quasi-static source or sink of heat.

Reversible work or heat sources that are very large are known as *reservoirs*; in particular, a very large reversible work source is a *volume reservoir*, and a very large reversible heat source is a *heat reservoir*.

The useful feature of a heat reservoir is that it remains at a fixed and constant temperature independent of the amount of heat put into or withdrawn from it. The derivative $(\partial T/\partial U)_{V,N_1,N_2...}$ which describes the change in temperature caused by the input of unit quantity of heat, is a homogeneous inverse-first-order function of the extensive parameters and therefore vanishes for an infinitely large system. A heat reservoir consequently is useful as a thermostating device; when in contact with a system through a diathermal wall, the heat reservoir will maintain the system at constant temperature independent of any manipulations of the extensive parameters X_0, $X_1 \cdots X_k \cdots$ of the system.

Similarly, the pressure of a volume reservoir is constant. In practice, the atmosphere frequently plays the role of both a heat and a volume reservoir. Thus chemical reactions carried out in open vessels necessarily begin and terminate in states with temperature and pressure determined by the ambient atmosphere.

4.4 Maximum Work Processes

A system in a particular state A may be coupled to a reversible work source and to a reversible heat source and may then be led by some process to a particular final state B. In this process heat is generally transferred to or from the reversible heat source and work is transferred to or from the reversible work source. The amount of work transferred is of particular interest, as it is made available for useful exploitation. In fact, we frequently wish to find that particular process, initiated and terminated in the given states A and B, that yields the maximum possible transfer of work to the reversible work source. We shall now see that the process that does so is reversible. That is, *of all processes occurring between a given initial and a given final state of a system, the flux of heat to an associated reversible heat source is minimum and the flux of work to an associated reversible work source is maximum for reversible processes. The fluxes of heat and work are the same for all reversible processes between the given states.*

Consider a closed composite system consisting of a reversible work source, a reversible heat source, and a subsystem of a general and unspecified nature. The subsystem undergoes some process that takes it from the initial state A to the final state B. If the internal energy of the subsystem in the state B is smaller than in the state A, the energy difference will be distributed between the reversible heat source and the reversible work source. The fraction of this energy that finally resides in the reversible work source is to be maximized; the remaining fraction that resides in the reversible heat source simultaneously is minimized. Now, the total entropy of the composite system necessarily increases in any real process, but a reversible process corresponds to the idealized limiting case in which this increase in total entropy is zero. Consequently, the entropy increase attending any real irreversible process is greater than that which attends a reversible process. The entropy changes in the various portions

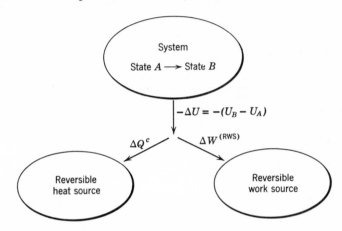

Figure 4.5 Maximum work processes. The delivered work $\Delta W^{(\mathrm{RWS})}$ is maximum and ΔQ^c is minimum if the system goes from A to B by a reversible process.

of the system, in both irreversible and reversible processes, are indicated in Table 4.1. At the conclusion of the process the entropy of the reversible heat source will be smaller if the process is reversible than if the process is irreversible. Thus the final energy of the reversible heat source is also least if the process is reversible, for the internal energy and entropy of the reversible heat source are connected by the relation* $dU = T\,dS$, with T positive. Thus we have shown that the energy delivered to the reversible heat source is smallest in a reversible process, and it therefore follows that the delivered work is greatest in such a process.

The actual amount of work delivered in a reversible process can be computed by considering the energy changes associated with the entropy changes listed in Table 4.1. The energy change of the subsystem is $U_B - U_A$, as listed in Table 4.2.

Let ΔQ^c be the heat transferred to the reversible heat source. Let

---

* The use of this quasi-static relation is valid *within* the reversible heat source where all processes are quasi-static by definition, even if the total process is irreversible.

$T^c(S^c)$ be the temperature of the reversible heat source; the temperature is effectively a function only of the entropy, for the volume and mole numbers of the reversible heat source are constants. Finally, let the entropy of the reversible heat source be S_0^c initially, so that its terminal value is $S_0^c - (S_B - S_A)$. The heat transfer to the reversible heat source is

$$\Delta Q^c = \int_{S_0^c}^{S_0^c - (S_B - S_A)} T^c(S^c)\, dS^c \tag{4.1}$$

Table 4.1
ENTROPY CHANGES IN IRREVERSIBLE AND REVERSIBLE PROCESSES

	Irreversible Processes	Reversible Processes
Total system	$\Delta S > 0$	$\Delta S = 0$
Subsystem	$S_B - S_A$	$S_B - S_A$
Reversible work source	0	0
Reversible heat source	$\Delta S - (S_B - S_A)$	$-(S_B - S_A)$

The work transferred to the reversible work source is equal to the energy withdrawn from the subsystem, minus the heat transfer to the reversible heat source, as shown in Table 4.2.

Table 4.2
ENERGY CHANGES IN REVERSIBLE PROCESSES

Total System	0
Subsystem	$U_B - U_A$
Reversible heat source	$\Delta Q^c = \int_{S_0^c}^{S_0^c - (S_B - S_A)} T^c(S^c)\, dS^c$
Reversible work source	$\Delta W^{(\text{RWS})} = -\Delta Q^c - (U_B - U_A)$

From the table we find then that

$$\Delta W^{(\text{RWS})} = -\int_{S_0^c}^{S_0^c - (S_B - S_A)} T^c(S^c)\, dS^c - (U_B - U_A) \tag{4.2}$$

For given states A and B, and for a given reversible heat source [described by $T^c(S^c)$], this equation gives the maximum work that can be extracted from the system.

It may happen, for given states A and B and given reversible work source, that the delivered work $\Delta W^{(\mathrm{RWS})}$ is negative. It is then necessary to do work *on* the system in order that the process occur. Our demonstration that the delivered work is algebraically maximum implies that the absolute value of the work done *on* the system is minimum in this case. The excess work done in an irreversible process, over that done in a reversible process, is called *dissipative work*.

4.5 Thermodynamic Engines

The heat and work transfers in a reversible process are shown in Figure 4.6 in greater detail than in Figure 4.5. The energy that leaves

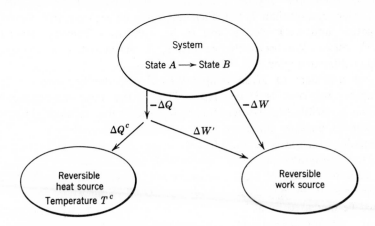

Figure 4.6 Work and heat transfers in a maximum work process.

the system $(-\Delta U)$ leaves partly in the form of work $(-\Delta W)$ and partly in the form of heat $(-\Delta Q)$. The work $(-\Delta W)$ is transferred directly to the reversible work source. But the heat $(-\Delta Q)$ is only partly delivered to the heat reservoir (ΔQ^c) and partly transformed into work for delivery to the reversible work source $(\Delta W')$. We compute the fraction of the heat $(-\Delta Q)$ which is transformed into work $(\Delta W')$ and delivered to the reversible work source.

Consider an infinitesimal step in the process, and let the temperature of the system be T. Then the heat flux $(-dQ)$ leaving the system is $-T\,dS$. The heat dQ^c entering the reversible heat source is $T^c\,dS^c = -T^c\,dS$, and the portion of this work dW' entering the reversible work source is

$$dW' = (-dQ) - dQ^c \tag{4.3}$$

$$= -T\,dS + T^c\,dS \tag{4.4}$$

$$= \left(1 - \frac{T^c}{T}\right)(-dQ) \tag{4.5}$$

The fraction of the withdrawn heat which can be transformed into work is called the *thermodynamic engine efficiency* ϵ_e. Thus

$$\epsilon_e \equiv \frac{dW'}{-dQ} = 1 - \frac{T^c}{T} \tag{4.6}$$

The fraction of the heat withdrawn from the subsystem that can be delivered as work is equal to the difference in temperature of subsystem and reversible heat source, divided by the temperature of the subsystem.

In order that a *positive* fraction of the withdrawn heat be delivered to the reversible work source, it is clearly necessary that T^c be less than T. If T^c were greater than T, the efficiency would be negative, dW' would be negative, and work would have to be withdrawn from the reversible work source. We discuss this case later; it corresponds to a refrigerator rather than an engine.

For a system of given temperature T, the thermodynamic engine efficiency increases as T^c decreases. That is, the lower the temperature of the reversible heat source, the higher the engine efficiency, and the maximum possible efficiency, $\epsilon_e = 1$, occurs if the temperature of the reversible heat source is equal to zero.

The underlying principle of the thermodynamic engine is quite intuitive. A certain amount of heat $(-dQ)$ is withdrawn from the subsystem, *decreasing* its entropy by an amount $(-dQ)/T$. Somewhere the entropy must be increased by at least as much. We do this by taking a portion of the withdrawn heat and inserting it into a reversible heat source. If the temperature of the reversible heat source is very low, we can get a very large entropy increase with a small heat input, and the remainder of the withdrawn heat is available as work. The lower the temperature of the reversible heat source, the less heat must be sacrificed to it in order to satisfy the condition that the *total* entropy should increase, and the more work we are able to salvage.

Our discussion has been on extremely general terms, but we have been able to arrive at a very specific and quantitative formula for the maximum engine efficiency. We have not concerned ourselves at all with particular processes or specific methods for conversion of the withdrawn heat into work. There are many such processes; a representative one called the *Carnot cycle* is described in section 4.7. But the beauty of our result lies in its very generality—for *any* reversible process the efficiency is given by equation 4.6 and for any irreversible process the efficiency is smaller.

Problems—Section 4.5

4.5-1. A vat of boiling water and another vat of ice are available. Each is enclosed by rigid and impermeable, but diathermal, walls. For each joule of work that can be done, how much heat must be withdrawn from the hot vat? How many grams of ice must be melted? (Every 80 cal delivered to the cold vat melts 1 gram of ice.)

4.5-2. On a summer day, at a temperature of 80°F, there is available an artesian well of temperature 55°F. A thermodynamic engine operating between these reservoirs is used to raise water from the well. If 50 lb of water is raised 20 ft, how much heat must be inserted into the well?

4.5-3. If the engine in problem 4.5-2 attains only 30 per cent of the ideal efficiency, what is the solution of that problem?

4.5-4. A locomotive weighing 100 tons is able to climb a grade of angle θ at a speed of 50 mph. The locomotive burns 1 ton of coal/hr and maintains the boiler temperature at 100°C. The temperature of the air is 70°F. Assuming that the locomotive is operating at 25 per cent of the thermodynamic efficiency, what is the angle θ of the grade?

The heat equivalent of the coal is 14,000 Btu/lb.

4.6 An Illustrative Problem

To illustrate an application of the theory of the thermodynamic engine efficiency, we consider the following problem. Two identical bodies have equations of state $U = NCT$, with C a constant. The values of N and C are the same for each system. The initial temperatures are T_1 and T_2, and they are to be used as a source of work by bringing them to a common final temperature T_f. What is the range of possible final temperatures? What final temperature corresponds to the maximum amount of delivered work, and what is this maximum amount of delivered work?

The process envisaged is the withdrawal of heat from the body of higher temperature, insertion of part of this heat into the body of lower temperature, and salvage of the remainder as available work. Body No. 1 is the analogue of the subsystem of section 4.5, and body No. 2 is the analogue of the reversible heat source.

The first evident fact is that in a completely irreversible process, in which no work is delivered, the final temperature will be greatest. If work is extracted, the final energy, and consequently the final temperature, will be lower. The highest final temperature, therefore, corresponds to the case in which the two bodies are merely brought together into thermal contact, delivering no work, and reaching the temperature $T_f = (T_1 + T_2)/2$.

The lowest attainable final temperature corresponds to the delivery of the largest possible amount of work and is associated with a reversible process.

In a reversible process we withdraw an infinitesimal amount of heat from the hot body, put some of it into the cold body, and deliver some as work. The efficiency is that given by equation 4.5. In the next infinitesimal step, however, we find that the temperature of each body has been changed by the heat transfer which occurred in the first infinitesimal step. We cannot merely apply equation 4.5 to the entire process, but we must trace it through, step-by-step, taking account of the fact that the efficiency continually changes.

Let us suppose that at some stage of the process the hotter body has attained the temperature $T^{(1)}$ and the colder body has attained the temperature $T^{(2)}$. We withdraw an amount of heat $-dQ^{(1)}$, decreasing the entropy by $-dS^{(1)} = -dQ^{(1)}/T^{(1)}$, and decreasing the temperature by $-dT^{(1)} = -dQ^{(1)}/NC$. Simultaneously, we insert an amount of heat $dQ^{(2)}$ into the colder body, increasing the entropy by $dS^{(2)} = dQ^{(2)}/T^{(2)}$, and increasing the temperature by $dT^{(2)} = dQ^{(2)}/NC$. The requirement that the total entropy remain unchanged is

$$\frac{dQ^{(1)}}{T^{(1)}} + \frac{dQ^{(2)}}{T^{(2)}} = 0 \qquad (4.7)$$

or

$$\frac{NC\,dT^{(1)}}{T^{(1)}} + \frac{NC\,dT^{(2)}}{T^{(2)}} = 0 \qquad (4.8)$$

Integrating over the entire process, we note that $T^{(1)}$ goes from T_1 to T_f, whereas $T^{(2)}$ goes from T_2 to T_f:

$$\int_{T_1}^{T_f} \frac{dT^{(1)}}{T^{(1)}} = -\int_{T_2}^{T_f} \frac{dT^{(2)}}{T^{(2)}} \qquad (4.9)$$

whence

$$\ln \frac{T_f}{T_1} = -\ln \frac{T_f}{T_2} \qquad (4.10)$$

or

$$T_f = \sqrt{T_1 T_2} \qquad (4.11)$$

This is the minimum attainable final temperature.

We must still find the delivered work. The most direct way to do this is to note that the final total energy is $U_f = 2NCT_f$, whereas the original energy was $U_i = NC(T_1 + T_2)$. The difference is the delivered work, or

$$\Delta W = NC[T_1 + T_2 - 2\sqrt{T_1 T_2}] \qquad (4.12)$$

The reader should find it instructive to corroborate this result by integrating the work delivered in each infinitesimal step of the total process.

The illustrative problem which we have worked in such detail is of negligible importance in itself. The principle of the thermodynamic engine efficiency finds its real application in the design of steam turbines, gasoline engines, and the like. And, of course, these never attain the ideal thermodynamic engine efficiency. Because of internal bearing friction and because they cannot be operated so slowly as to be truly quasi-static, they seldom attain more than 30 or 40 per cent of the thermodynamic efficiency. Nevertheless, the upper limit on the efficiency, set by basic thermodynamic principles, is an extremely important factor in engineering design.

Problems—Section 4.6

4.6-1.   In the illustrative problem in the text heat is withdrawn quasi-statically from the hotter body and introduced quasi-statically into the colder body, delivering no work. Compute the irreversible increase in the total entropy.

4.6-2.   If $NC = 2$ cal/°K for each of the bodies in the illustrative problem and if $T_1 = 100°C$ and $T_2 = 0°C$, what is the maximum delivered work?

4.6-3.   A system maintained at constant volume has a "heat capacity at constant volume" $C_v \equiv Nc_v$, which is independent of temperature. The system is initially at a temperature T_1, and a heat reservoir at the lower temperature T_0 is available. Show that the maximum work recoverable, as the system is cooled to the temperature of the reservoir, is

$$ W = -C_v \int_{T_1}^{T_0} \left(1 - \frac{T_0}{T} \right) dT = C_v \left[(T_1 - T_0) - T_0 \ln \frac{T_1}{T_0} \right] $$

4.6-4.   If the temperature of the atmosphere is 5°C on a winter day and if 1 kg of water at 90°C is available, how much work can be obtained? Assume that the volume of the water is constant, and assume that the specific heat at constant volume is 18 cal/mole°K and is independent of temperature.

4.6-5.   A body with the equation of state $U = NCT$ is heated from temperature T_1 to T_2 by a series of reservoirs ranging from T_1 to T_2. The body is then brought back to its initial state by contact with a single reservoir at temperature T_1. Calculate the change of entropy of the body and of the reservoirs. What is the total change in entropy of the whole system?

If the initial heating were accomplished merely by bringing the body into contact with a single reservoir at temperature T_2, what would the various entropy changes be?

4.6-6.   Each of three identical bodies has an equation of state $U = NCT$, with $NC = 2$ cal/°K. Their initial temperatures are 200°K, 250°K, and 540°K. What is the maximum amount of work that can be extracted in a process in which these three bodies are brought to a final common temperature?

4.6–7. Each of two bodies has a heat capacity at constant volume given by

$$C_v \equiv Nc_v = A + 2BT$$

where $A = 2$ cal/$°$K and $B = 0.5 \times 10^{-2}$ cal/($°$K)^2.

If the bodies are initially at temperatures of 200$°$K and 400$°$K and if a reversible work source is available, what are the maximum and minimum final common temperatures to which the two bodies can be brought? What is the maximum amount of work that can be transferred to the reversible work source? It is to be assumed throughout that each body is maintained at constant volume.

Answer: $T_{\min} = 292°$K

4.6–8. In the temperature range between 0$°$C and 100$°$C a particular system maintained at constant volume has a heat capacity

$$C_v = Nc_v = A + 2BT$$

with $A = 1/300$ cal/$°$K, and $B = 10^{-4}$ cal/($°$K).^{2}

A heat reservoir at 0$°$C and a reversible work source are available. What is the maximum amount of work that can be transferred to the reversible work source as the system is cooled from 100$°$C to the temperature of the reservoir?

4.6–9. A system has a heat capacity (at constant volume) of

$$C_v = AT^2$$

where $A = 0{\cdot}01$ cal/($°$K)^3.

The system is originally at 200$°$K, and a thermal reservoir at 100$°$K is available. What is the maximum amount of work that can be recovered as the system is cooled down to the temperature of the reservoir?

4.7 Refrigerators and Heat Pumps

The useful function of an engine is to deliver work, which it does by extracting heat from a high-temperature system and by passing some of this heat on to a low-temperature system. Suppose we operate such an engine in reverse: heat is extracted from the low-temperature system, work is extracted from an external agent, and the sum of these energies is inserted as heat into the hot system. *Both* the hot and cold systems here are assumed to be reversible heat sources. Such an operation can be useful in two ways. If the purpose is to cool the cold system further, the device is called a *refrigerator*. If the purpose is to heat the hot system further, the device is called a *heat pump*. Basically, engines, refrigerators, and heat pumps are identical devices, operated for different purposes but subject to the same underlying principles.

Consider first the refrigerator. The cold system, from which heat is extracted, is the "inside" of the refrigerator. The hot system, to which heat is delivered is the "outside" of the refrigerator; usually the ambient atmosphere. The work that must be supplied by the external agent is the commodity which we ruefully purchase from the electric company.

Clearly, we would like this work, which must be paid for, to be as small as possible. We want to minimize the absorbed work, or, in algebraic terms, we want to maximize the (intrinsically negative) delivered work. Again we recognize that the optimum operation is achieved by a reversible process.

Although the analysis of section 4.6 applies to the refrigerator, the engine efficiency there derived is not the interesting measure of the performance of the refrigerator. Rather, we are interested in the number of calories removed from the cold system for every calorie of work purchased from the power company. The *coefficient of refrigerator performance*, ϵ_r, is defined as the ratio of extracted heat to absorbed work.

To adapt the analysis of section 4.5 to the refrigerator, we denote the subsystem there by the superscript h (rather than the absence of a super-script). The temperature T^h of this system is greater than T^c, but dQ^h is now to be considered as a positive quantity and dQ^c as a negative quantity. Equation 4.5 shows that the delivered work dW' is negative, as expected. The energy $-dQ^c$ is extracted from the cold system, the energy $-dW'$ is taken from the reversible work source, and the energy $dQ^h = -dQ^c - dW'$ is inserted in the hot system. The condition of reversibility demands that

$$\frac{dQ^c}{T^c} + \frac{dQ^h}{T^h} = 0 \tag{4.13}$$

or

$$\frac{dQ^c}{T^c} - \frac{dQ^c + dW'}{T^h} = 0 \tag{4.14}$$

The coefficient of refrigerator performance consequently is

$$\epsilon_r \equiv \frac{-dQ^c}{-dW'} = \frac{T^c}{T^h - T^c} \tag{4.15}$$

If the temperatures of the two systems are equal, the coefficient of refrigerator performance becomes infinite: no work is then required to transfer heat from one system to the other. The coefficient of performance becomes progressively smaller as the temperature T^c of the refrigerator decreases relative to T^h. And if the temperature of the refrigerator approaches zero, the coefficient of performance also approaches zero (assuming T^h fixed). It therefore requires huge amounts of work to extract even trivially small quantities of heat from a system near $T^c = 0$.

We now turn our attention to the heat pump. In this case we are interested in heating a warm system, extracting some heat from a cold system, and extracting some work from a reversible work source. In a practical case the warm system may be the interior of a home in winter, the cold system is the outdoors, and the reversible work source is again the power company. In effect, we heat our home by removing the door of our refrigerator and pushing it up to an open window. The inside of the refrigerator is exposed to the outdoors, and the refrigerator attempts (with negligible success) further to cool the great outdoors. The heat extracted from this huge reservoir, together with the energy purchased from the power company, is ejected directly into the room from the cooling coils in the back of the refrigerator. Despite the fact that an ordinary household refrigerator would not have the capacity to heat any but the smallest room effectively in this way, the principle is correct, and practical heat pumps for industrial and domestic heating are commercially available.

The *coefficient of heat pump performance* ϵ_p is the ratio of the heat delivered to the hot system to the work extracted from the reversible work source.

$$\epsilon_p = \frac{dQ^h}{-dW} = \frac{T^h}{T^h - T^c} \tag{4.16}$$

Problems—Section 4.7

4.7-1. The lowest temperatures that have been reached are of the order of $0.001°K$. If the price of work is $2.5¢/kw\text{-}hr$, what would be the minimum cost of extraction of 1 cal of heat from a system at $0.001°K$? (The "warm system" is the ambient atmosphere.)

4.7-2. A home is to be maintained at $70°F$, and the external temperature is $50°F$. One method of heating the home is to purchase work from the power company and to convert it directly into heat: this is the method used in common electric room heaters. Alternatively, the purchased work can be used to operate a heat pump. What is the ratio of the costs if the heat pump attains the ideal thermodynamic coefficient of performance?

4.7-3. A household refrigerator is maintained at a temperature of $35°F$. Every time the door is opened, warm material is placed inside, introducing an average of 50 kcal, but making only a small change in the temperature of the refrigerator. The door is opened fifteen times a day, and the refrigerator operates at 15 per cent of the ideal coefficient of performance. The cost of work is $2.5¢/kw\text{-}hr$. What is the monthly bill for operating this refrigerator?

4.7-4. Heat is extracted from a bath of liquid helium at a temperature of $4.2°K$. The high-temperature reservoir is a bath of liquid nitrogen at a temperature of $77.3°K$. How many calories of heat are introduced into the nitrogen bath for each calorie extracted from the helium bath?

4.7-5. Assume that a particular body has the equation of state $U = NCT$, with $NC = 2 \text{ cal}/°K$ and assume that this equation of state is valid throughout the temperature range from $0.5°K$ to room temperature. How much work must be expended to cool this body from room temperature $(300°K)$ to $0.5°K$, using the ambient atmosphere as the hot reservoir?

4.7–6.   One mole of a monatomic ideal gas is allowed to expand isothermally from an initial volume of 10 liters to a final volume of 15 liters, the temperature being maintained at 400°K. The work delivered is used to drive a thermodynamic refrigerator operating between reservoirs of temperatures 200 and 300°K. What is the maximum amount of heat withdrawn from the low-temperature reservoir?

4.8   The Carnot Cycle

We have seen that in a process in which heat is extracted from a hot system, partly injected into a cold system, and partly made available as work the delivered work is maximum if the process is reversible. We now describe the Carnot cycle, which is a specific procedure whereby these reversible heat and work transfers can be accomplished.

To carry out the required process we introduce an "auxiliary system," in addition to the two reversible heat sources and the reversible work source. The auxiliary system is, in effect, a tool, and at the end of the process it is left in precisely the same state as it was in at the beginning. It is this cyclic nature of the process within the auxiliary system that is reflected in the name of the Carnot "cycle."

In general, the auxiliary system can be a magnetic system, an electric system, or any other type of thermodynamic system. We consider a representative form of the Carnot cycle, in which the auxiliary system is a gas contained in a cylinder with a movable piston.

We further temporarily assume that the hot and cold systems are not only reversible heat sources but heat reservoirs. This restriction merely permits us to consider finite heat and work transfers rather than infinitesimal transfers. We shall return later to consider infinitesimal Carnot cycles between reversible heat sources other than reservoirs.

The cycle is accomplished in four steps, and the changes of the temperature and the entropy of the auxiliary system are plotted for each of these steps in Figure 4.7.

1. The auxiliary system, originally at the same temperature T^h as the hot reservoir, is placed in contact with this reservoir and with the reversible work source and is caused to expand isothermally. In this process a flux of heat occurs from the hot reservoir to the auxiliary system, and a transfer of work ($\int P\, dV$) occurs from the auxiliary system to the reversible work source. This is the isothermal step $A \rightarrow B$ in Figure 4.7.

2. The auxiliary system, now in contact only with the reversible work source, is adiabatically expanded until its temperature falls to that of the cold reservoir. A further transfer of work occurs from the auxiliary system to the reversible work source. The quasi-static adiabatic process

occurs at constant entropy of the auxiliary system, as in $B \rightarrow C$ of Figure 4.7.

3. The auxiliary system is isothermally compressed while in contact with the cold reservoir and the reversible work source. This compression is continued until the entropy of the auxiliary system attains its initial value.

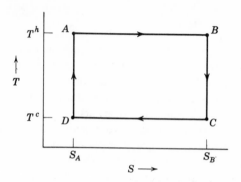

Figure 4.7 The T–S diagram for the auxiliary system in the Carnot cycle.

During this process there is a transfer of work from the reversible work source to the auxiliary system and a transfer of heat from the auxiliary system to the cold reservoir. This is the step $C \rightarrow D$ in Figure 4.7.

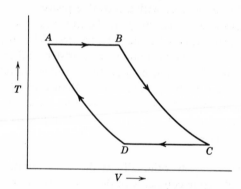

Figure 4.8 The T–V diagram for the auxiliary system in the Carnot cycle.

4. The auxiliary system is finally adiabatically compressed and receives work from the reversible work source. The compression brings the auxiliary system to its initial state and completes the cycle. Again the entropy of the auxiliary system is constant, from D to A in Figure 4.7.

The heat withdrawn from the first reservoir in process 1 is $T^h \Delta S$, and the heat transferred to the second reservoir in process 3 is $T^c \Delta S$. The difference $(T^h - T^c) \Delta S$ is the net work transferred to the reversible work source in the complete cycle. On the diagram of Figure 4.7 the heat $T^h \Delta S$ withdrawn from the first reservoir is represented by the area bounded by the four points labeled $ABS_B S_A$, the heat ejected to the second reservoir is represented by the area $CDS_A S_B$ and the net work delivered is represented by the area $ABCD$. The coefficient of performance is the ratio of the area $ABCD$ to the area $ABS_B S_A$, or $(T^h - T^c)/T^h$.

The Carnot cycle may be represented on any of a number of other diagrams, such as a P-V diagram, a T-V diagram, or a μ-S diagram. The representation on a T-V diagram is indicated in Figure 4.8. The precise form of the curve BC, representing the dependence of T on V in an adiabatic (isentropic) expansion, would follow from the equation of state $T = T(s, v)$.

If the hot and cold systems are merely reversible heat sources rather than reservoirs, the Carnot cycle must be carried out in infinitesimal steps. The heat withdrawn from the hot system in process 1 is then $T^h \, dS$ rather than $T^h \Delta S$, and similarly for the other steps. There is clearly no difference in the essential results.

Several other common and practical cyclic processes are described in Appendix F.

Problems—Section 4.8

4.8–1. Assuming that the auxiliary system in the Carnot cycle is an ideal monatomic gas, with a fundamental equation as found in section 3.4, find the form of the curves BC and DA in Figure 4.8.

4.8–2. Assuming that the auxiliary system of the Carnot cycle is an ideal monatomic gas, plot a P-V diagram of the cycle.

4.8–3. Describe the operation of the Carnot cycle as a refrigerator. Give a graphical representation of the coefficient of refrigerator performance.

4.8–4. Describe the operation of the Carnot cycle as a heat pump. Give a graphical representation of the coefficient of heat pump performance.

4.9 Measurability of the Temperature

The Carnot cycle not only illustrates the general principle of reversible processes as maximum work processes, but it provides us with an operational method for measurements of temperature. We recall that the entropy was introduced merely as an abstract function, the maxima of which determine the equilibrium states. The temperature was then defined in terms of a partial derivative of this function. It is clear that such a definition does not provide a direct recipe for an operational measurement of the temperature and that it is necessary therefore for such a procedure to be formulated explicitly. The importance of this problem is evident when we recall that the utility of thermodynamics depends upon the empirical determination of fundamental equations, to which the thermodynamic formalism may then be applied. The empirical determination of the fundamental equation of a given system is most conveniently done by empirical measurement of the equations of state, and such measurements entail a direct experimental measurement of the temperature.

Now, in our discussion of the efficiency of thermodynamic engines we have seen that the efficiency of an engine working by reversible processes between two systems, of temperatures T^h and T^c, is,

$$\epsilon_e = 1 - T^c/T^h \tag{4.17}$$

The thermodynamic engine efficiency is defined in terms of fluxes of heat and work and is consequently operationally measurable. Thus a Carnot cycle provides us with an operational method of measuring the ratio of two temperatures.

Unfortunately, real processes are never truly quasi-static, so that real engines never quite exhibit the theoretical engine efficiency. Therefore, the ratio of two given temperatures must actually be determined in terms of the limiting maximum efficiency of all real engines, but this is a difficulty of practice rather than of principle.

The statement that the ratio of temperatures is a measurable quantity is tantamount to the statement that the scale of temperature is determined within an arbitrary multiplicative constant. The temperature of some arbitrarily chosen standard system may be assigned at will, and the temperatures of all other systems are then uniquely determined, with values directly proportional to the chosen temperature of the fiducial system.

The choice of a standard system, and the arbitrary assignment of some definite temperature to it, has been discussed in section 2.6. We recall that the assignment of the number 273.16° to a system of ice, water, and vapor in mutual equilibrium leads to the absolute Kelvin scale of temperature. A Carnot cycle operating between this system and another system determines the ratio of the second temperature to 273.16°K and consequently determines the second temperature on the absolute Kelvin scale.

Practical thermometry generally employs secondary thermometers, the calibration of which eventually traces back to the Carnot-cycle method we have described. A representative "practical" thermometer is the ideal gas thermometer. Let us suppose that we have available a system that obeys the equation of state

$$PV = NRT \tag{4.18}$$

As P, V, and N are measurable, T is easily obtained. Consequently, to measure the temperature of any given system, we merely bring a sample of our ideal gas into thermal equilibrium with it, and we then use equation 4.18 to compute the temperature. The critical question, however, is this: how did we originally know that our gas obeyed equation 4.18 as an equation of state? To test the equation of state required measurements of P, V, N, and T, and the temperature measurement had to be made by some more fundamental method that was not predicated on equation 4.18. Presumably, a Carnot cycle method was used initially to corroborate equation 4.18, and thereafter the ideal gas could be used as a more convenient secondary thermometer.

In practice, real gases are found to have equations of state that deviate from equation 4.18, and corresponding corrections must be made in gas thermometers. There are also all sorts of corrections that must be made for expansion or contraction of the vessel containing the gas, for absorption on the walls of the vessel, and for myriads of other elusive effects which affect high-precision measurements.

The equations of state of other systems also provide convenient methods of temperature measurement. Both alcohol and mercury are commonly enclosed in capillary tubes, in which their changes of volume are easily observed, and are used to indicate temperature. The expansion of solid metals is also frequently used, as in the bimetallic strips which actuate home thermostats.

4.10 The T^* Method for Low Temperatures

At low temperatures, of the order of $1°K$ or less, the measurement of temperature becomes particularly difficult. A number of effects conspire to make this region troublesome. The heat transfers involved in Carnot cycles become awkwardly small and difficult to measure. All real gases condense to the liquid or solid phases, and natural processes become slow, so that thermal equilibrium is difficult to establish or maintain. However, there is a method of extrapolation of the high-temperature scale into the low-temperature region, which is commonly referred to as the T^* *method.* Because of its importance in low temperature physics and because of its relation to the theoretical structure of thermodynamics, we shall describe a representative form of the method.

Let us suppose that we adopt some system as a thermometer, despite the fact that we do not know its equation of state in the low-temperature region. The system most often used is a paramagnetic salt, but we consider here a compressible fluid in a cylinder with a movable piston. We *define* a *starred temperature*, T^*, as being directly proportional to the volume at some particular specified pressure, choosing a constant of proportionality that makes the starred temperature agree with the true temperature at the lowest temperature at which the true temperature can conveniently be measured accurately. The starred temperature can then be measured easily in the range of low temperatures, and the problem is to convert starred temperatures to true temperatures. The starred temperature is really introduced as a sort of bookkeeping device—it merely serves to label the states of which the true temperature is to be measured.

Consider the T-P diagram of Figure 4.9. The ordinate is the temperature scale, measured in true temperature above T_0 and in starred temperature below T_0. The two scales agree at T_0, that is, $T_0 = T_0^*$. We attempt to find the relation between true and starred temperatures below T_0 along the line $P = 0$. The zero pressure line is particularly interesting because, for liquids and solids, atmospheric pressure is negligibly small (in a sense that will become evident momentarily) and because the magnetic analogy is zero external magnetic field.

Now let us for a moment suppose that we can establish an entropy scale along the $P = 0$ line. We first show that this entropy scale permits us to translate the T^* scale into a T scale, and we then return to demonstrate how the entropy scale itself can be established.

Assuming that we know the molar entropy s of our thermometric substance as a function of T^* for zero P, we recall that

$$du = T \, ds - P \, dv \qquad (4.19)$$

which reduces, along the $P = 0$ line, to

$$du = dQ = T \, ds \qquad (4.20)$$

or

$$\left(\frac{du}{dT^*}\right)_{P=0} = \left(\frac{dQ}{dT^*}\right)_{P=0} = T\left(\frac{ds}{dT^*}\right)_{P=0} \qquad (4.21)$$

The quantity $(dQ/dT^*)_{P=0}$ is the specific heat, as measured on the starred scale, and is a measurable quantity. We adopt the usual notation

$$\left(\frac{dQ}{dT^*}\right)_{P=0} = c_P^* \qquad (4.22)$$

whence

$$T = c_P^* \Big/ \left(\frac{ds}{dT^*}\right)_{P=0} \qquad (4.23)$$

Knowledge of s as a function of T^*, for $P = 0$, consequently would permit us to evaluate T.

Of course, we still have to show that an entropy scale can be established along the $P = 0$ line. Consider a representative point such as $(0, T_1^*)$ in

Figure 4.9. By starting at this state and carrying out a quasi-static adiabatic process, we can trace out the curve labeled $s = s_1$, along which the entropy is constant. The entropy at the point $(0, T_1^*)$ therefore is the same as the entropy at (P_2, T_0). We might now say justifiably that the point (P_2, T_0) lies in the region of established temperature scale and that its entropy can therefore be assumed to be known by standard means. The entire demonstration of the establishment of the T scale in the low-temperature region is thereby completed.

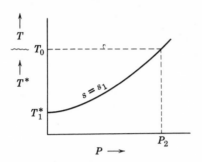

Figure 4.9   The T–P diagram for the T^* method of
low temperature measurement.

However, to make the demonstration fully explicit, we describe a method of evaluating the entropy at the point (P_2, T_0). To set the scale of entropy we assume that the entropy is known at some convenient point; we choose the point $(0, T_0)$ and assign it the entropy s_0. Then the entropy s_1 at (P_2, T_0) can clearly be written as

$$s_1 = s_0 + \int_0^{P_2} \left(\frac{\partial s}{\partial P} \right)_{T=T_0} dP \tag{4.24}$$

One method of evaluating the integrand would be to write

$$\left(\frac{\partial s}{\partial P} \right)_{T=T_0} = \frac{1}{T_0} \left(\frac{dQ}{dP} \right)_{T=T_0} \tag{4.25}$$

An evaluation of the heat absorbed per unit increase in pressure at each point along the $T = T_0$ line would enable us to carry out the numerical or graphical integration in equation 4.24, evaluating s_1.

A more convenient way of evaluating the integrand in equation 4.24 is based on the identities referred to in section 3.5. By the identity 3.50, equation 4.24 can be rewritten in the particularly convenient form

$$s_1 = s_0 - \int_0^{P_2} v\alpha \, dP \tag{4.26}$$

Measurement of the molar volume and the coefficient of thermal expansion α along the horizontal line from $(0, T_0)$ to (P_2, T_0) in Figure 4.9, and numerical or graphical integration, again evaluates s_1.

To recapitulate, equation 4.24 or 4.26 evaluates s_1, the entropy at any point $(0, T_1{}^*)$. Having thus established an entropy scale along the $P = 0$ line, equation 4.23 evaluates the true temperature T at any point along this line. The T^* method is extremely useful in low-temperature physics, although magnetic variables usually play the roles of the mechanical variables P, V of our discussion.

CHAPTER 5

Alternative Formulations and Legendre Transformations

5.1 The Energy Minimum Principle

The principle of maximum entropy, which is the fundamental principle of thermodynamics, has been developed in much of its essential content in the preceding chapters. We do not imply that we have yet discussed all that is significant in thermodynamics—on the contrary, most of the useful results of thermodynamics have not yet been mentioned. But we have established the basic principles, and we have illustrated the manner in which physical inferences can be drawn from the equilibrium condition $dS = 0$. Further inferences of great significance follow from the stability criterion $d^2S < 0$ and from the Nernst postulate (that $S = 0$ at $T = 0$), but the general character of thermodynamic inference already has been well illustrated. Before we proceed to the further developments, we shall find it convenient to reformulate all we have done to this point, in a mathematically equivalent alternative representation. And then, in the following sections, we shall present a host of other reformulations. Each of these alternatives will be found to be particularly convenient in particular types of problems. Only after we have treated the complete class of equivalent representations of the basic thermodynamic formalism shall we proceed with the further development of the theory.

The peculiar multiplicity of formulation and reformulation of the basic thermodynamic formalism is responsible for the apparent complexity of a subject which in its naked form is quite simple. The theoretical structure developed in the first three chapters is certainly simple, and the reader will

85

do well to keep constantly in his mind the fact that the next several chapters merely rephrase this simple theoretical structure.

The fundamental equation of a thermodynamic system can be written with either the entropy or the energy as the dependent quantity. This interchangeability of the roles of energy and entropy suggests the first reformulation of the thermodynamic formalism. In this restatement the

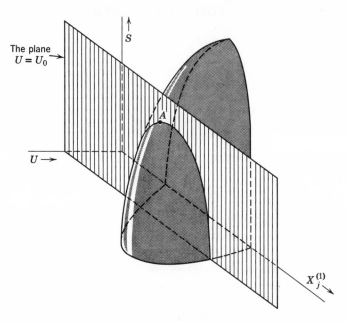

Figure 5.1   The equilibrium state A as a point of maximum S for constant U.

principle of maximum entropy is shown to be equivalent to, and is replaced by, a principle of minimum energy. Whereas the entropy maximum principle characterizes the equilibrium state as one having maximum entropy for given total energy, the energy minimum principle characterizes the equilibrium state as one having minimum energy for given total entropy.

In Figure 5.1 we show a section of the thermodynamic configuration space for a composite system, as discussed in section 4.1. The axes labeled S and U correspond to the total entropy and energy of the composite system, and the axis labeled $X_j^{(1)}$ corresponds to a particular extensive parameter of the first subsystem. Other axes, not shown explicitly in the figure, are $U^{(1)}$, X_j, and other pairs $X_k^{(1)}$, X_k.

The total energy of the composite system is a constant determined by the closure condition. The geometrical representation of this closure condition is the requirement that the state of the system lie on the plane $U = U_0$ in Figure 5.1. The fundamental equation of the system is represented by the surface shown, and the representative point of the system therefore must be on the curve of intersection of the plane and

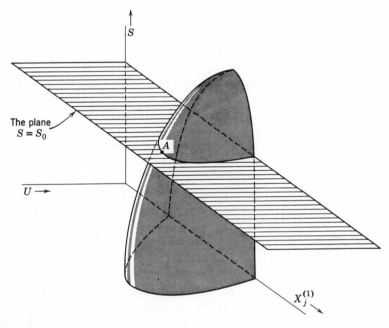

Figure 5.2 The equilibrium state A as a point of minimum U for constant S.

surface. If the parameter $X_j^{(1)}$ is unconstrained, the equilibrium state is that particular state which maximizes the entropy along the permitted curve, that is, the state labeled A in Figure 5.1.

The alternative representation of the equilibrium state A as a state of minimum energy for a given entropy is illustrated in Figure 5.2. Through the equilibrium point A is passed the plane $S = S_0$, which determines a curve of intersection with the fundamental surface. This curve consists of a family of states of constant entropy, and the equilibrium state A is the state that minimizes the energy along this curve.

The equivalence of the entropy maximum and the energy minimum principle clearly depends upon the fact that the geometrical form of the fundamental surface is generally as shown in Figures 5.1 and 5.2. As discussed in section 4.1, the form of the surface shown in the figures is determined by the postulates that $\partial S/\partial U > 0$ and that U is a single-valued continuous function of S; these analytic postulates, consequently, are the underlying conditions for the equivalence of the two principles.

To recapitulate, we have made plausible, though we have not yet proved, that the following two principles are equivalent:

✳ **Entropy Maximum Principle.** *The equilibrium value of any unconstrained internal parameter is such as to maximize the entropy for the given value of the total internal energy.*

✳ **Energy Minimum Principle.** *The equilibrium value of any unconstrained internal parameter is such as to minimize the energy for the given value of the total entropy.*

To prove the equivalence of the two extremal criteria, we simply show that if the energy were *not* minimum the entropy could not be maximum in equilibrium.

Assuming, for the sake of argument, that the energy has not the smallest possible value consistent with the given entropy, we withdraw energy from the system in the form of work, maintaining the entropy constant. We now return this energy to the system in the form of heat. The entropy of the system necessarily increases, in accordance with the quasi-static relationship $dQ = T\,dS$. The system is restored to its original energy but with an increased entropy. As this is inconsistent with the requirement that the original state be the state of maximum entropy, we are led to an inconsistency. We conclude that the original equilibrium state is the state of minimum energy for given entropy.

As already indicated, the fact that precisely the same situation is described by the two extremal criteria is analogous to the isoperimetric problem in geometry. Thus a circle may be characterized either as the two dimensional figure of maximum area for given perimeter or, alternatively, as the two dimensional figure of minimum perimeter for given area.

The two alternative extremal criteria which characterize a circle are completely equivalent, and each applies to every circle. Yet they suggest two different ways of generating a circle. Suppose we are given a square and we wish to distort it continuously to generate a circle. We may keep its area constant and allow its bounding curve to contract as if it were a rubber band. We thereby generate a circle as the figure of minimum perimeter for the given area. Alternatively we might keep the perimeter of the given square constant and allow the area to increase, thereby obtaining a (different) circle, as the figure of maximum area for the given perimeter. However, after each of these circles is obtained, each satisfies *both* extremal conditions for its final values of area and perimeter.

The physical situation pertaining to a thermodynamic system is very closely analogous to the geometrical situation described. Again, any equilibrium state can be characterized either as a state of maximum entropy for given energy or as a state of minimum energy for given entropy. But these two criteria nevertheless suggest two different ways of attaining equilibrium. As a specific illustration of these two approaches to equilibrium, consider a piston originally fixed at some point in a closed cylinder. We are interested in bringing the system to equilibrium without the constraint on the position of the piston. We can simply remove the constraint and allow the equilibrium to establish itself spontaneously; the entropy increases and the energy is maintained constant by the closure condition. This is the process suggested by the entropy maximum principle. Alternatively, we can permit the piston to move very slowly, doing work on an external agent until it has moved to the position that equalizes the pressure on the two sides. During this process energy is withdrawn from the system, but its entropy remains constant (the process is quasi-static and no heat flows). This is the process suggested by the energy minimum principle. The vital fact we wish to stress, however, is that *independent of whether the equilibrium is brought about by either of these two processes, or by any other process, the final equilibrium state satisfies both extremal conditions.*

Finally, we illustrate the energy minimum principle by using it in place of the entropy maximum principle to solve the problem of thermal equilibrium, as treated in section 2.4. We consider a closed composite system with an internal rigid impermeable diathermal wall. Heat is free to flow between the two subsystems, and we wish to find the equilibrium state. The fundamental equation in the energy representation is

$$U = U^{(1)}(S^{(1)}, V^{(1)}, N_1^{(1)} \cdots) + U^{(2)}(S^{(2)}, V^{(2)}, N_1^{(2)} \cdots) \quad (5.1)$$

All volume and mole-number parameters are constant and known. The variables which must be computed are $S^{(1)}$ and $S^{(2)}$. Now, despite the fact that the system is actually closed and that the total energy is fixed, the equilibrium state can be characterized as the state that would minimize the energy if energy changes were permitted. The virtual change in total energy associated with virtual heat fluxes in the two systems is, by differentiation of equation 5.1,

$$dU = T^{(1)} \, dS^{(1)} + T^{(2)} \, dS^{(2)} \quad (5.2)$$

The energy minimum condition states that $dU = 0$, subject to the condition of fixed total entropy: $S^{(1)} + S^{(2)} = \text{constant}$ \quad (5.3)

whence

$$dU = (T^{(1)} - T^{(2)}) \, dS^{(1)} = 0 \qquad (5.4)$$

and we conclude that

$$T^{(1)} = T^{(2)} \qquad (5.5)$$

The energy minimum principle thus provides us with the same condition of thermal equilibrium as we previously found by using the entropy maximum principle.

Equation 5.5 is one equation in $S^{(1)}$ and $S^{(2)}$. The second equation is most conveniently taken as equation 5.1, in which the total energy U is known and which consequently involves only the two unknown quantities $S^{(1)}$ and $S^{(2)}$. Equations 5.1 and 5.5, in principle, permit a fully explicit solution of the problem.

Problems—Section 5.1

5.1–1.   One mole of a monatomic ideal gas and two moles of a diatomic ideal gas (with $U = \frac{5}{2}NRT$) form the two subsystems of a composite system with an internal rigid impermeable diathermal wall. The volume of the first subsystem is $2 \times 10^4 \, cm^3$, and the volume of the second subsystem is $3 \times 10^4 \, cm^3$. The total energy of the composite system is 2500 cal. Find the equilibrium state. What is the pressure in each subsystem, and what is the temperature?

5.1–2.   Solve the problem of section 2.7, using the energy minimum principle.

5.1–3.   Solve the problem of section 2.8, using the energy minimum principle.

5.2   Legendre Transformations

In both the energy and entropy representations the extensive parameters play the roles of mathematically independent variables, whereas the intensive parameters arise as derived concepts. This situation is in direct contrast to the practical situation dictated by convenience in the laboratory. The experimenter frequently finds that the intensive parameters are the more easily measured and controlled and therefore is likely to think of the intensive parameters as operationally independent variables and of the extensive parameters as operationally derived quantities. The extreme instance of this situation is provided by the conjugate variables entropy and temperature. No practical instruments exist for the measurement and control of entropy, whereas thermometers and thermostats, for the measurement and control of the temperature, are common laboratory equipment. The question therefore arises as to the possibility of recasting the mathematical formalism in such a way that intensive parameters will replace extensive parameters as mathematically independent variables.

We shall see that such a reformulation is, in fact, possible and that it leads to various other thermodynamic representations.

It is, perhaps, superfluous at this point to stress again that thermodynamics is logically complete and self-contained within either the entropy or the energy representations and that the introduction of the transformed representations is purely a matter of convenience. This is, admittedly, a convenience without which thermodynamics would be almost unusably awkward, but in principle it is still only a luxury rather than a logical necessity.

The purely formal aspects of our problem are as follows. We are given an equation (the fundamental relation) of the form

$$Y = Y(X_0, X_1 \cdots X_t) \tag{5.6}$$

and it is desired to find a method whereby the derivatives

$$P_k \equiv \frac{\partial Y}{\partial X_k} \tag{5.7}$$

can be considered as independent variables without sacrificing any of the mathematical content of the given fundamental relation (5.6). This formal problem has its counterpart in geometry and several other phases of physics. The solution of the problem, employing the mathematical technique of Legendre transformations, is most intuitive when given its geometrical interpretation, and it is this geometrical interpretation that we shall develop in this section.

For simplicity, we first consider the mathematical case in which the fundamental relation is a function of only a single independent variable X:

$$Y = Y(X) \tag{5.8}$$

Geometrically, the fundamental relation is represented by a curve in a space with cartesian coordinates X and Y, and the derivative

$$P \equiv \frac{\partial Y}{\partial X} \tag{5.9}$$

is the slope of this curve. Now, if we desire to consider P as an independent variable in place of X, our first impulse might be simply to eliminate X between equations 5.8 and 5.9, thereby obtaining Y as a function of P

$$Y = Y(P) \tag{5.10}$$

A moment's reflection indicates, however, that we would sacrifice some of the mathematical content of the given fundamental relation (5.8), for, from the geometrical point of view, it is clear that knowledge of Y as a function of the slope dY/dX would not permit us to reconstruct the curve

$Y = Y(X)$. In fact, each of the displaced curves shown in Figure 5.4 corresponds equally well to the relation $Y = Y(P)$. From the analytical point of view the relation $Y = Y(P)$ is a first-order differential equation, and its integration gives $Y = Y(X)$ only to within an undetermined integration constant. Therefore, we see that acceptance of $Y = Y(P)$ as a basic equation in place of $Y = Y(X)$ would involve the sacrifice of some information originally contained in our fundamental relation.

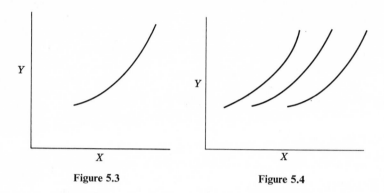

Figure 5.3   Figure 5.4

Despite the desirability of having P as a mathematically independent variable, this sacrifice of the informational content of the formalism would be completely unacceptable.

The practicable solution to the problem is supplied by the duality between conventional *point geometry* and the Pluecker *line geometry*. The essential concept in line geometry is that a given curve may be represented equally well either as the envelope of a family of tangent lines (Figure 5.5) or by the locus of points satisfying the relation $Y = Y(X)$. Any equation that enables us to construct the family of tangent lines therefore determines the curve equally as well as the relation $Y = Y(X)$.

Just as every point in the plane is described by the two numbers X and Y, so every straight line in the plane may be described by the two numbers P and ψ, where P is the slope of the line and ψ is its intercept along the Y-axis. Then just as a relation $Y = Y(X)$ selects a subset of all possible points (X, Y), a relation $\psi = \psi(P)$ selects a subset of all possible lines (P, ψ). A knowledge of the intercepts ψ of the tangent lines as a function of the slopes P enables us to construct the family of tangent lines and thence the curve of which they are the envelope. Thus the relation

$$\psi = \psi(P) \tag{5.11}$$

is completely equivalent to the fundamental relation $Y = Y(X)$. In this relation the independent variable is P, so that equation 5.11 provides a complete and satisfactory solution to our problem. As the relation $\psi = \psi(P)$ is mathematically equivalent to the relation $Y = Y(X)$, it can also be considered a fundamental relation; $Y = Y(X)$ is a fundamental relation in the "Y-representation," whereas $\psi = \psi(P)$ is a fundamental relation in the "ψ-representation."

The question now arises as to how we can compute the relation $\psi = \psi(P)$ if we are given the relation $Y = Y(X)$. The appropriate mathematical

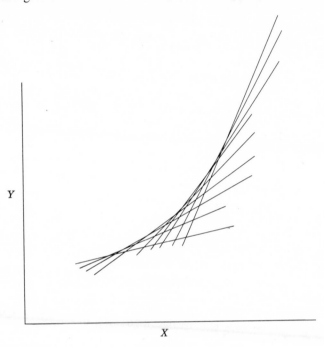

Figure 5.5

manipulation is known as a Legendre transformation. We consider a tangent line that goes through the point X, Y and has a slope P. If the intercept is ψ, we have (see Figure 5.6)

$$P = \frac{Y - \psi}{X - 0} \qquad (5.12)$$

or

$$\psi = Y - PX \qquad (5.13)$$

Let us now suppose that we are given the equation

$$Y = Y(X) \qquad (5.14)$$

and by differentiation we find

$$P = P(X) \qquad (5.15)$$

Then by elimination* of X and Y among equations 5.13, 5.14, and 5.15 we obtain the desired relation between ψ and P. The basic identity of the Legendre transformation is equation 5.13, and this equation can be taken as the analytic definition of the function ψ. The function ψ is referred to as a *Legendre transform* of Y.

The inverse problem to that discussed in the preceding paragraph is that of recovering the relation $Y = Y(X)$ if the relation $\psi = \psi(P)$ is given. We shall see here that the relationship between (X, Y) and (P, ψ) is

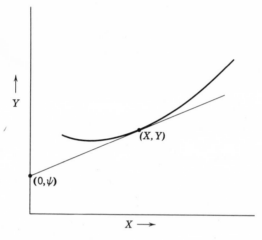

Figure 5.6

symmetrical with its inverse, except for a sign in the equation of the Legendre transformation. Taking the differential of equation 5.13 and recalling that $dY = P \, dX$, we find

$$d\psi = -P \, dX - X \, dP + dY \qquad (5.16)$$
$$= -X \, dP$$

or

$$-X = \frac{d\psi}{dP} \qquad (5.17)$$

If the two variables ψ and P are eliminated† from the given equation

---

* This elimination is possible if P is not independent of X; that is, if $d^2Y/dX^2 \neq 0$. In the thermodynamic application this criterion will turn out to be identical to the criterion of stability. The criterion fails only at the "critical points," which are discussed in detail in Chapter 8.

† The condition that this be possible is that $d^2\psi/\partial P^2 \neq 0$, which will, in the thermodynamic application, be guaranteed by the stability of the system under consideration.

$\psi = \psi(P)$ and from equations 5.17 and 5.13, we recover the relation $Y = Y(X)$. The symmetry between the Legendre transformation and its inverse is indicated by the following schematic comparison:

$Y = Y(X)$	$\psi = \psi(P)$
$P = \dfrac{dY}{dX}$	$-X = \dfrac{d\psi}{dP}$
$\psi = -PX + Y$	$Y = XP + \psi$
Elimination of X and Y yields $\psi = \psi(P)$	Elimination of P and ψ yields $Y = Y(X)$

The generalization of the Legendre transformation to functions of more than a single independent variable is simple and straightforward. In three dimensions Y is a function of X_0 and X_1, and the fundamental equation represents a surface. This surface can be considered as the locus of points satisfying the fundamental equation $Y = Y(X_0, X_1)$, or it can be considered as the envelope of tangent planes. A plane can be characterized by its intercept ψ on the Y-axis and by the slopes P_0 and P_1 of its traces on the $Y - X_0$ and $Y - X_1$ planes. The fundamental equation then selects from all possible planes a subset described by $\psi = \psi(P_0, P_1)$.

In general the given fundamental relation

$$Y = Y(X_0, X_1 \cdots X_t) \qquad (5.18)$$

represents a hyper-surface in a $(t + 2)$-dimensional space with cartesian coordinates $Y, X_0, X_1 \cdots X_t$. The derivative

$$P_k = \frac{\partial Y}{\partial X_k} \qquad (5.19)$$

is the partial slope of this hyper-surface. The hyper-surface may be equally well represented as the locus of points satisfying equation 5.18 or as the envelope of the tangent hyper-planes. The family of tangent hyper-planes may be characterized by giving the intercept of a hyper-plane, ψ, as a function of the slopes $P_0, P_1 \cdots P_t$. Then

$$\psi = Y - \sum_k P_k X_k \qquad (5.20)$$

Taking the differential of this equation, we find

$$d\psi = -\sum_k X_k \, dP_k \qquad (5.21)$$

whence

$$-X_k = \frac{\partial \psi}{\partial P_k} \qquad (5.22)$$

A Legendre transformation is effected by eliminating Y and the X_k from $Y = Y(X_0, X_1 \cdots X_t)$, the set of equations 5.19, and equation 5.20. The inverse transformation is effected by eliminating ψ and the P_k from $\psi = \psi(P_1, P_2 \cdots P_r)$, the set of equations 5.22, and equation 5.20.

Finally, a Legendre transformation may be made only in some $(n + 2)$-dimensional subspace of the full $(t + 2)$-dimensional space of the relation $Y = Y(X_0, X_1 \cdots X_t)$. Of course, the subspace must contain the Y-coordinate but may involve any choice of $n + 1$ coordinates from the set $X_0, X_1 \cdots X_t$. For convenience of notation, we order the coordinates so that the Legendre transformation is made in the subspace of the first $n + 1$ coordinates (and of Y); the coordinates $X_{n+1}, X_{n+2} \cdots X_t$ are left untransformed. Such a partial Legendre transformation is effected merely by considering the variables $X_{n+1}, X_{n+2} \cdots X_t$ as constants in the transformation. The resulting Legendre transform must be denoted by some explicit notation that indicates which of the independent variables have participated in the transformation. We employ the notation $Y[P_0, P_1 \cdots P_n]$ to denote the function obtained by making a Legendre transformation with respect to $X_0, X_1 \cdots X_n$ on the function $Y(X_0, X_1 \cdots X_t)$. Thus $Y[P_0, P_1 \cdots P_n]$ is a function of the independent variables $P_0, P_1 \cdots P_n, X_{n+1} \cdots X_t$. The various relations involved in a partial Legendre transformation and its inverse are indicated in the table shown on page 97.

In this section we have divorced the mathematical aspects of Legendre transformations from the physical applications. Before proceeding to the thermodynamic applications in the succeeding sections of this chapter, it may be of interest to indicate very briefly the application of the formalism to Lagrangian and Hamiltonian mechanics, which perhaps may be a more familiar field of physics than thermodynamics. The Lagrangian principle guarantees that a particular function, the Lagrangian, completely characterizes the dynamics of a mechanical system. The Lagrangian is a function of $2r$ variables, r of which are *generalized coordinates* and r of which are *generalized velocities.*" Thus the equation

$$L = L(v_1, v_2 \cdots v_r, q_1, q_2 \cdots q_r) \qquad (5.27)$$

plays the role of a fundamental relation. The *generalized momenta* are defined as derivatives of the Lagrangian function

$$P_k \equiv \frac{\partial L}{\partial v_k} \qquad (5.28)$$

$$Y = Y(X_0, X_1 \cdots X_t)$$

$$P_k = \frac{\partial Y}{\partial X_k}$$

The partial differentiation denotes a constancy of all the natural variables of Y other than X_k (i.e. of all X_j with $j \neq k$)

$$dY = \sum_0^t P_k \, dX_k$$

$$Y[P_0 \cdots P_n] = Y - \sum_0^n P_k X_k$$

Elimination of Y and $X_0, X_1 \cdots X_n$ from (5.23), (5.26), and the first $n + 1$ equations of (5.24) yields the transformed fundamental relation.

$$Y[P_0, P_1 \cdots, P_n] = \text{function of}$$
$$P_0, P_1 \cdots P_n, X_{n+1} \cdots X_t \quad (5.23)$$

$$-X_k = \frac{\partial Y[P_0 \cdots P_n]}{\partial P_k}, \quad k \leq n \tag{5.24}$$

$$P_k = \frac{\partial Y[P_0 \cdots P_n]}{\partial X_k}, \quad k > n$$

The partial differentiation denotes constancy of all the natural variables of $Y[P_0 \cdots P_n]$ other than that with respect to which the differentiation is being carried out.

$$dY[P_0 \cdots P_n] = -\sum_0^n X_k \, dP_k$$
$$+ \sum_{n+1}^t P_k \, dX_k \tag{5.25}$$

$$Y = Y[P_0 \cdots P_n] + \sum_0^n X_k P_k \tag{5.26}$$

Elimination of $Y[P_0 \cdots P_n]$ and P_0, $P_1 \cdots P_n$ from (5.23), (5.26), and the first $n + 1$ equations of (5.24) yields the original fundamental relation.

If it is desired to replace the velocities by the momenta as independent variables, we must make a partial Legendre transformation with respect to the velocities. We thereby introduce a new function, called the Hamiltonian and defined by*

$$(-H) = L - \sum_1^r P_k v_k \tag{5.29}$$

A complete dynamical formalism can then be based on the new fundamental relation

$$H = H(P_1, P_2 \cdots P_r, q_1, q_2 \cdots q_r) \tag{5.30}$$

Furthermore, by equation 5.24 the derivative of H with respect to P_k is the velocity v_k, which is one of the Hamiltonian dynamical equations.

---

* In our usage the Legendre transform of the Lagrangian is the *negative* Hamiltonian. Actually, the accepted mathematical convention agrees with the usage in mechanics, and the function $-\psi$ would be called the Legendre transform of Y.

Thus, if an equation of the form 5.27 is considered as a dynamical fundamental equation in the Lagrangian representation, the Hamiltonian equation (5.30) is the equivalent fundamental equation expressed in the Hamiltonian representation.

5.3 Thermodynamic Potentials

The application of the preceding formalism to thermodynamics is self-evident. The fundamental relation $Y = Y(X_0, X_1 \cdots)$ can be interpreted as the energy-language fundamental relation $U = U(S, X_1, X_2 \cdots X_t)$ or $U = U(S, V, N_1, N_2 \cdots)$. The derivatives $P_0, P_1 \cdots$ correspond to the intensive parameters $T, -P, \mu_1, \mu_2 \cdots$. The Legendre transformed functions are called *thermodynamic potentials*, and we now specifically define several of the commonest of them. In Chapter 6 we continue the discussion of these functions by deriving extremum principles for each potential, indicating the intuitive significance of each, and discussing its particular role in thermodynamic theory, but for the moment we concern ourselves merely with the formal aspects of the definitions of the several particular functions.

The *Helmholtz potential*, or the *Helmholtz free energy*, is that partial Legendre transform of U which replaces the entropy by the temperature as independent variable. The Helmholtz potential is generally indicated by the notation F or A; the notation F has been endorsed by the 1948 International Union of Physics and by the 1947 International Union of Pure and Applied Chemistry. Consequently, it is adopted here. The natural variables of the Helmholtz potential are $T, V, N_1, N_2 \cdots$. That is, the functional relation $F = F(T, V, N_1, N_2 \cdots)$ constitutes a fundamental relation. In the systematic notation introduced in section 5.2

$$\boxed{F \equiv U[T]} \tag{5.31}$$

The full relationship between the energy and the Helmholtz potential representations is summarized in the following schematic comparison:

$U = U(S, V, N_1, N_2 \cdots)$	$F = F(T, V, N_1, N_2 \cdots)$ (5.32)
$T = \partial U/\partial S$	$-S = \partial F/\partial T$ (5.33)
$F = U - TS$	$U = F + TS$ (5.34)
Elimination of U and S yields	Elimination of F and T yields
$F = F(T, V, N_1, N_2 \cdots)$	$U = U(S, V, N_1, N_2 \cdots)$

The complete differential dF is

$$dF = -S\, dT - P\, dV + \mu_1\, dN_1 + \mu_2\, dN_2 + \cdots \tag{5.35}$$

The *enthalpy* is that partial Legendre transform of U that replaces the volume by the pressure as independent variable. Following the recommendations of the International Unions of Physics and of Chemistry, and in agreement with almost universal usage, we adopt the symbol H for the enthalpy. The natural variables of this potential are $S, P, N_1, N_2 \cdots$ and

$$\boxed{H \equiv U[P]} \qquad (5.36)$$

The schematic representation of the relationship of energy and enthalpy representations is as follows:

$U = U(S, V, N_1, N_2 \cdots)$	$H = H(S, P, N_1, N_2 \cdots)$ (5.37)
$-P = \partial U / \partial V$	$V = \partial H / \partial P$ (5.38)
$H = U + PV$	$U = H - PV$ (5.39)
Elimination of U and V yields	Elimination of H and P yields
$H = H(S, P, N_1, N_2 \cdots)$	$U = U(S, V, N_1, N_2 \cdots)$

The inversion of the signs in equations 5.38 and 5.39, resulting from the fact that $-P$ is the intensive parameter associated with V, should be noted. The complete differential dH is

$$dH = T \, dS + V \, dP + \mu_1 \, dN_1 + \mu_2 \, dN_2 + \cdots \qquad (5.40)$$

The third of the common Legendre transforms of the energy is the *Gibbs function*, or *Gibbs free energy*. This potential is the Legendre transform which simultaneously replaces the entropy by the temperature and the volume by the pressure as independent variables. The standard notation is G, and the natural variables are $T, P, N_1, N_2 \cdots$. We thus have

$$\boxed{G \equiv U[T, P]} \qquad (5.41)$$

and

$U = U(S, V, N_1, N_2 \cdots)$	$G = G(T, P, N_1, N_2 \cdots)$ (5.42)
$T = \partial U / \partial S$	$-S = \partial G / \partial T$ (5.43)
$-P = \partial U / \partial V$	$V = \partial G / \partial P$ (5.44)
$G = U - TS + PV$	$U = G + TS - PV$ (5.45)
Elimination of $U, S,$ and V yields	Elimination of $G, T,$ and P yields
$G = G(T, P, N_1, N_2 \cdots)$	$U = U(S, V, N_1, N_2 \cdots)$

The complete differential dG is

$$dG = -S \, dT + V \, dP + \mu_1 \, dN_1 + \mu_2 \, dN_2 + \cdots \qquad (5.46)$$

A thermodynamic potential which arises naturally in the statistical mechanical theory of a single-component simple system is the *grand canonical potential*, $U[T, \mu]$. For this potential we have

$U = U(S, V, N)$	$U[T, \mu] = $ function of T, V, and μ $\qquad$ (5.47)
$T = \partial U / \partial S$	$-S = \partial U[T, \mu] / \partial T \qquad (5.48)$
$\mu = \partial U / \partial N$	$-N = \partial U[T, \mu] / \partial \mu \qquad (5.49)$
$U[T, \mu] = U - TS - \mu N$	$U = U[T, \mu] + TS + \mu N$ $\qquad (5.50)$
Elimination of U, S, and N yields $U[T, \mu]$ as a function of T, V, μ	Elimination of $U[T, \mu]$, T, and μ yields $U = U(S, V, N)$

and

$$dU[T, \mu] = -S \, dT - P \, dV - N \, d\mu \qquad (5.51)$$

Other possible transforms of the energy for a simple system, which are used only infrequently and which consequently are unnamed, are $U[\mu_1]$, $U[P, \mu_1]$, $U[T, \mu_1, \mu_2]$, etc. The complete Legendre transform is $U[T, P, \mu_1, \mu_2 \cdots \mu_r]$. The fact that $U(S, V, N_1, N_2 \cdots N_t)$ is a homogeneous first-order function of its arguments causes this latter function to vanish identically. For

$$U[T, P, \mu_1 \cdots \mu_r] = U - TS + PV - \mu_1 N_1 - \mu_2 N_2 \cdots - \mu_r N_r$$
$$(5.52)$$

which, by the Euler relation (3.6), is identically zero:

$$\boxed{U[T, P, \mu_1 \cdots \mu_r] \equiv 0} \qquad (5.53)$$

Problems—Section 5.3

5.3-1. Find the fundamental equation of a monatomic ideal gas in the Helmholtz potential representation, in the enthalpy representation, and in the Gibbs function representation. Assume the fundamental equation computed in section 3.4. In each case find the equations of state by differentiation of the fundamental equation.

5.3-2. Find the fundamental equation of oxygen in the Helmholtz potential representation. Assume that oxygen is an ideal gas with a specific heat as given in Table D.2.

5.3-3. Find the fundamental equation of a mixture of monatomic ideal gases in the Helmholtz and Gibbs function representations. (See section D.6.)

5.3–4. Find the fundamental equation in the Helmholtz potential representation of a mixture of general ideal gases. (See section D.6.)

5.4 Generalized Massieu Functions

Whereas the commonest and most useful functions definable in terms of Legendre transformations are those mentioned in section 5.3, another set can be defined by performing the Legendre transformation on the entropy rather than on the energy. That is, the fundamental relation in the form $S = S(U, V, N_1, N_2 \cdots)$ can be taken as the relation on which the transformation is performed. Such Legendre transforms of the entropy were invented by Massieu in 1869 and actually predated the transforms of the energy introduced by Gibbs in 1875. We refer to the transforms of the entropy as *Massieu functions*, as distinguished from the *thermodynamic potentials* transformed from the energy. The Massieu functions will turn out to be particularly useful in the theory of irreversible thermodynamics, and they also arise naturally in statistical mechanics and in the theory of thermal fluctuations. Three representative Massieu functions are $S[1/T]$, in which the internal energy is replaced by the reciprocal temperature as independent variable; $S[P/T]$, in which the volume is replaced by P/T as independent variable; and $S[1/T, P/T]$, in which both replacements are made simultaneously. Clearly

$$S[1/T] \equiv S - \frac{1}{T}U = -F/T \tag{5.54}$$

$$S[P/T] \equiv S - \frac{P}{T} \cdot V \tag{5.55}$$

and

$$S[1/T, P/T] = S - \frac{1}{T}U - \frac{P}{T} \cdot V = -G/T \tag{5.56}$$

Thus, of the three, only $S[P/T]$ is not trivially related to one of the previously introduced thermodynamic potentials. For this function

$S = S(U, V, N_1, N_2 \cdots)$	$S[P/T] = \text{function of } U, P/T, N_1,$
	$\qquad\qquad\qquad N_2 \cdots \quad$ (5.57)
$P/T = \partial S/\partial V$	$-V = \partial S[P/T]/\partial(P/T) \quad$ (5.58)
$S[P/T] = S - (P/T)V$	$S = S[P/T] + (P/T)V \quad$ (5.59)
Elimination of S and V yields $S[P/T]$ as function of $U, P/T, N_1, N_2 \cdots$	Elimination of $S[P/T]$ and P/T yields $S = S(U, V, N_1, N_2 \cdots)$

and

$$dS[P/T] = (1/T)\,dU - V\,d(P/T) - (\mu_1/T)\,dN_1 - \frac{\mu_2}{T}\,dN_2 \cdots \quad (5.60)$$

Other Massieu functions may be invented and analyzed by the reader as a particular need for them arises.

Problems—Section 5.4

5.4-1. Find the fundamental equation of a monatomic ideal gas in the representation

$$S\left[\frac{P}{T}, \frac{\mu}{T}\right]$$

Find the equations of state by differentiation of this fundamental equation.

CHAPTER 6

The Extremum Principle in the Legendre Transformed Representations

6.1 The Minimum Principles for the Potentials

We have seen that the Legendre transformation permits us to express the fundamental equation in terms of a set of independent variables chosen to be particularly convenient for a given problem. Clearly, however, the advantage of being able to write the fundamental equation in various representations would be lost if the extremum principle were not itself expressible also in those representations. We are concerned, therefore, with the reformulation of the basic extremum principle in forms appropriate to the Legendre transformed representations.

The straightforward way to translate the basic extremum principle to another representation is to write the energy minimum principle formally in the energy representation and simply to change variables to those appropriate to the new representation, using the formal techniques of the Legendre transformation. We shall follow precisely this technique, but we shall attempt to guide the analysis on the basis of physical considerations in the hope thereby of investing the restated principle with a more evident physical interpretation.

For definiteness we consider a composite system in diathermal contact with a heat reservoir. We further suppose that some internal constraint within the composite system has been removed, and we are interested in the mathematical condition that will permit us to predict the equilibrium state of the composite system.

103

In the equilibrium state the total energy of the composite system plus reservoir is minimum:

$$d(U + U^r) = 0 \qquad (6.1)$$

and

$$d^2(U + U^r) = d^2U > 0 \qquad (6.2)$$

subject to the isentropic condition

$$d(S + S^r) = 0 \qquad (6.3)$$

The quantity d^2U^r has been put equal to zero in equation 6.2 because d^2U^r is a sum of products of the form $dP_k{}^r \, dX_k{}^r$, or   not true

$$\frac{\partial^2 U^r}{\partial X_j{}^r \, \partial X_k{}^r} dX_j{}^r \, dX_k{}^r \qquad \downarrow$$

which vanish for a reservoir.

The other closure conditions depend upon the particular form of the internal constraints in the composite system. If the internal wall is movable and impermeable, we have

$$dN_j^{(1)} = dN_j^{(2)} = d(V^{(1)} + V^{(2)}) = 0 \qquad \text{for all } j \qquad (6.4)$$

whereas, if the internal wall is rigid and permeable to the kth component, we have

$$d(N_k^{(1)} + N_k^{(2)}) = dN_j^{(2)} = dV^{(1)} = dV^{(2)} = 0, \qquad j \neq k \qquad (6.5)$$

These equations suffice to determine the equilibrium state.

The differential dU in equation 6.1 involves the terms $T^{(1)} \, dS^{(1)} + T^{(2)} \, dS^{(2)}$, which arise from heat flux between the composite system and the reservoir, and terms such as $-P^{(1)} \, dV^{(1)} - P^{(2)} \, dV^{(2)}$ and $\mu_k^{(1)} \, dN_k^{(1)} + \mu_k^{(2)} \, dN_k^{(2)}$, which arise from the virtual process of interest within the composite system. The terms $T^{(1)} \, dS^{(1)} + T^{(2)} \, dS^{(2)}$ combine with the term $dU^r = T^r \, dS^r$ in equation 6.1 to yield

$$T^{(1)} \, dS^{(1)} + T^{(2)} \, dS^{(2)} + T^r \, dS^r = T^{(1)} \, dS^{(1)}$$
$$+ \, T^{(2)} \, dS^{(2)} - T^r \, d(S^{(1)} + S^{(2)}) = 0 \qquad (6.6)$$

whence

$$T^{(1)} = T^{(2)} = T^r \qquad (6.7)$$

Thus one evident aspect of the final equilibrium state is the fact that the reservoir maintains a constancy of temperature throughout the system. The remaining conditions of equilibrium naturally depend upon the specific form of the internal constraints in the composite system.

We now re-examine equation 6.1 with the purpose of recasting it into a form suitable to another representation. We may write

$$d(U + U^r) = dU + T^r \, dS^r = 0 \qquad (6.8)$$

or, by equation 6.3,

$$dU - T^r \, dS = 0 \qquad (6.9)$$

As T^r is a constant, we commute it with the differential operator to write

$$d(U - T^rS) = 0 \qquad (6.10)$$

Furthermore, since T^r is a constant, $d^2(T^rS) = 0$, and $N \cdot T$

$$d^2(U - T^rS) = d^2U > 0 \qquad (6.11)$$

Thus the quantity $(U - T^rS)$ is minimum in the equilibrium state. Now the quantity $U - T^rS$ is suggestive by its form of the Helmholtz potential $U - TS$. We are therefore led to examine further the extremum properties of the quantity $(U - T^rS)$ and to ask how these may be related to the extremum properties of the Helmholtz potential. We have seen that an evident feature of the equilibrium is that the temperature of the composite system (that is, of each of its subsystems) is equal to T^r. If we accept that part of the solution, we may immediately restrict our search for the equilibrium state among the manifold of states for which $T = T^r$. But over this manifold of states $U - TS$ is identical to $U - T^rS$. Then we may write equation 6.10 as

$$dF = d(U - TS) = 0 \qquad (6.12)$$

subject to the auxiliary condition that

$$\boxed{T = T^r} \qquad (6.13)$$

That is, the equilibrium state minimizes the Helmholtz potential, not absolutely, but over the manifold of states for which $T = T^r$. We thus arrive at the equilibrium condition in the Helmholtz potential representation.

✳ **Helmholtz Potential Minimum Principle.** *The equilibrium value of any unconstrained internal parameter in a system in diathermal contact with a heat reservoir minimizes the Helmholtz potential at constant temperature (equal to that of the heat reservoir).*

The intuitive significance of this principle is clearly evident in equations 6.8–6.10. The energy of the system plus the reservoir is, of course, minimum. But the statement that the Helmholtz potential of the system alone is minimum is just another way of saying this, for $dF = d(U - TS)$, and the term $d(-TS)$ actually represents the change in energy of the reservoir (since $T = T^r$ and $-dS = dS^r$).

It is now a simple matter to extend the foregoing considerations to the other common representations.

Consider a composite system in which each subsystem is in contact with a single pressure reservoir through walls nonrestrictive with respect to volume. We further assume that some internal constraint within the composite system has been removed. The first condition of equilibrium may be written

$$d(U + U^r) = dU - P^r \, dV^r = dU + P^r \, dV = 0 \qquad (6.14)$$

or

$$d(U + P^r V) = 0 \qquad (6.15)$$

Accepting the evident condition that $P = P^r$, we can write

$$dH = d(U + PV) = 0 \qquad (6.16)$$

subject to the auxiliary restriction

$$\boxed{P = P^r} \qquad (6.17)$$

✱ **Enthalpy Minimum Principle.** *The equilibrium value of any unconstrained internal parameter in a system in contact with a pressure reservoir minimizes the enthalpy at constant pressure (equal to that of the pressure reservoir).*

Finally, consider a system in simultaneous contact with a heat and a pressure reservoir. Again

$$d(U + U^r) = dU - T^r \, dS + P^r \, dV = 0 \qquad (6.18)$$

Accepting the evident conditions that $T = T^r$ and $P = P^r$, we may write

$$dG = d(U - TS + PV) = 0 \qquad (6.19)$$

subject to the auxiliary restrictions

$$\boxed{T = T^r, \qquad P = P^r} \qquad (6.20)$$

We thus obtain the equilibrium condition in the Gibbs representation.

✱ **Gibbs Function Minimum Principle.** *The equilibrium value of any unconstrained internal parameter in a system in contact with a temperature and a pressure reservoir minimizes the Gibbs function at constant temperature and pressure (equal to those of the respective reservoirs).*

The general result is now clear. *The equilibrium value of any unconstrained internal parameter in a system in contact with a set of reservoirs (with intensive parameters $P_1^r, P_2^r \cdots$) minimizes the thermodynamic potential $U[P_1, P_2 \cdots]$ at constant $P_1, P_2 \cdots$ (equal to $P_1^r, P_2^r \cdots$).*

We now consider the specific physical significance and utility of the Helmholtz potential, enthalpy, and Gibbs function in turn.

6.2 The Helmholtz Potential

For a composite system in diathermal contact with a heat reservoir the equilibrium state minimizes the Helmholtz potential over the manifold of states of constant temperature (equal to that of the reservoir).

The Helmholtz potential is a natural function of the variables T, V, N_1, $N_2 \cdots$ and this potential consequently is extremely convenient in problems in which the temperature is constant. The condition that T is constant reduces the number of variables in the problem, and F effectively becomes a function only of the variables V and N_1, $N_2 \cdots$. This is in marked contrast with the manner in which constancy of T would have to be handled in the energy representation: there U would be a function of S, V, N_1, $N_2 \cdots$ but the auxiliary condition $T = T^r$ would imply a relation among these variables. In the absence of explicit knowledge of the equation of state $T = T(S, V, N)$ this auxiliary restriction would lead to considerable awkwardness in the analytic procedures in the energy representation. In practice, many processes are carried out under conditions in which the ambient atmosphere acts as a heat reservoir to maintain the temperature constant; for these the Helmholtz potential representation is admirably suited.

As an illustration of the use of the Helmholtz potential, we consider a composite system composed of two simple systems separated by a movable adiabatic impermeable wall. The systems are also in diathermal contact with a heat reservoir of temperature T^r. The problem, then, is to predict the volumes V_1 and V_2 of the two subsystems. We write

$$F = F^{(1)}(T^r, V^{(1)}, N_1^{(1)}, N_2^{(1)} \cdots) + F^{(2)}(T^r, V^{(2)}, N_1^{(2)}, N_2^{(2)} \cdots) \quad (6.21)$$

and

$$dF = 0 \quad (6.22)$$

Thus

$$\frac{\partial F^{(1)}}{\partial V^{(1)}} dV^{(1)} + \frac{\partial F^{(2)}}{\partial V^{(2)}} dV^{(2)} = -P^{(1)} dV^{(1)} - P^{(2)} dV^{(2)} = 0 \quad (6.23)$$

and, with the conservation condition $dV^{(1)} = -dV^{(2)}$, we find, as expected

$$P^{(1)} = P^{(2)} \quad (6.24)$$

A more interesting problem is that of the *osmotic pressure difference* across a semipermeable membrane. We again consider a composite system composed of two simple systems separated by a rigid wall permeable to component No. 1 and impermeable to all other components. The systems are also in diathermal contact with a heat reservoir. The problem is to find the pressure difference in the two subsystems.

The fundamental equation corresponds to equation 6.21, and an analogous calculation leads to

$$\mu_1^{(1)}(T^r, V^{(1)}, N_1^{(1)} \cdots) = \mu_1^{(2)}(T^r, V^{(2)}, N_1^{(2)} \cdots) \quad (6.25)$$

which, with the conservation condition,

$$N_1^{(1)} + N_1^{(2)} = N_1^0 \quad (6.26)$$

permits us to find $N_1^{(1)}$ and $N_1^{(2)}$. Knowing these values, we can then evaluate the pressures from

$$P^{(1)} = -\frac{\partial F^{(1)}}{\partial V^{(1)}} = P^{(1)}(T^r, V^{(1)}, N_1^{(1)} \cdots) \tag{6.27}$$

and similarly for $P^{(2)}$. The difference $P^{(1)} - P^{(2)}$ is the osmotic pressure difference.

A common laboratory demonstration of the osmotic pressure difference is illustrated in Figure 6.1. Pure water is in a U tube with a membrane

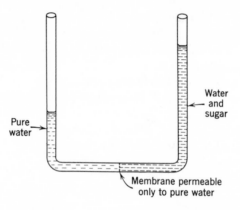

Figure 6.1   Demonstration of osmotic pressure difference.

permeable to water. Sugar is then put into one side of the U tube. The electrochemical potential of the water is decreased by the presence of the sugar, and the water flows through the membrane into the region containing sugar. The osmotic pressure difference is made visual by the difference in level of the liquids in the two arms of the U tube. This is not quite the situation analyzed above, for the volumes of the two subsystems are not constants in this case. However, the essential idea is the same.

It is of interest to carry out the calculation of $P^{(1)} - P^{(2)}$ explicitly in a case for which we know the full fundamental equation. We therefore consider a mixture of ideal gases, although we shall see that the osmotic pressure difference is trivial in this case. For a mixture of ideal gases the electrochemical potential has the form (see equations D.46, D.47, and D.40)

$$\mu_1 = RT\left[\phi_1(T) + \ln\frac{N_1 RT}{V}\right] \tag{6.28}$$

where $\phi_1(T)$ is a function of temperature only. Then equation 6.25 gives

$$\frac{N_1^{(1)}}{V^{(1)}} = \frac{N_1^{(2)}}{V^{(2)}} \tag{6.29}$$

With equation 6.26, we find that the mole numbers in equilibrium are

$$\frac{N_1^{(1)}}{N_1^0} = \frac{V^{(1)}}{V^{(1)} + V^{(2)}}, \qquad \frac{N_1^{(2)}}{N_1^0} = \frac{V^{(2)}}{V^{(1)} + V^{(2)}} \tag{6.30}$$

whence

$$P^{(1)} - P^{(2)} = RT\left[\frac{N^{(1)}}{V^{(1)}} - \frac{N^{(2)}}{V^{(2)}}\right] \tag{6.31}$$

$$= RT\left[\frac{N_2^{(1)} + N_3^{(1)} + \cdots}{V^{(1)}} - \frac{N_2^{(2)} + N_3^{(2)} + \cdots}{V^{(2)}}\right] \tag{6.32}$$

This result is independent of component No. 1. The pressure difference is precisely that which would have existed had there not been any of the first component in the system. This trivial result traces back to the fact that μ_1, in equation 6.28, depends only on N_1, independent of N_2, $N_3 \cdots$. For other systems than ideal gases we would find a less trivial solution, and the pressure difference would be dependent on the properties of the component to which the membrane is permeable.

Returning to the general aspects of the Helmholtz potential, we now show that a physical significance, arising out of a formalism very similar to that which led to its minimal properties, can be imputed to the Helmholtz potential. Consider a thermodynamic system in interaction with a reversible work source and also in diathermal contact with a heat reservoir. We consider some reversible process, and we inquire about the amount of work transferred to the reversible work source. By the conservation of energy, the work input to the reversible work source $dW^{(\text{RWS})}$ is equal to the decrease in energy of the system and the reservoir.

$$dW^{(\text{RWS})} = -d(U + U^r) \tag{6.33}$$

By the same line of reasoning employed in equations 6.8–6.12,

$$\boxed{dW^{(\text{RWS})} = -dF} \tag{6.34}$$

Thus the work delivered in a reversible process, by a system in contact with a heat reservoir, is equal to the decrease in the Helmholtz potential. For this reason the Helmholtz potential is sometimes referred to as *the available work at constant temperature*, or the *Helmholtz free energy*.

As an illustration of this property of the Helmholtz potential, we consider the following problem. A cylinder contains an internal piston on each side of which is one mole of a monatomic ideal gas. The walls of the cylinder are diathermal, and the system is immersed in a large bath of liquid (a heat reservoir) at temperature 0°C. The initial volumes of the two gaseous subsystems (on either side of the piston) are 10 liters and 1 liter, respectively. The piston is now moved reversibly, so that the final volumes are 6 liters and 5 liters, respectively. How much work is delivered?

As the reader has shown in problem 5.3–1, the fundamental equation of a monatomic ideal gas in the Helmholtz potential representation is

$$F = NRT \left\{ \frac{F_0}{N_0 R T_0} - \ln \left[\left(\frac{T}{T_0}\right)^{3/2} \frac{V}{V_0} \left(\frac{N}{N_0}\right)^{-1} \right] \right\} \tag{6.35}$$

At constant T and N this is simply

$$F = \text{constant} - NRT^r \ln V \tag{6.36}$$

The change in Helmholtz potential is

$$\Delta F = -NRT^r[\ln 6 + \ln 5 - \ln 10 - \ln 1] = -NRT^r \ln 3 = -596 \text{ cal} \tag{6.37}$$

Thus 596 cal of work are delivered in this process.

It is interesting to note that all of the work done comes from the thermal reservoir. The energy of a monatomic ideal gas is simply $\frac{3}{2}NRT$ and is constant at constant temperature. The fact that we withdraw heat from the temperature reservoir and deliver it *entirely* as work to the reversible work source does not, however, violate the Carnot efficiency principle because the gaseous subsystems are not left in their initial state. Despite the fact that the energy of these subsystems remains constant, their *entropy* increases.

Problems—Section 6.2

6.2–1. Two simple systems are contained within a cylinder and are separated by a piston. Each subsystem is a mixture of $\frac{1}{2}$ mole of N_2 and $\frac{1}{2}$ mole of H_2 (to be considered as ideal gases). The piston is in the center of the cylinder, each subsystem occupying a volume of 10 liters. The walls of the cylinder are diathermal, and the system is in contact with a heat reservoir at a temperature of 0°C. The piston is permeable to H_2 but impermeable to N_2. How much work is required to push the piston to such a position that the volumes of the subsystems are 5 liters and 15 liters?

6.2–2. By direct integration of $dW = -P\,dV$, corroborate the result (6.37).

6.3 The Enthalpy

For a composite system in interaction with a pressure reservoir the equilibrium state minimizes the enthalpy over the manifold of states of constant pressure (equal to that of the reservoir).

The enthalpy is a natural function of the variables S, P, N_1, $N_2 \cdots$. The enthalpy representation is therefore particularly convenient in the analysis of problems in which the pressure is maintained constant by a pressure reservoir. In processes carried out in open vessels the ambient atmosphere acts as such a reservoir, and the enthalpy representation consequently is of common usefulness.

The enthalpy may also be looked on as the available work from a system in contact with a pressure reservoir. We consider a system in simultaneous contact with a pressure reservoir and with a reversible work source. The work input to the reversible work source is equal to the decrease in energy of the system and the reservoir

$$dW^{(\mathrm{RWS})} = -d(U + U^r) \tag{6.38}$$

or, by the logic of equations 6.14–6.16,

$$dW^{(\mathrm{RWS})} = -dH \tag{6.39}$$

Thus, just as the energy U acts as a "potential for work" for systems of constant entropy and the Helmholtz potential acts as a potential for work for systems of constant temperature, the enthalpy acts as a potential for work for systems of constant pressure.

The generalization of the foregoing result, and the analogous result for the Helmholtz potential, is clear. *The work delivered in a reversible process by a system in contact with a set of reservoirs (with intensive parameters $P_1{}^r$, $P_2{}^r \cdots$) is equal to the decrease in $U[P_1, P_2 \cdots]$.*

There is yet another interpretation arising from considerations of heat transfer, rather than of work transfer, that can be given specifically to the enthalpy. We consider a simple system, enclosed in an impermeable wall, in contact with a pressure reservoir, and with various other unspecified systems. In some arbitrary process both heat and work may be transferred. The change in enthalpy is, in general,

$$dH = T\,dS + V\,dP + \mu_1\,dN_1 + \mu_2\,dN_2 + \cdots \tag{6.40}$$

Under the assumed conditions, all but the first term on the right vanishes, so that

$$dQ = (dH)_{P,N_1,N_2\cdots} \tag{6.41}$$

Thus heat added to a system at constant mole numbers and pressure appears as an increase in the enthalpy. This may be compared to the role of the internal energy U; heat added to a system at constant mole numbers and volume appears as an increase in the internal energy.

$$dQ = (dU)_{V,N_1,N_2\cdots} \tag{6.42}$$

Because heating of a system is so frequently done while the system is maintained at constant pressure by the ambient atmosphere, the enthalpy is generally useful in discussion of heat transfers. The enthalpy accordingly is sometimes referred to as the *heat content* of the system, although this terminology is not strictly correct, since heat refers to a mode of energy *flux* rather than to an attribute of a state of a thermodynamic system.

To illustrate the significance of the enthalpy as a potential for heat, we pose the following problem. A simple system is maintained at constant pressure, and its volume is changed from V_i to V_f. We desire to compute the heat absorbed by the system. As the pressure is constant, the heat flux is equal to the change in the enthalpy

$$\int dQ = H_f - H_i \tag{6.43}$$

If we were to know the fundamental equation

$$H = H(S, P, N) \tag{6.44}$$

and, by differentiation,

$$V = \frac{\partial H}{\partial P} = V(S, P, N) \tag{6.45}$$

we could eliminate the entropy to find H as a function of V, P, and N. Then

$$\int dQ = H(V_f, P, N) - H(V_i, P, N) \tag{6.46}$$

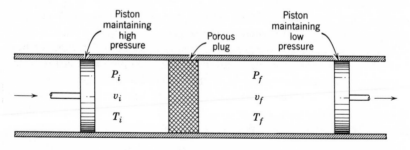

Figure 6.2 Schematic representation of the Joule–Thomson process.

As another and independent application of the enthalpy, we consider the *Joule–Thomson*, or *porous plug*, experiment. A gas at high pressure is allowed to seep through a porous plug into a region of low pressure (Figure 6.2). The porous plug can be made, for instance, by tamping a wad of glass wool into a pipe, and the process can be made continuous by using a mechanical pump to return the gas from the region of low pressure to the region of high pressure. Depending upon certain conditions, to be developed in a moment, the gas is either heated or cooled in passing through the plug. Systems in contact with the pipe on either side of the plug can thereby be cooled or heated, and the Joule–Thomson effect can be employed as a practical refrigerator or heater.

The Joule–Thomson effect is frequently employed in cryogenics laboratories in the production of low temperatures. For real gases, and for given initial and final pressures, the change in temperature, on passing through the plug, is positive down to a particular temperature and negative below that temperature. The temperature at which the change in temperature changes sign is called the *inversion temperature;* it depends upon the gas and upon the given pressures. In order that the Joule–Thomson effect may be an effective cooling mechanism, the gas must first be precooled to a temperature below its inversion temperature, and it can then be used down to the temperature at which the gas liquifies. The Joule–Thomson process is a convenient intermediate step in a sequence of operations leading to very low temperatures.

We now show that the Joule–Thomson process occurs at constant enthalpy. Consider one mole of the gas, which we shall consider as having a single component. The piston which pushes this quantity of gas through the plug does an amount of work $P_i v_i$, in which v_i is the molar volume of the gas on the high pressure side of the plug. As the gas emerges from the plug, it does work on the piston which maintains the low pressure P_f, and this amount of work is $P_f v_f$. Thus the conservation of energy enables us to compute the final molar energy of the gas; it is the initial molar energy, plus the work $P_i v_i$ done on the gas, minus the work $P_f v_f$ done by the gas.

$$u_f = u_i + P_i v_i - P_f v_f \qquad (6.47)$$

or

$$u_f + P_f v_f = u_i + P_i v_i \qquad (6.48)$$

which can be written in terms of the molar enthalpy h as

$$h_f = h_i \qquad (6.49)$$

Although, on the basis of equation 6.49, we say that the Joule–Thomson process occurs at constant enthalpy, we stress that this simply implies that the final enthalpy is equal to the initial enthalpy. We do not imply anything about the enthalpy during the process; the intermediate states of the gas are nonequilibrium states for which the enthalpy is not even defined.

The observation that the Joule–Thomson process occurs at constant enthalpy provides the key to the quantitative analysis of the process. Thus the change in temperature is, for a small pressure difference dP,

$$dT = \left(\frac{\partial T}{\partial P}\right)_{h,N_1,N_2\cdots} dP = \left(\frac{\partial T}{\partial P}\right)_{H,N_1,N_2\cdots} dP \qquad (6.50)$$

By straightforward mathematical manipulations, guided by a general pattern, which we discuss in detail in the following chapter, equation 6.50 can be rewritten as follows (the mole numbers are constant throughout):

$$dT = -\left[\left(\frac{\partial H}{\partial P}\right)_T \middle/ \left(\frac{\partial H}{\partial T}\right)_P\right] dP \tag{6.51}$$

Recalling that $dH = T\, dS + V\, dP$ at constant mole numbers,

$$dT = -\frac{T(\partial S/\partial P)_T + V}{T(\partial S/\partial T)_P}\, dP \tag{6.52}$$

Invoking the identity 3.50 and definitions 3.39 and 3.41, we find

$$dT = \frac{v}{c_P}\,(T\alpha - 1)\, dP \tag{6.53}$$

This is the fundamental equation of the Joule–Thomson effect. As the change in pressure dP is negative, the sign of dT is opposite that of the quantity in parentheses.

We have seen that for an ideal gas the coefficient of thermal expansion α is equal to $1/T$ (equation D-11), so that there is no change in temperature for an ideal gas. The Joule–Thomson effect depends upon the deviation from ideal gas behavior. It is left to the problems to show that dT is negative at low temperatures and positive at high temperatures for real gases. The inversion temperature is determined by the equation

$$T\alpha = 1 \tag{6.54}$$

which can be solved if α is known as a function of T and of the (mean) pressure P.

Problems—Section 6.3

6.3-1. A hole is opened in the wall separating two chemically identical single-component subsystems of a composite system. Each of the subsystems is also in interaction with a pressure reservoir of pressure P^r. Use the enthalpy minimum principle to show that the conditions of equilibrium are $T^{(1)} = T^{(2)}$ and $\mu^{(1)} = \mu^{(2)}$.

6.3-2. Find the change in temperature per unit change in pressure in a Joule–Thomson experiment if the gas used is CO_2, the mean pressure is 1 atm, and the mean temperature is $0°C$. Assume CO_2 satisfies the van der Waals equation, with constants as given in Table D.3, and that its specific heat is as given in Table D.2.

6.3–3.   Compute the inversion temperatures for Cl_2 and N_2O, assuming that these gases satisfy the van der Waals equation of state, with constants as given in Table D.3, and assuming a mean pressure of 2 atm. (Recall problem 3.5–3.)

6.3–4.   One mole of a monatomic ideal gas is in a cylinder with a movable piston, on the other side of which is a pressure reservoir with $P^r = 1$ atm. How much heat must be added to the gas to increase its volume from 20 to 50 liters?

6.4   The Gibbs Function

For a composite system in interaction with both heat and pressure reservoirs the equilibrium state minimizes the Gibbs function over the manifold of states of constant temperature and pressure (equal to those of the reservoirs).

The Gibbs function is a natural function of the variables $T, P, N_1, N_2 \cdots$ and is particularly convenient in the analysis of problems involving constant T and P. Chemical processes are frequently carried out in open vessels, so that they begin and terminate at atmospheric temperature and pressure. The Gibbs function correspondingly plays a dominant role in modern theoretical chemistry.

For a system in contact with a reversible work source, and also with heat and pressure reservoirs, the Gibbs function acts as a *potential for work*.

$$dW^{(RWS)} = -dG \tag{6.55}$$

The Gibbs function thus measures the work available in a reversible process from a system at constant T and P. It is often referred to as the *Gibbs free energy*.

The Gibbs function is closely related to the chemical potential, for

$$G = U - TS + PV \tag{6.56}$$

and inserting the Euler relation

$$U = TS - PV + \mu_1 N_1 + \mu_2 N_2 + \cdots \tag{6.57}$$

we find

$$G = \mu_1 N_1 + \mu_2 N_2 + \cdots \tag{6.58}$$

For a single component system the molar Gibbs function is identical with μ.

$$g \equiv \frac{G}{N} = \mu \tag{6.59}$$

The chemical potential is ofttimes referred to as the *molar Gibbs function* in single-component systems or as the *partial molar Gibbs function* in multicomponent systems.

6.5   The Maximum Principles for the Massieu Functions

In the energy representation the energy is minimum for constant entropy, and from this it follows that each Legendre transform of the energy is minimum for constant values of the transformed (intensive) variables.

Similarly, in the entropy representation the entropy is maximum for constant energy, and from this it follows that each Legendre transform of the entropy is maximum for constant values of the transformed (intensive) variables.

For two of the three common Massieu functions the maximum principles can be very easily obtained, for these functions are directly related to potentials (i.e., to transforms of the energy). By equation 5.54, we have

$$S[1/T] = -F/T \qquad (6.60)$$

and, as F is minimum at constant temperature, $S[1/T]$ is clearly maximum. Again, by equation 5.56,

$$S[1/T, P/T] = -G/T \qquad (6.61)$$

and, as G is minimum at constant pressure and temperature, $S[1/T, P/T]$ is clearly maximum.

For the remaining common Massieu function $S[P/T]$ we may repeat the logic of section 6.1. We are concerned with a system in contact with a reservoir that maintains P/T constant, although permitting $1/T$ to vary. It is readily recognized that such a reservoir is more of a mathematical fiction than a physically practical device, and the extremum principle for the function $S[P/T]$ is correspondingly artificial. Nevertheless, the derivation of this principle along the lines of section 6.1 is an interesting exercise that we leave to the curious student.

CHAPTER 7

Maxwell Relations

7.1 The Maxwell Relations

A formal aspect of thermodynamics, which is discussed most conveniently in terms of the Legendre transformation, is the set of Maxwell relations. It will be recalled (see equation 3.43) that the mathematical equality of the two mixed second derivatives $\partial^2 U/\partial S\, \partial V$ and $\partial^2 U/\partial V\, \partial S$ yielded a physical prediction which was one of the most immediate consequences of the existence of a fundamental equation. We had, in particular,

$$\frac{\partial^2 U}{\partial S\, \partial V} = \frac{\partial^2 U}{\partial V\, \partial S} \tag{7.1}$$

or

$$-\left(\frac{\partial P}{\partial S}\right)_{V,N_1,N_2\cdots} = \left(\frac{\partial T}{\partial V}\right)_{S,N_1,N_2\cdots} \tag{7.2}$$

This relation is the prototype of a whole class of similar equalities known as the *Maxwell relations*. These relations arise from the equality of the mixed partial derivatives of the fundamental relation expressed in any of the various possible alternative representations.

Given a particular thermodynamic potential, expressed in terms of its $(t + 1)$ natural variables, there are $t(t + 1)/2$ separate pairs of mixed second derivatives. Thus each potential yields $t(t + 1)/2$ Maxwell relations.

For a single-component simple system the internal energy is a function of three variables ($t = 2$), and the three [$= (2 \cdot 3)/2$] pairs of mixed second derivatives are $\partial^2 U/\partial S\, \partial V = \partial^2 U/\partial V\, \partial S$, $\partial^2 U/\partial S\, \partial N = \partial^2 U/\partial N\, \partial S$, and $\partial^2 U/\partial V\, \partial N = \partial^2 U/\partial N\, \partial V$. The complete set of Maxwell relations for a

117

single-component simple system is given in the following listing, in which the first column states the potential from which the relation derives, the second column states the pair of independent variables with respect to which the mixed partial derivatives are taken, and the last column states the Maxwell relations themselves. The mnemonic device given in section 7.2 provides a mental device for recalling relations of this form. In section 7.3 we present a procedure for utilizing these relations in the solution of thermodynamic problems.

U S, V $\left(\dfrac{\partial T}{\partial V}\right)_{S,N} = -\left(\dfrac{\partial P}{\partial S}\right)_{V,N}$ (7.3)

$dU = T\,dS - P\,dV + \mu\,dN$ S, N $\left(\dfrac{\partial T}{\partial N}\right)_{S,V} = \left(\dfrac{\partial \mu}{\partial S}\right)_{V,N}$ (7.4)

                         V, N $-\left(\dfrac{\partial P}{\partial N}\right)_{S,V} = \left(\dfrac{\partial \mu}{\partial V}\right)_{S,N}$ (7.5)

$U[T] \equiv F$ T, V $\left(\dfrac{\partial S}{\partial V}\right)_{T,N} = \left(\dfrac{\partial P}{\partial T}\right)_{V,N}$ (7.6)

$dF = -S\,dT - P\,dV + \mu\,dN$ T, N $-\left(\dfrac{\partial S}{\partial N}\right)_{T,V} = \left(\dfrac{\partial \mu}{\partial T}\right)_{V,N}$ (7.7)

                         V, N $-\left(\dfrac{\partial P}{\partial N}\right)_{T,V} = \left(\dfrac{\partial \mu}{\partial V}\right)_{T,N}$ (7.8)

$U[P] \equiv H$ S, P $\left(\dfrac{\partial T}{\partial P}\right)_{S,N} = \left(\dfrac{\partial V}{\partial S}\right)_{P,N}$ (7.9)

$dH = T\,dS + V\,dP + \mu\,dN$ S, N $\left(\dfrac{\partial T}{\partial N}\right)_{S,P} = \left(\dfrac{\partial \mu}{\partial S}\right)_{P,N}$ (7.10)

                         P, N $\left(\dfrac{\partial V}{\partial N}\right)_{S,P} = \left(\dfrac{\partial \mu}{\partial P}\right)_{S,N}$ (7.11)

$U[\mu]$ S, V $\left(\dfrac{\partial T}{\partial V}\right)_{S,\mu} = -\left(\dfrac{\partial P}{\partial S}\right)_{V,\mu}$ (7.12)

$dU[\mu] = T\,dS - P\,dV - N\,d\mu$ S, μ $\left(\dfrac{\partial T}{\partial \mu}\right)_{S,V} = -\left(\dfrac{\partial N}{\partial S}\right)_{V,\mu}$ (7.13)

                         V, μ $\left(\dfrac{\partial P}{\partial \mu}\right)_{S,V} = \left(\dfrac{\partial N}{\partial V}\right)_{S,\mu}$ (7.14)

$U[T, P] \equiv G$ T, P $-\left(\dfrac{\partial S}{\partial P}\right)_{T,N} = \left(\dfrac{\partial V}{\partial T}\right)_{P,N}$ (7.15)

$dG = -S\,dT + V\,dP + \mu\,dN$ T, N $-\left(\dfrac{\partial S}{\partial N}\right)_{T,P} = \left(\dfrac{\partial \mu}{\partial T}\right)_{P,N}$ (7.16)

                         P, N $\left(\dfrac{\partial V}{\partial N}\right)_{T,P} = \left(\dfrac{\partial \mu}{\partial P}\right)_{T,N}$ (7.17)

$U[T, \mu]$ T, V $\left(\dfrac{\partial S}{\partial V}\right)_{T,\mu} = \left(\dfrac{\partial P}{\partial T}\right)_{V,\mu}$ (7.18)

$dU[T, \mu] = -S\,dT - P\,dV - N\,d\mu$ T, μ $\left(\dfrac{\partial S}{\partial \mu}\right)_{T,V} = \left(\dfrac{\partial N}{\partial T}\right)_{V,\mu}$ (7.19)

V, μ $\left(\dfrac{\partial P}{\partial \mu}\right)_{T,V} = \left(\dfrac{\partial N}{\partial V}\right)_{T,\mu}$ (7.20)

$U[P, \mu]$ S, P $\left(\dfrac{\partial T}{\partial P}\right)_{S,\mu} = \left(\dfrac{\partial V}{\partial S}\right)_{P,\mu}$ (7.21)

$dU[P, \mu] = T\,dS + V\,dP - N\,d\mu$ S, μ $\left(\dfrac{\partial T}{\partial \mu}\right)_{S,P} = -\left(\dfrac{\partial N}{\partial S}\right)_{P,\mu}$ (7.22)

P, μ $\left(\dfrac{\partial V}{\partial \mu}\right)_{S,P} = -\left(\dfrac{\partial N}{\partial P}\right)_{S,\mu}$ (7.23)

7.2   A Thermodynamic Mnemonic Diagram

A number of the most useful Maxwell relations can be remembered conveniently in terms of a simple mnemonic diagram.* This diagram, given in Figure 7.1, consists of a square with arrows pointing upward

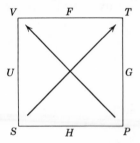

Figure 7.1   The thermodynamic square.

along the two diagonals. The sides are labeled with the four common thermodynamic potentials, F, G, H, and U, in alphabetical order clockwise around the diagram, the Helmholtz potential F at the top. The two corners at the left are labeled with the extensive parameters V and S, and the two corners at the right are labeled with the intensive parameters T and P.

Each of the four thermodynamic potentials appearing on the square is flanked by its natural independent variables. Thus U is a natural function of V and S; F is a natural function of V and T; and G is a natural function

---

* This diagram was presented by Professor Max Born in 1929 in a lecture heard by Professor Tisza. It appeared in the literature in a paper by F. O. Koenig, *J. Chem. Phys.* **3**, 29 (1935).

of T and P. Each of the potentials also depends on the mole numbers, but since these variables are common to all, they are not indicated explicitly on the diagram.

In writing the differential expression for each of the potentials in terms of the differentials of its natural (flanking) variables, the coefficient of each differential is indicated by the diagonal arrow. An arrow pointing away from a natural variable implies a positive coefficient, whereas an arrow pointing toward a natural variable implies a negative coefficient. This scheme becomes evident by inspection of the diagram and of each of the following equations:

$$dU = \quad T\,dS - P\,dV + \sum_k \mu_k\,dN_k \qquad (7.24)$$

$$dF = -S\,dT - P\,dV + \sum_k \mu_k\,dN_k \qquad (7.25)$$

$$dG = -S\,dT + V\,dP + \sum_k \mu_k\,dN_k \qquad (7.26)$$

$$dH = \quad T\,dS + V\,dP + \sum_k \mu_k\,dN_k \qquad (7.27)$$

Finally, the Maxwell relations can be read from the diagram. We then deal only with the corners of the diagram. The labeling of the four corners of the square may easily be seen to be suggestive of the relationship

$$\left(\frac{\partial V}{\partial S}\right)_P = \left(\frac{\partial T}{\partial P}\right)_S \qquad \text{(constant } N_1, N_2 \cdots) \qquad (7.28)$$

By rotating the square on its right side, we find, by exactly the same construction,

$$\left(\frac{\partial S}{\partial P}\right)_T = -\left(\frac{\partial V}{\partial T}\right)_P \qquad \text{(constant } N_1, N_2 \cdots) \qquad (7.29)$$

The minus sign in this equation is to be inferred from the unsymmetrical placement of the arrows in this case. The two remaining positions of the square give the two additional Maxwell relations:

$$\left(\frac{\partial P}{\partial T}\right)_V = \left(\frac{\partial S}{\partial V}\right)_T \qquad \text{(constant } N_1, N_2 \cdots) \qquad (7.30)$$

and

$$\left(\frac{\partial T}{\partial V}\right)_S = -\left(\frac{\partial P}{\partial S}\right)_V \qquad \text{(constant } N_1, N_2 \cdots) \qquad (7.31)$$

These are the four most useful Maxwell relations in the conventional applications of thermodynamics.

The mnemonic diagram may be adapted to other pairs of variables than S and V. If we are interested in Legendre transformations dealing with S and N_j, the diagram takes the form shown in Figure 7.2.

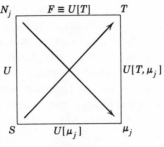

Figure 7.2

The arrow connecting N_j and μ_j has been reversed in relation to that which previously connected V and P to take account of the fact that μ_j is analogous to $(-P)$. Equations 7.4, 7.7, 7.13, and 7.19 may be read directly from this diagram. Other diagrams can be constructed in a similar fashion.

Problems—Section 7.2

7.2–1. Show that the relation

$$\alpha = \frac{1}{T}$$

implies that c_P is independent of the pressure

$$\left(\frac{\partial c_P}{\partial P} \right)_T = 0$$

7.3 A Procedure for the Reduction of Derivatives in Single-Component Systems

In the practical applications of thermodynamics the experimental situation to be analyzed frequently dictates a partial derivative to be evaluated. For instance, we may be concerned with the analysis of the temperature change which is required to maintain the volume of a single-component system constant if the pressure is increased slightly. This temperature change is evidently

$$dT = \left(\frac{\partial T}{\partial P} \right)_{V,N} dP \tag{7.32}$$

and consequently we are interested in an evaluation of the derivative $(\partial T/\partial P)_{V,N}$. A number of similar problems are considered in section 7.4. A general feature of the derivatives that arise in this way is that they are likely to involve constant mole numbers and that they generally involve both intensive and extensive parameters. *Of all such derivatives, only three can be independent, and any given derivative can be expressed by an identity in terms of an arbitrarily chosen set of three basic derivatives.* This set is conventionally chosen as c_P, α, and κ_T.

To see that only three derivatives can be independent, we recall that any first derivative involving intensive parameters is expressible in terms of second derivatives involving extensive parameters only—this merely by replacing the intensive parameters by their fundamental definitions. But, if N is maintained constant, the fundamental relation of a single-component system is a function of two variables only and has only three independent second derivatives: these may be $\partial^2 U/\partial S^2$, $\partial^2 U/\partial V^2$, and $\partial^2 U/\partial S\,\partial V = \partial^2 U/\partial V\,\partial S$.

The foregoing argument suggests a definite procedure for expressing any given derivatives at constant N in terms of three arbitrarily chosen basic derivatives. We could proceed by taking the given derivative and each of the three basic derivatives in turn, replacing all intensive parameters by their definitions, and thereby expressing each of the four derivatives in terms of the three quantities $\partial^2 U/\partial S^2$, $\partial^2 U/\partial V^2$, and $\partial^2 U/\partial S\,\partial V$. Elimination of these quantities from among the four equations then would yield the sought-for equation of identity among the four derivatives.

Although the foregoing procedure is simple in principle, it is not convenient in practice. And it is very important that such manipulations be mastered by the student of thermodynamics. Consequently, we present a procedure which makes free use of the Maxwell relations contained in the thermodynamic diagram and which reduces the formal manipulation of derivatives to a simple recipe.

Consider a partial derivative involving constant mole numbers. It is desired to express this derivative in terms of c_P, α, and κ_T. We first recall the following identities, which are to be employed in the mathematical manipulations (see Appendix A):

$$\left(\frac{\partial X}{\partial Y}\right)_Z = 1 \bigg/ \left(\frac{\partial Y}{\partial X}\right)_Z \tag{7.33}$$

and

$$\left(\frac{\partial X}{\partial Y}\right)_Z = \left(\frac{\partial X}{\partial W}\right)_Z \bigg/ \left(\frac{\partial Y}{\partial W}\right)_Z \tag{7.34}$$

$$\left(\frac{\partial X}{\partial Y}\right)_Z = -\left(\frac{\partial Z}{\partial Y}\right)_X \bigg/ \left(\frac{\partial Z}{\partial X}\right)_Y \tag{7.35}$$

The following steps are then to be taken in order:

1. If the derivative contains any potentials, bring them, one by one to the numerator and eliminate by the thermodynamic square (equations 7.24–7.27).

Example. Reduce the derivative $(\partial P/\partial U)_{G,N}$

$$\left(\frac{\partial P}{\partial U}\right)_{G,N} = \left[\left(\frac{\partial U}{\partial P}\right)_{G,N}\right]^{-1} \qquad \text{(by 7.33)}$$

$$= \left[T\left(\frac{\partial S}{\partial P}\right)_{G,N} - P\left(\frac{\partial V}{\partial P}\right)_{G,N}\right]^{-1} \qquad \text{(by 7.24)}$$

$$= \left[-T\left(\frac{\partial G}{\partial P}\right)_{S,N} \bigg/ \left(\frac{\partial G}{\partial S}\right)_{P,N} + P\left(\frac{\partial G}{\partial P}\right)_{V,N} \bigg/ \left(\frac{\partial G}{\partial V}\right)_{P,N}\right]^{-1} \qquad \text{(by 7.35)}$$

$$= \left[-T\frac{-S(\partial T/\partial P)_{S,N} + V}{-S(\partial T/\partial S)_{P,N}} + P\frac{-S(\partial T/\partial P)_{V,N} + V}{-S(\partial T/\partial V)_{P,N}}\right]^{-1} \qquad \text{(by 7.26)}$$

The remaining expression does not contain any potentials but may involve a number of derivatives. Choose these one by one and treat each according to the following procedure.

2. If the derivative contains the chemical potential, bring it to the numerator and eliminate by means of the Gibbs–Duhem relation, $d\mu = -s\,dT + v\,dP$.

Example. Reduce $(\partial\mu/\partial V)_{S,N}$

$$\left(\frac{\partial\mu}{\partial V}\right)_{S,N} = -s\left(\frac{\partial T}{\partial V}\right)_{S,N} + v\left(\frac{\partial P}{\partial V}\right)_{S,N}$$

3. If the derivative contains the entropy, bring it to the numerator. If one of the four Maxwell relations of the thermodynamic square now eliminates the entropy, invoke it. If the Maxwell relations do not eliminate the entropy put a ∂T under ∂S (employ equation 7.34 with $w = T$). The numerator will then be expressible as one of the specific heats (either c_v or c_P).

Example. Consider the derivative $(\partial T/\partial P)_{S,N}$ appearing in the example of step 1:

$$\left(\frac{\partial T}{\partial P}\right)_{S,N} = -\left(\frac{\partial S}{\partial P}\right)_{T,N} \bigg/ \left(\frac{\partial S}{\partial T}\right)_{P,N} \qquad \text{(by 7.35)}$$

$$= \left(\frac{\partial V}{\partial T}\right)_{P,N} \bigg/ \frac{N}{T}c_P \qquad \text{(by 7.29)}$$

Example. Consider the derivative $(\partial S/\partial V)_{P,N}$. The Maxwell relation would give $(\partial S/\partial V)_{P,N} = (\partial P/\partial T)_{S,N}$ (equation 7.28), which would not eliminate the entropy. We therefore do not invoke the Maxwell relation but write

$$\left(\frac{\partial S}{\partial V}\right)_{P,N} = \frac{(\partial S/\partial T)_{P,N}}{(\partial V/\partial T)_{P,N}} = \frac{(N/T)c_P}{(\partial V/\partial T)_{P,N}} \qquad \text{(by 7.34)}$$

The derivative now contains neither any potential nor the entropy. It consequently contains only V, P, T (and N).

4. Bring the volume to the numerator. The remaining derivative will be expressible in terms of α and κ_T.

Example. Given $(\partial T/\partial P)_{V,N}$,

$$\left(\frac{\partial T}{\partial P}\right)_{V,N} = -\left(\frac{\partial V}{\partial P}\right)_{T,N} \bigg/ \left(\frac{\partial V}{\partial T}\right)_{P,N} = \frac{\kappa_T}{\alpha} \qquad \text{(by 7.35)}$$

5. The originally given derivative has now been expressed in terms of the four quantities c_v, c_P, α, and κ_T. The specific heat at constant volume is eliminated by the equation

$$c_v = c_P - Tv\,\alpha^2/\kappa_T \qquad (7.36)$$

This useful relation, which should be committed to memory, was alluded to in equation 3.47. The reader should be able to derive it as an exercise, although a derivation is given in equations 7.60–7.64.

This method of reduction of derivatives can be applied to multicomponent systems as well as to single-component systems, provided that the chemical potentials μ_j do not appear in the derivative. For the Gibbs–Duhem relation, which eliminates the chemical potential for single-component systems, merely introduces the chemical potentials of other components for multicomponent systems. Nevertheless, the foregoing method is very often useful. A more general method is given in section 7.5.

7.4 Some Simple Applications

In this section we indicate several representative applications of the manipulations described in section 7.3.

In each case to be considered we first pose a problem. Typically, we are asked to find the change in one parameter when some other parameter is changed. Thus, in the simplest case, we might be asked to find the increase in the pressure of a system if its temperature is increased by ΔT, its volume being kept constant.

In the examples to be given we consider two types of solutions. First, the straightforward solution that assumes complete knowledge of the fundamental equation; and, second, the solution that can be obtained if c_P, α, and κ_T are assumed known and if the changes in parameters are small.

Adiabatic Compression

Consider a single-component system of some definite quantity of matter (characterized by the mole number N) enclosed within an adiabatic wall. The initial temperature and pressure of the system are known. The system is compressed quasi-statically so that the pressure increases from its initial value P_i to some definite final value P_f. We attempt to predict the changes in the various thermodynamic parameters (i.e., in the volume, temperature, internal energy, and chemical potential) of the system.

The essential key to the analysis of the problem is the fact that for a quasi-static process the adiabatic constraint implies constancy of the entropy. This fact follows, of course, from the quasi-static correspondence $dQ = T \, dS$.

We consider in particular the change in temperature. First, we assume the fundamental equation to be known. By differentiation, we can find the two equations of state $T = T(S, V, N)$ and $P = P(S, V, N)$. By knowing the initial temperature and pressure, we can thereby find the initial volume and entropy. Elimination of V between the two equations of state gives the temperature as a function of $S, P,$ and N. Then, obviously,

$$T = T(S, P_f, N) - T(S, P_i, N) \tag{7.37}$$

If the fundamental equation is not known, but c_P, α, and κ_T are given, and if the pressure change is small, we have

$$dT = \left(\frac{\partial T}{\partial P}\right)_{S,N} dP \tag{7.38}$$

By the method of section 7.3, we then obtain

$$dT = \frac{Tv\alpha}{c_P} dP \tag{7.39}$$

The change in chemical potential can be found similarly. Thus, for a small pressure change

$$d\mu = \left(\frac{\partial \mu}{\partial P}\right)_{S,N} dP \tag{7.40}$$

$$= \left(v - \frac{sTv\alpha}{c_P}\right) dP \tag{7.41}$$

where again it is left to the reader to use the methods of the preceding section to reduce $(\partial \mu / \partial P)_{S,N}$, as in equation 7.41.

Isothermal Compression

We now consider a system maintained at constant temperature and mole number and quasi-statically compressed from an initial pressure P_i to a final pressure P_f. We shall be interested in the prediction of the changes in the values of U, S, V, and μ. By appropriate elimination of variables among the fundamental equation and the equations of state, any parameter can be expressed in terms of T, P, and N, and the change in that parameter can then be computed directly.

For small changes in pressure we find

$$dS = \left(\frac{\partial S}{\partial P}\right)_{T,N} dP \tag{7.42}$$

$$= -\alpha V \, dP \tag{7.43}$$

Also

$$dU = \left(\frac{\partial U}{\partial P}\right)_{T,N} dP \tag{7.44}$$

$$= (-T\alpha V + PV\kappa_T) \, dP \tag{7.45}$$

and similarly for the other parameters.

One may inquire about the total quantity of heat that must be extracted from the system by the heat reservoir in order to keep the system at constant temperature during the isothermal compression. First, assume that the fundamental equation is known. Then

$$\Delta Q = U_f[P, \mu] - U_i[P, \mu] \tag{7.46}$$

where the Legendre transform $U[P, \mu]$ is most conveniently expressed as a function of T, P, and N. It is left to the reader to show that $U[P, \mu]$ is a "potential for heat at constant temperature and mole number," thereby justifying the foregoing solution.

For an infinitesimal process we have, from equation 7.43,

$$dQ = -T\alpha V \, dP \tag{7.47}$$

If the pressure change is not small and if both α and V are known as a function of T and P, we integrate equation 7.47 at constant temperature.

$$\Delta Q = -T \int_{P_i}^{P_f} \alpha V \, dP \tag{7.48}$$

This solution must be equivalent to that given in equation 7.46.

Free Expansion

The third process we shall consider is a free expansion. The constraints that require the system to have a volume V_i are suddenly relaxed, allowing it to expand to a volume V_f. If the system is a gas (which, of course, need not necessarily be the case), the expansion may be accomplished conveniently by confining the gas in one section of a rigid container, the other section of which is evacuated. If the septum separating the sections is suddenly fractured, the gas spontaneously expands to the volume of the whole container. The problem to which we address ourselves is the prediction of the change in the temperature and in the various other parameters of the system.

The essential element of the analysis in this case is the fact that the total internal energy of the system remains constant during the free expansion. Neither heat nor work are transferred to the system by any external agency.

If the temperature is expressed in terms of U, V, and N, we find

$$T_f - T_i = T(U, V_f, N) - T(U, V_i, N) \qquad (7.49)$$

If the volume change is small, we find

$$dT = \left(\frac{\partial T}{\partial V}\right)_{U,N} dV \qquad (7.50)$$

$$= \left(\frac{P}{Nc_v} + \frac{T\alpha}{Nc_v\kappa_T}\right)dV \qquad (7.51)$$

The process here treated, unlike the two previously treated, is essentially irreversible and is definitely not a quasi-static process.

Problems—Section 7.4

7.4–1. The adiabatic bulk modulus is defined by

$$\beta_S \equiv -v\left(\frac{\partial P}{\partial v}\right)_S = -V\left(\frac{\partial P}{\partial V}\right)_{S,N}$$

Show that

$$\beta_S = \frac{c_P}{c_v\kappa_T}$$

7.4–2. Two moles of an imperfect gas occupy a volume of 1 liter and are at a temperature of $100°K$ and a pressure of 0.2 atm. The gas is allowed to expand freely into an additional volume, initially evacuated, of $10 \ cm^3$. Find the change in enthalpy.

At the initial conditions

$$c_P = 0.8 \ \text{joules/mole}°K$$
$$\kappa_T = 0.3 \ (\text{atm})^{-1}$$
$$\alpha = 0.002/°K$$

7.4–3. A 1 per cent decrease in the volume of a system is carried out at constant mole number and under adiabatic conditions. Find the change in the electrochemical potential. Assume that c_P, α, and κ_T are known.

7.4–4. Two moles of O_2 are initially at a pressure of 1 atm and a temperature of $0°C$. An adiabatic compression is carried out to a final temperature of $300°C$. Find the final pressure by integration of equation 7.39. Assume that O_2 is an ideal gas with a specific heat as given in Table D.2, and recall problem 7.2–1.

Hint: Show that $\displaystyle\int_{T_0}^{T_f} \frac{c_P}{T} \, dT = R \int_{P_0}^{P_f} \frac{dP}{P}$.

7.4–5. Express the derivative $(\partial T/\partial V)_H$ in terms of c_P, α, and κ_T. Show that this derivative vanishes for a general ideal gas.

7.4–6. A ball bearing of mass 10 grams is placed in a vertical glass tube of cross-sectional area $2 \ cm^2$. The bottom of the tube is connected to a vessel of volume 5 liters, filled with oxygen at a temperature of $30°C$. The top of the tube is open to the atmosphere, which is at the same temperature and a pressure of 1 atm. What is the period of oscillation of the ball? Assume that the compressions and expansions of the oxygen are slow enough to be essentially quasi-static, and fast enough to be adiabatic. Assume that O_2 is an ideal gas with a specific heat as given in Table D.2.

7.5 Jacobian Transformations

A method of manipulation of thermodynamic derivatives alternative to, and more general than, the procedure described in section 7.3 is based on the mathematical properties of Jacobians. We state briefly the relevant properties of Jacobians and refer the reader to any standard text on differential calculus for proofs and for a more complete discussion.

If $u, v \cdots w$ are functions of $x, y \cdots z$, the Jacobian is defined as

$$\frac{\partial(u, v \cdots w)}{\partial(x, y \cdots z)} \equiv
\begin{vmatrix}
\dfrac{\partial u}{\partial x} & \dfrac{\partial u}{\partial y} & \cdots & \dfrac{\partial u}{\partial z} \\
\dfrac{\partial v}{\partial x} & \dfrac{\partial v}{\partial y} & \cdots \cdots \\
\dfrac{\partial w}{\partial x} & \cdots \cdots & \dfrac{\partial w}{\partial z}
\end{vmatrix}
\tag{7.52}$$

The property that makes it particularly useful in thermodynamic applications is the relationship

$$\left(\frac{\partial u}{\partial x}\right)_{y \cdots z} = \frac{\partial(u, y \cdots z)}{\partial(x, y \cdots z)} \tag{7.53}$$

By means of this relationship, a thermodynamic derivative of interest can be expressed in terms of Jacobians, and the well-developed calculus of these quantities can then be invoked.

An evident property which follows directly from the definition of Jacobians in terms of determinants is

$$\frac{\partial(u \ v \cdots w)}{\partial(x, y \cdots z)} = -\frac{\partial(v, u \cdots w)}{\partial(x, y \cdots z)} \tag{7.54}$$

Furthermore, in direct analogy to ordinary derivatives,

$$\frac{\partial(u, v \cdots w)}{\partial(x, y \cdots z)} = \frac{\partial(u, v \cdots w)}{\partial(r, s \cdots t)} \frac{\partial(r, s \cdots t)}{\partial(x, y \cdots z)} \tag{7.55}$$

and

$$\frac{\partial(u, v \cdots w)}{\partial(x, y \cdots z)} = 1 \Big/ \frac{\partial(x, y \cdots z)}{\partial(u, v \cdots w)} \tag{7.56}$$

These simple relationships are sufficient for most of the standard thermodynamic applications.

To employ the method of Jacobians in order to transform a given derivative in terms of c_P, α, and κ_T, we note that in each of the three quantities

$$c_P = T\left(\frac{\partial s}{\partial T}\right)_P, \qquad \alpha = \frac{1}{V}\left(\frac{\partial V}{\partial T}\right)_P, \qquad \kappa_T = \frac{-1}{V}\left(\frac{\partial V}{\partial P}\right)_T \tag{7.57}$$

the independent parameters are T, P, (and the mole numbers). *The problem of reduction of a given derivative to c_P, α, and κ_T is equivalent to the coordination transformation to T, P, and the N_j as independent parameters.* Alternatively stated, the introduction of c_P, α, and κ_T is equivalent to a transformation to the Gibbs function representation.

To illustrate the use of Jacobians, we consider the derivative that arose in our discussion of adiabatic compression (equation 7.38). Suppressing N in our notation, since it remains constant throughout, we introduce P and T as independent variables rather than P and S:

$$\left(\frac{\partial T}{\partial P}\right)_S = \frac{\partial(T, S)}{\partial(P, S)} = \frac{\partial(T, S)}{\partial(P, T)} \Big/ \frac{\partial(P, S)}{\partial(P, T)} \tag{7.58}$$

$$= -\left(\frac{\partial S}{\partial P}\right)_T \Big/ \left(\frac{\partial S}{\partial T}\right)_P \tag{7.59}$$

and by the Maxwell relation

$$\left(\frac{\partial T}{\partial P}\right)_S = \left(\frac{\partial V}{\partial T}\right)_P \bigg/ \left(\frac{\partial S}{\partial T}\right)_P = \frac{Tv\alpha}{c_P} \qquad (7.60)$$

which coincides with equation 7.39.

As another illustration of the method, we consider the derivation of equation 3.47, expressing c_v in terms of c_P, α, and κ_T. We have

$$c_v = T\left(\frac{\partial s}{\partial T}\right)_v = T\frac{\partial(s, v)}{\partial(T, v)} = T\frac{\partial(s, v)}{\partial(T, P)} \bigg/ \frac{\partial(T, v)}{\partial(T, P)} \qquad (7.61)$$

$$= -\frac{T}{v\kappa_T}\frac{\partial(s, v)}{\partial(T, P)} \qquad (7.62)$$

Expanding the Jacobian as a determinant,

$$c_v = -\frac{T}{v\kappa_T}\left[\left(\frac{\partial s}{\partial T}\right)_P\left(\frac{\partial v}{\partial P}\right)_T - \left(\frac{\partial s}{\partial P}\right)_T\left(\frac{\partial v}{\partial T}\right)_P\right] \qquad (7.63)$$

$$c_v = -\frac{T}{v\kappa_T}\left\{-\frac{c_P}{T}v\kappa_T + \left[\left(\frac{\partial v}{\partial T}\right)_P\right]^2\right\} \qquad (7.64)$$

$$= c_P - Tv\alpha^2/\kappa_T \qquad (7.65)$$

CHAPTER 8

Stability
of Thermodynamic
Systems

8.1 Intrinsic Stability of Single-Component Systems

The basic extremum principle of thermodynamics implies that $dS = 0$ and that $d^2S < 0$. The first condition, which states that the entropy is an extremum, has been exploited fully in the preceding chapters. The second condition, which states that the entropy is a maximum, remains to be investigated. The condition that the entropy be a maximum is the requirement of *stability* of the predicted equilibrium states. Considerations of stability lead to some of the most interesting and significant predictions of thermodynamics. In this chapter we investigate the conditions under which a system is stable, following the formulation given by L. Tisza in 1950. In Chapter 9 we consider the consequences of instability, that is, phase transitions and "critical points."

The problem of stability arises on two distinct levels. There is the problem of *mutual* stability of two simple systems which concerns the stability of a predicted partition of energy, volume, or mole numbers between two simple systems separated by an appropriate wall. But there is also a problem of *intrinsic* stability, which arises even within a single closed simple system. It is this subject of intrinsic stability that we discuss first.

It is evident that the concept of a single closed simple system is rather arbitrary, for we may mentally subdivide the system into two or more portions, and by this purely mental procedure our erstwhile simple system is transformed into a composite system. By this stratagem we formally

131

reduce the problem of intrinsic stability to a problem of mutual stability. We apply the requirement that the equilibrium between the two conceptual subsystems be mutually stable, and we thereby derive certain mathematical conditions which must apply to the fundamental equation of any given homogeneous simple system.

For the special case of single-component simple systems the discussion of intrinsic stability is particularly transparent and the results are particularly perspicuous. We therefore develop the analysis in this special case first.

We consider a single-component simple system of energy U', entropy S', volume V', and mole number N'. A conceptual spherical surface may be defined such that at any instant it encloses N moles of material at the center of the given system. The N moles enclosed within this hypothetical sphere then constitute a subsystem of the given system, and the material external to the sphere constitutes a second subsystem, which we refer to as the *complementary subsystem*. The "wall" that separates the subsystem and the complementary subsystem is diathermal and nonrigid, but it is restrictive with respect to the mole number by definition. For later convenience we assume that the subsystem is very small in relation to the total system, hence also in relation to the complementary subsystem.

$$N \ll N' \tag{8.1}$$

We employ the energy representation, and we write the fundamental equation in terms of molar quantities. Then

$$U' = Nu(s, v) + \tilde{N}\tilde{u}(\tilde{s}, \tilde{v}) \tag{8.2}$$

in which u, s, and v are the molar parameters of the subsystem and $\tilde{u}$, $\tilde{s}$, and $\tilde{v}$ are the molar parameters of the complementary subsystem. The mole number of the subsystem is N and that of the complementary subsystem is $\tilde{N} \equiv N' - N$. The closure condition on the volume is

$$Nv + \tilde{N}\tilde{v} = V' \tag{8.3}$$

and in virtual changes of volume of the subsystems

$$N\,dv + \tilde{N}\,d\tilde{v} = 0 \tag{8.4}$$

In applying the energy minimum principle, the total entropy must be held constant:

$$Ns + \tilde{N}\tilde{s} = S' \tag{8.5}$$

and

$$N\,ds + \tilde{N}\,d\tilde{s} = 0 \tag{8.6}$$

By virtue of equation 8.1, we see that

$$|d\tilde{v}| \ll |dv| \tag{8.7}$$

and

$$|d\tilde{s}| \ll |ds| \tag{8.8}$$

The smallness of $|d\tilde{v}|$ and $|d\tilde{s}|$ in comparison to $|dv|$ and $|ds|$ permits us to neglect higher powers of $d\tilde{v}$ and $d\tilde{s}$ in the analysis. This simplification is the sole reason for our assumption that the subsystem is small—an assumption with no essential effect on the final results.

We now proceed to our central considerations. A virtual transfer of entropy and volume across the hypothetical surface leads to a change in the total energy, given by a Taylor expansion. In accordance with equations 8.7 and 8.8, this expansion involves an infinite series of terms relating to the subsystem, whereas all but the first-order terms relating to the complementary subsystem can be neglected.

$$\Delta U' = N[du + d^2u + d^3u + \cdots] + \tilde{N}\,d\tilde{u} \tag{8.9}$$

where

$$du = \frac{\partial u}{\partial s}\,ds + \frac{\partial u}{\partial v}\,dv = T\,ds - P\,dv \tag{8.10}$$

$$d^2u = \tfrac{1}{2}[u_{ss}(ds)^2 + 2u_{sv}\,ds\,dv + u_{vv}(dv)^2] \tag{8.11}$$

$$d^3u = \frac{1}{3!}\left[\frac{\partial^3 u}{\partial s^3}(ds)^3 + 3\frac{\partial^3 u}{(\partial s)^2\,\partial v}(ds)^2\,dv + \cdots\right]$$

$$d\tilde{u} = \frac{\partial \tilde{u}}{\partial \tilde{s}}\,d\tilde{s} + \frac{\partial \tilde{u}}{\partial \tilde{v}}\,d\tilde{v} = \tilde{T}\,d\tilde{s} - \tilde{P}\,d\tilde{v} \tag{8.12}$$

and where, in turn,

$$u_{ss} \equiv \frac{\partial^2 u}{\partial s^2} = \frac{\partial T}{\partial s} \tag{8.13}$$

$$u_{sv} = u_{vs} \equiv \frac{\partial^2 u}{\partial s\,\partial v} = -\frac{\partial P}{\partial s} = \frac{\partial T}{\partial v} \tag{8.14}$$

$$u_{vv} \equiv \frac{\partial^2 u}{\partial v^2} = -\frac{\partial P}{\partial v} \tag{8.15}$$

Application of our usual formalism to the composite system requires first the vanishing of the first-order terms $N\,du + \tilde{N}\,d\tilde{u}$. This leads to the equality of the temperatures and pressures of subsystem and environment and merely confirms our original assumption that the entire system is homogeneous.

The requirement of stability is that the second-order terms be positive for any conceivable virtual process. That is,

$$d^2u = \tfrac{1}{2}[u_{ss}(ds)^2 + 2u_{sv}\,ds\,dv + u_{vv}(dv)^2] > 0 \qquad (8.16)$$

for all possible pairs of values of ds and dv, except the trivial pair $ds = dv = 0$. The quantity in brackets is a *homogeneous quadratic form* in the two variables ds and dv. The condition that it be positive for all pairs of values of ds and dv (except the trivial pair $ds = dv = 0$) is referred to mathematically as the condition that the quadratic form be *positive-definite.*

Now suppose we were to have a quadratic form in the special form of a sum of squares with no cross terms, such as $A\xi_1{}^2 + B\xi_2{}^2$. The condition that this form be positive-definite is obviously that both constants A and B be positive and nonzero. To analyze the positive-definiteness of equation 8.16, we therefore attempt to express it in terms of new variables, such that it will be a sum of squares of these new variables. The new variables will be linear functions of the old variables ds and dv and will prove to have direct physical significance. The coefficients of the new terms will be functions of the constants u_{ss}, u_{sv}, and u_{vv} and will also prove to have direct physical significance.

In order to eliminate the cross-term in equation 8.16, we introduce as a new variable in place of ds the temperature differential

$$dT \equiv u_{ss}\,ds + u_{sv}\,dv \qquad (8.17)$$

whence

$$O.K. \qquad d^2u = \frac{1}{2}\left[\frac{1}{u_{ss}}\,(dT)^2 + \left(u_{vv} - \frac{u_{sv}^2}{u_{ss}}\right)(dv)^2 \right] \qquad (8.18)$$

Although we have now succeeded in reducing d^2u to a sum of squares, we briefly delay the consideration of stability while we seek the physical interpretation of the coefficient of $(dv)^2$. By examination of equation 8.18, it is clear that the coefficient can be written as

$$O.K. \qquad \left(u_{vv} - \frac{u_{sv}^2}{u_{ss}}\right) = \left(\frac{\partial^2 u}{\partial v^2}\right)_T \qquad (8.19)$$

A more natural way to write it is in terms of the molar Helmholtz potential

$$F/N \equiv f \equiv u - Ts \qquad (8.20)$$

for which the natural variables are T and v. At constant T the term Ts is a linear term and can be subtracted from u in equation 8.19 without affecting the second derivative. That is, *True if Δ is a linear function of $\forall$ at const. T yes!*

$$2 \quad \left(u_{vv} - \frac{u_{sv}^2}{u_{ss}}\right) = \left(\frac{\partial^2 u}{\partial v^2}\right)_T = \left(\frac{\partial^2(u - Ts)}{\partial v^2}\right)_T = \frac{\partial^2 f}{\partial v^2} \qquad (8.21)$$

$u = u(\Delta, v)$ *$f = f(T, v)$*

Furthermore, since $\partial f/\partial v = -P$, we have

$$\left(u_{vv} - \frac{u_{sv}^2}{u_{ss}}\right) = \frac{\partial^2 f}{\partial v^2} = -\left(\frac{\partial P}{\partial v}\right)_T = \frac{1}{v\kappa_T} \qquad (8.22)$$

The reader can corroborate equation 8.22 by the direct methods of section 7.3.

The quadratic form 8.18 becomes

$$d^2u = \frac{1}{2}\left[\frac{1}{u_{ss}}(dT)^2 + f_{vv}(dv)^2\right] \qquad (8.23)$$

The criteria of positive definiteness, hence of stability, are

$$u_{ss} \equiv \left(\frac{\partial T}{\partial s}\right)_v = T/c_v > 0 \qquad (8.24)$$

and

$$\frac{u_{ss}u_{vv} - u_{sv}^2}{u_{ss}} = f_{vv} = -\left(\frac{\partial P}{\partial v}\right)_T = \frac{1}{v\kappa_T} > 0 \qquad (8.25)$$

The two criteria (8.24) and (8.25) imply also that

$$u_{vv} = -\left(\frac{\partial P}{\partial v}\right)_s > 0 \qquad (8.26)$$

The first of the stability criteria (8.24) can be interpreted easily. Dividing by the temperature, which is intrinsically positive,

$$\frac{1}{T}\frac{\partial T}{\partial s} = \frac{N}{T}\frac{\partial T}{\partial S} = N\frac{dT}{dQ} > 0 \qquad (8.27)$$

which states that <u>addition of heat to a stable system must increase its temperature.</u>

The physical significance of the second stability criterion is expressed in equation 8.25 as the requirement that <u>an isothermal expansion of a stable system must decrease its pressure.</u>

The physical content of the two stability criteria is known as *Le Châtelier's principle*. According to this principle, the criterion for stability is that the spontaneous processes induced by a deviation from equilibrium be in a direction to restore the system to equilibrium. As an example, consider two portions of a system, which have temperatures $T^{(1)}$ and $T^{(2)}$.

If $T^{(1)}$ is greater than $T^{(2)}$, the system has undergone a deviation from the equilibrium state. The spontaneous process which then occurs is a flow of heat from the higher temperature $T^{(1)}$ to the lower $T^{(2)}$. The Le Châtelier principle requires that this process equalize the temperatures, reducing $T^{(1)}$ and increasing $T^{(2)}$. That is, we require that an outflow of heat tend to reduce the temperature and that an inflow of heat tend to increase the temperature. This is precisely the formal statement of the first stability criterion (equation 8.24).

The second stability criterion can be similarly pictorialized in terms of Le Châtelier's principle. Consider two small portions of a large system. These subsystems are separated by a movable diathermal imaginary wall. Each subsystem is in diathermal contact with the large remainder of the system, which acts as a heat reservoir to maintain constant temperature. If the pressures of the two subsystems are unequal, the wall moves from the region of high pressure to the region of low pressure. Equation 8.25 then guarantees that this process will tend to equalize the pressures.

In any single-component simple system an arbitrarily chosen portion will be in stable equilibrium with the remainder of the system only if the fundamental equation conforms to the inequalities demanded by the stability criteria (8.24) and (8.25). If the fundamental equation were such that the inequalities were not satisfied, the system could not remain homogeneous. We are thus led to the conclusion that *the fundamental equation of every homogeneous simple system is perforce consistent with the inequalities (8.24) and (8.25)*.

It is frequently observed that a simple system satisfies the stability criteria but that as the external constraints are changed in a particular way the inequalities approach more and more closely to equalities. If we were to extrapolate the behavior of the system in a continuous fashion, we would then expect that at some particular values of the extensive parameters the system would come into conflict with the stability criteria. In such cases we observe that the system actually does cease to be homogeneous and suddenly splits into two or more *phases*. The phenomena of melting of a solid and of partial liquefaction of a gas are intimately related to the violation of the stability criteria. We give detailed and explicit treatment to the theory of phase transitions in Chapter 9.

Problems—Section 8.1

8.1–1. Show that the fundamental equation of a monatomic ideal gas satisfies the criteria of intrinsic stability.

8.1–2. Show that the van der Waals equation of state does not satisfy the criteria of intrinsic stability for all values of the parameters. Plot the curves of P versus V for constant T (the isotherms of the gas) and show the region of instability.

8.1–3.   Show that if the conceptual subsystem of section 8.1 is taken as one of constant volume rather than of constant mole number a set of intrinsic stability criteria completely equivalent to equations 8.24 and 8.25 is obtained.

Hint: The Gibbs–Duhem relation $s\,dT - v\,dP + d\mu = 0$ can be divided by ds and interpreted at constant v, yielding $su_{ss} + vu_{sv} + \dfrac{\partial \mu}{\partial s} = 0$. This equation and the two analogous equations obtained by dividing by dv and by dN relate the quantities occurring in the new form of the stability criteria to those occurring in equations 8.24 and 8.25.

8.1–4.   If the roles of ds and dv are interchanged in the analysis and, in particular, in equations 8.17–8.18, the stability criteria developed become, analogous to equation 8.24,

$$u_{vv} \equiv -\left(\frac{\partial P}{\partial v}\right)_s > 0$$

and, analogous to equation 8.25,

$$\left(\frac{\partial T}{\partial s}\right)_P > 0$$

Show that these criteria are completely equivalent to those derived in the text.

8.2   Mutual Stability of Single-Component Systems

The inequalities (8.24) and (8.25) represent the criteria that a single-component simple system be stable within itself. If two such intrinsically stable systems are allowed to interact through a nonrestrictive wall, the mutual equilibrium state is determined by the principle of minimum energy, and we are confronted with the problem of analyzing the stability of this mutual equilibrium state. We now show that the equilibrium state predicted by the condition $dU = 0$ will always be stable, provided that each of the subsystems is itself intrinsically stable. The problem of intrinsic stability thus dominates the problem of mutual stability.

We consider two single-component simple subsystems of a given composite system, and we denote the two subsystems by the superscripts 1 and 2. The internal wall is assumed to be diathermal and nonrestrictive with respect to volume. The change in energy in a virtual process is

$$\Delta U = N^{(1)}(du^{(1)} + d^2u^{(1)} + \cdots) + N^{(2)}(du^{(2)} + d^2u^{(2)} + \cdots) \quad (8.28)$$

and the quantities $du^{(1)}$, $du^{(2)}$, $d^2u^{(1)}$, $d^2u^{(2)} \cdots$ are given by the analogues of equations 8.9–8.11. The first-order terms $N^{(1)}\,du^{(1)} + N^{(2)}\,du^{(2)}$ determine the equilibrium state, and the second-order terms $N^{(1)}\,d^2u^{(1)} + N^{(2)}\,d^2u^{(2)}$ determine the stability. With the closure condition

$$N^{(1)}\,dv^{(1)} + N^{(2)}\,dv^{(2)} = 0 \quad (8.29)$$

and the restriction of constant entropy

$$N^{(1)} \, ds^{(1)} + N^{(2)} \, ds^{(2)} = 0 \tag{8.30}$$

the second-order terms take the form

$$d^2 U = N^{(1)} \, d^2 u^{(1)} + N^{(2)} \, d^2 u^{(2)} = \frac{(N^{(1)})^2}{2} \left[\left(\frac{u_{ss}^{(1)}}{N^{(1)}} + \frac{u_{ss}^{(2)}}{N^{(2)}} \right) (ds^{(1)})^2 \right.$$

$$\left. + 2 \left(\frac{u_{sv}^{(1)}}{N^{(1)}} + \frac{u_{sv}^{(2)}}{N^{(2)}} \right) ds^{(1)} \, dv^{(1)} + \left(\frac{u_{vv}^{(1)}}{N^{(1)}} + \frac{u_{vv}^{(2)}}{N^{(2)}} \right) (dv^{(1)})^2 \right] \tag{8.31}$$

This construct is a homogeneous quadratic form in the variables $ds^{(1)}$ and $dv^{(1)}$, and the condition of mutual stability is that this quadratic form be positive-definite. By analogy with equations 8.24 and 8.25, the criteria of stability are

$$\frac{u_{ss}^{(1)}}{N^{(1)}} + \frac{u_{ss}^{(2)}}{N^{(2)}} > 0 \tag{8.32}$$

and

$$\left(\frac{u_{ss}^{(1)}}{N^{(1)}} + \frac{u_{ss}^{(2)}}{N^{(2)}} \right) \left(\frac{u_{vv}^{(1)}}{N^{(1)}} + \frac{u_{vv}^{(2)}}{N^{(2)}} \right) - \left(\frac{u_{sv}^{(1)}}{N^{(1)}} + \frac{u_{sv}^{(2)}}{N^{(2)}} \right)^2 > 0 \tag{8.33}$$

The criteria of intrinsic stability of the two subsystems imply

$$\frac{u_{ss}^{(1)}}{N^{(1)}} > 0, \qquad \frac{u_{ss}^{(2)}}{N^{(2)}} > 0 \tag{8.34}$$

and

$$\frac{u_{ss}^{(1)}}{N^{(1)}} \frac{u_{vv}^{(1)}}{N^{(1)}} - \left(\frac{u_{sv}^{(1)}}{N^{(1)}} \right)^2 > 0, \qquad \frac{u_{ss}^{(2)}}{N^{(2)}} \frac{u_{vv}^{(2)}}{N^{(2)}} - \left(\frac{u_{sv}^{(2)}}{N^{(2)}} \right)^2 > 0 \tag{8.35}$$

We may see easily that equations 8.34 and 8.35 imply equations 8.32 and 8.33. Equation 8.34 obviously implies equation 8.32, so that only equation 8.33 remains to be verified. The identity

$$(A_1 + A_2)(C_1 + C_2) - (B_1 + B_2)^2 \equiv \left(1 + \frac{A_1}{A_2} \right) (A_2 C_2 - B_2^2)$$

$$+ \left(1 + \frac{A_2}{A_1} \right) (A_1 C_1 - B_1^2) + (A_1 B_2 - A_2 B_1)^2 / A_1 A_2 \tag{8.36}$$

can be verified easily by straightforward algebraic manipulation. If we identify A as u_{ss}/N, B as u_{sv}/N, and C as u_{vv}/N, the left member becomes the construct of equation 8.33, whereas the right member is clearly positive by equations 8.34 and 8.35. We thus establish the inequality of equation 8.33.

We have now demonstrated that *the stability of the mutual equilibrium state of two single-component simple systems is guaranteed by the intrinsic stability of the individual systems.* All significant aspects of the thermodynamic stability problem therefore are included in the criteria of intrinsic stability.

8.3 The Le Châtelier–Braun Principle

Although the interpretation of the stability criteria in terms of the Le Châtelier principle appears to be almost self-evident, a more subtle interpretation is also possible. This deeper significance is known as the *Le Châtelier–Braun principle.* We consider a system that is taken out of equilibrium by some imposed perturbation. The perturbation directly

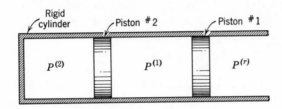

Figure 8.1 Illustration of the Le Châtelier–Braun principle.

induces a process that, by the Le Châtelier principle, reduces the perturbation. But various other internal processes are simultaneously but indirectly induced. The content of the Le Châtelier–Braun principle is that these indirectly induced processes also tend to reduce the applied perturbation.

A simple example makes the meaning of this principle clear. Consider a cylinder with one end closed and with two movable pistons, as shown in Figure 8.1. The two enclosed subsystems have pressures $P^{(2)}$ and $P^{(1)}$, and the external pressure reservoir has the constant pressure $P^{(r)}$. In equilibrium all the pressures are equal, and this condition determines the positions of the two pistons. Now we perturb the system by moving piston No. 1 outward, reducing $P^{(1)}$. The induced pressure difference $P^{(r)} - P^{(1)}$ tends to move piston No. 1 inward, increasing $P^{(1)}$ in accordance with the Le Châtelier principle. But, simultaneously, piston No. 2 tends to move outward, driven by the pressure difference $P^{(2)} - P^{(1)}$. By thus increasing $P^{(1)}$, this secondary process also tends to diminish the primary pressure difference $P^{(r)} - P^{(1)}$.

A second example is provided by a cylinder with a single movable diathermal piston. If the piston is moved outward, decreasing the internal pressure, the internal temperature also is changed. Not only will the piston be moved inward, but heat will flow across the diathermal piston. Both of these processes tend to increase the internal pressure.

To demonstrate the Le Châtelier–Braun principle formally, we consider two extensive parameters, which we denote by X_1 and X_2. Let

$$\mathscr{P}_1 \equiv \frac{\partial U}{\partial X_1} \tag{8.37}$$

and

$$\mathscr{P}_2 \equiv \frac{\partial U}{\partial X_2} \tag{8.38}$$

in which the energy refers to the entire composite system considered. If X_1 is the volume of the system in the foregoing example, $\mathscr{P}_1$ is the difference in pressure of system and reservoir. And, if X_2 is the system entropy, $\mathscr{P}_2$ is the temperature difference.

In equilibrium both $\mathscr{P}_1$ and $\mathscr{P}_2$ are zero, and the deviation from equilibrium is measured by the values of these quantities.

Consider that X_1 is altered, whereas X_2 is constrained. The $\mathscr{P}_1$ becomes nonzero; for definiteness say positive. The spontaneous change in X_1 which follows is such as to decrease U. That is, $dU\,(=\mathscr{P}_1\,dX_1)$ must be negative, so that dX_1 is negative. The Le Châtelier principle demands that this negative change in X_1 tend to decrease $\mathscr{P}_1$, and we have the stability criterion

$$\left(\frac{\partial \mathscr{P}_1}{\partial X_1}\right)_{X_2} > 0 \tag{8.39}$$

Consider now that X_1 is altered, but X_2 is kept at its original value. Then the constraints on *both* X_1 and X_2 are released, and each is allowed to change spontaneously. Let us see in which direction X_2 will change and the effect it will have on $\mathscr{P}_1$. The original alteration of X_1 not only made $\mathscr{P}_1$ nonzero, but it also made $\mathscr{P}_2$ nonzero. In fact the value of $\mathscr{P}_2$ was

$$\mathscr{P}_2 = \left(\frac{\partial \mathscr{P}_2}{\partial \mathscr{P}_1}\right)_{X_2} \mathscr{P}_1 \tag{8.40}$$

In order to decrease the energy, X_2 spontaneously changes, and the sign of dX_2 is opposite to the sign of $\mathscr{P}_2$.

$$\text{sign of } dX_2 = -\text{sign of } \left(\frac{\partial \mathscr{P}_2}{\partial \mathscr{P}_1}\right)_{X_2} \mathscr{P}_1 = -\text{sign of } \left(\frac{\partial \mathscr{P}_2}{\partial \mathscr{P}_1}\right)_{X_2}$$

$$\tag{8.41}$$

The spontaneous change in X_2 produces a change in $\mathscr{P}_1$, which we denote by $d_2\mathscr{P}_1$:

$$d_2\mathscr{P}_1 \equiv \left(\frac{\partial \mathscr{P}_1}{\partial X_2}\right)_{X_1} dX_2 \qquad (8.42)$$

From equations 8.41 and 8.42, it follows that

$$\text{sign of } d_2\mathscr{P}_1 = -\text{sign of } \left(\frac{\partial \mathscr{P}_1}{\partial X_2}\right)_{X_1} \left(\frac{\partial \mathscr{P}_2}{\partial \mathscr{P}_1}\right)_{X_2} \qquad (8.43)$$

$$= -\text{sign of } \left[\left(\frac{\partial \mathscr{P}_1}{\partial X_2}\right)_{X_1} \left(\frac{\partial \mathscr{P}_2}{\partial X_1}\right)_{X_2} \bigg/ \left(\frac{\partial \mathscr{P}_1}{\partial X_1}\right)_{X_2}\right] \qquad (8.44)$$

and, by the appropriate Maxwell equation,

$$\text{sign of } d_2\mathscr{P}_1 = -\text{sign of } \left[\left(\frac{\partial \mathscr{P}_1}{\partial X_2}\right)_{X_1}^2 \bigg/ \left(\frac{\partial \mathscr{P}_1}{\partial X_1}\right)_{X_2}\right] \qquad (8.45)$$

whence, by the stability criterion (8.39),

$$d_2\mathscr{P}_1 < 0 \qquad (8.46)$$

We therefore have shown that the spontaneous change in X_2 is such as to diminish the primary perturbation $\mathscr{P}_1$.

The reader has very probably noticed that the Le Châtelier–Braun principle comes very close to making statements about the dynamics of processes rather than merely about the statics. On close examination the principle proves to be purely static, but at least it creates the impression of being related to dynamic considerations. In fact, it provides a natural point of departure for the theory of irreversible thermodynamics. The Le Châtelier–Braun principle, stated in the entropy representation rather than in the energy representation, and suitably extended by an additional dynamic postulate, is fundamental in the theory of irreversible processes.

Problems—Section 8.3

8.3–1. Show that the stability criteria imply that $(1/\alpha)(\partial T/\partial P)_{S,N} > 0$, and discuss the relevance of this inequality to the second specific example of the Le Châtelier–Braun principle given in section 8.3.

8.4 Intrinsic Stability of General Systems

The results we shall obtain in this section are straightforward generalizations of the results for single-component systems. We recall that for a single-component system, with fundamental equation

$$u = u(s, v) \qquad (8.47)$$

the criteria of stability are (see equations 8.24 and 8.25)

$$u_{ss} > 0 \quad \text{for a single} \tag{8.48}$$

and

$$u[T]_{vv} \equiv f_{vv} > 0 \quad \text{component system} \tag{8.49}$$

For a general system we have

$$U = U(S, X_1, X_2 \cdots X_t) \tag{8.50}$$

and defining

$$u \equiv U/X_t, \quad x_0 = S/X_t \quad \text{and} \quad x_j = X_j/X_t \tag{8.51}$$

the fundamental equation is

$$u = u(x_0, x_1 \cdots x_{t-1}) \tag{8.52}$$

The quantity X_t can be chosen as a particular mole number, as the total mole number $\sum_j N_j$, as the volume, or in any other convenient way. In our special case of a single-component system, X_t was chosen as the mole number. We shall see that the criteria of stability are

$$u_{00} > 0 \tag{8.53}$$

$$u[P_0]_{11} > 0 \tag{8.54}$$

$$u[P_0, P_1]_{22} > 0 \tag{8.55}$$

$$u[P_0, P_1, P_2]_{33} > 0 \tag{8.56}$$

We again consider a system, with the fundamental equation

$$U' = U'(S', X_1', X_2' \cdots X_t') \tag{8.57}$$

The X_j' can be thought of as the volume and the various mole numbers, but the analysis is more general. For nonsimple systems the X_j' include electric, magnetic, and other extensive parameters.

A small subsystem with a constant value of X_t is considered, the remainder of the system constituting the complementary subsystem. With the notation of equation 8.51, the fundamental equation becomes

$$U' = X_t u(x_0, x_1, x_2 \cdots x_{t-1}) + \tilde{X}_t \tilde{u}(\tilde{x}_0, \tilde{x}_1, \tilde{x}_2 \cdots \tilde{x}_{t-1}) \tag{8.58}$$

where the unprimed quantities refer to the subsystem, and the tilde designates the complementary subsystem.

Repeating the logic of section 8.1, the stability depends upon the following form being positive-definite:

$$d^2 u = \frac{1}{2} \sum_0^{t-1} u_{jk} \, dx_j \, dx_k \tag{8.59}$$

The procedure to be followed is to make a nonsingular linear transformation of variables such that the quadratic form is a sum of squares in the new variables. Although the transformation is not unique, a theorem of algebra, called *Sylvester's law of inertia*, guarantees that the number of positive, negative, and zero coefficients is invariant to the choice of the transformation. The condition of stability is that all the coefficients be positive, and this condition consequently is invariant to the choice of transformation.

In transforming the quadratic form of equation 8.59 to diagonal form, we proceed by completion of the square. The terms are ordered in a particular way, and one by one the cross-terms are eliminated in equation 8.59. Therefore, it is the ordering of the terms in equation 8.59 that determines the final transformation. Our remarks about invariance of transformation may be restated by observing that the criteria of stability are independent of the ordering of the terms in equation 8.59, although the detailed procedure depends upon that ordering.

To exhibit all the terms involving dx_0, we rewrite equation 8.59 as

$$d^2u = \frac{1}{2}\left[u_{00}(dx_0)^2 + 2\sum_1^{t-1} u_{0k}\, dx_0\, dx_k + \sum_1^{t-1} u_{jk}\, dx_j\, dx_k \right] \qquad (8.60)$$

To eliminate the cross-terms involving dx_0, we introduce the new variable

$$dP_0 = u_{00}\, dx_0 + \sum_1^{t-1} u_{0k}\, dx_k \qquad (8.61)$$

The square of dP_0 is

$$(dP_0)^2 = u_{00}{}^2(dx_0)^2 + 2u_{00}\sum_1^{t-1} u_{0k}\, dx_0\, dx_k + \sum_1^{t-1} u_{0j}u_{0k}\, dx_j\, dx_k \qquad (8.62)$$

whence equation 8.60 can be rewritten

$$d^2u = \frac{1}{2}\left[\frac{1}{u_{00}}(dP_0)^2 + \sum_1^{t-1}\left(u_{jk} - \frac{u_{0j}u_{0k}}{u_{00}} \right) dx_j\, dx_k \right] \qquad (8.63)$$

In carrying out this step, we have assumed that u_{00} is nonzero. Before proceeding, we examine the physical significance of the coefficients in the summation terms of equation 8.63.

By examination of equation 8.63, it is clear that

$$\left(u_{jk} - \frac{u_{0j}u_{0k}}{u_{00}} \right) = \left(\frac{\partial^2 u}{\partial x_j\, \partial x_k} \right)_{P_0, x_1, x_2 \cdots} \qquad (8.64)$$

in which the partial derivatives are carried out at constant P_0 and constant values of the remaining x_k. A more natural way to write this equation is to note that at constant P_0 the term $P_0 x_0$ is only linear in the x_k, so that

$$\left(u_{jk} - \frac{u_{0j}u_{0k}}{u_{00}}\right) = \left(\frac{\partial^2(u - P_0 x_0)}{\partial x_j \, \partial x_k}\right)_{P_0, x_1 \cdots} = \frac{\partial^2 \psi^{(0)}}{\partial x_j \, \partial x_k} \qquad (8.65)$$

The function $\psi^{(0)}$ is the Legendre transform of u with respect to P_0, and the partial derivatives in equation 8.65 are the natural derivatives of $\psi^{(0)}$. Equation 8.65 can now be written as

$$d^2 u = \frac{1}{2}\left[\frac{1}{u_{00}}(dP_0)^2 + \sum_1^{t-1} \psi_{jk}^{(0)} \, dx_j \, dx_k\right] \qquad (8.66)$$

The entire procedure is now repeated, with the variable dx_1 playing the role previously played by dx_0. To eliminate the cross-terms involving dx_1, we introduce the new variable

$$dP_1^{(0)} = \sum_1^{t-1} \psi_{1k}^{(0)} \, dx_k \qquad (8.67)$$

Assuming $\psi_{11}^{(0)} \equiv u_{11}^{(0)}$ nonzero, we obtain

$$d^2 u = \frac{1}{2}\left[\frac{1}{u_{00}}(dP_0)^2 + \frac{1}{\psi_{11}^{(0)}}(dP_1^{(0)})^2 + \sum_2^{t-1}\left(\psi_{jk}^{(0)} - \frac{\psi_{1j}^{(0)}\psi_{1k}^{(0)}}{\psi_{11}^{(0)}}\right) dx_j \, dx_k\right] \qquad (8.68)$$

The physical significance of the quantity $dP_1^{(0)}$ is made evident by writing

$$P_1 = \frac{\partial \psi^{(0)}}{\partial x_1} \qquad (8.69)$$

whence

$$dP_1 = \frac{\partial^2 \psi^{(0)}}{\partial P_0 \, \partial x_1} dP_0 + \sum_1^{t-1} \psi_{1k}^{(0)} \, dx_k \qquad (8.70)$$

Comparison with equation 8.67 shows that $dP_1^{(0)}$ is the total variation of dP_1 at constant P_0.

The physical significance of the coefficients in the summation terms of equation 8.68 is also readily apparent. We first note that $dP_0 = dP_1^{(1)} = 0$ implies $dP_0 = dP_1 = 0$. Then, just as in equations 8.64 and 8.65, we observe that

$$\left(\psi_{jk}^{(0)} - \frac{\psi_{1j}^{(0)}\psi_{1k}^{(0)}}{\psi_{11}^{(0)}}\right) = \left(\frac{\partial^2 u}{\partial x_j \, \partial x_k}\right)_{P_0, P_1, x_2 \cdots} = \left(\frac{\partial^2(u - P_0 x_0 - P_1 x_1)}{\partial x_j \, \partial x_k}\right)_{P_0, P_1, x_2 \cdots} \qquad (8.71)$$

or

$$\left(\psi_{jk}^{(0)} - \frac{\psi_{1j}^{(0)}\psi_{1k}^{(0)}}{\psi_{11}^{(0)}}\right) = \psi_{jk}^{(1)} \qquad (8.72)$$

where

$$\psi^{(1)} = u - P_0 x_0 - P_1 x_1 \equiv u[P_0, P_1] \tag{8.73}$$

The quadratic form has now been reduced to the form

$$d^2u = \frac{1}{2}\left[\frac{1}{u_{00}}(dP_0)^2 + \frac{1}{\psi_{11}^{(0)}}(dP_1^{(0)})^2 + \sum_2^{t-1} \psi_{jk}^{(1)} dx_j\, dx_k\right] \tag{8.74}$$

Successive repetition of the process yields, finally,

$$d^2u = \frac{1}{2}\sum_0^{t-1} \frac{1}{\psi_{jj}^{(j-1)}}(dP_j^{(j-1)})^2 \tag{8.75}$$

where

$$\psi^{(k)} \equiv u - \sum_0^k P_j x_j \equiv u[P_0, P_1 \cdots P_k] \tag{8.76}$$

and where $dP_j^{\ k}$ is the total differential of P_j at constant $P_0, P_1 \cdots P_k$.

The criteria of stability are that all the coefficients in equation 8.76 be positive, or

$$\text{\Large ✳} \quad \psi_{jj}^{(j-1)} = \left(\frac{\partial P_j}{\partial x_j}\right)_{P_0, P_1 \cdots P_{j-1}, x_{j+1}, x_{j+2} \cdots x_{t-1}} > 0 \qquad \text{for all } j \tag{8.77}$$

The previously obtained results of equations 8.24 and 8.25 for single-component systems are obvious special cases of equation 8.77.

There are well-known relationships between quadratic forms and certain matrices, and the analysis of quadratic forms can be recast in terms of an algebra of matrices. Although no essential new results follow from such a recasting of the analysis, the matrix formulation is of some interest and is developed in Appendix G. The reader may, at his discretion, include or omit that appendix without loss of continuity or content.

CHAPTER 9

First- and Second-Order
Phase Transitions

9.1 First-Order Phase Transitions in Single-Component Systems

The criteria of stability must be satisfied by the fundamental equation of any system that is to remain homogeneous and stable. If the stability criteria are *not* satisfied, the system breaks up into two or more portions. This separation is called a *phase transition*.

Examples of phase transitions are very common. At a pressure of 1 atm and a temperature of 0°C water becomes unstable and separates into a solid portion (ice) and a liquid portion, which coexist in equilibrium. At a pressure of 1 atm and a temperature of 2.18°K liquid helium separates into two phases, designated as liquid helium I and liquid helium II. Both phases are liquids, and both coexist in equilibrium. Other phase transitions are the polymorphic transitions in solids (e.g., the transformation from tetragonal to cubic modifications), the boiling of liquids, and the onset of ferromagnetism or ferroelectricity. The classification of these phase transitions into *first-order* and *second-order* phase transitions will be made as the discussion proceeds.

Let us for a moment consider how we might conceivably obtain a fundamental equation that would not satisfy the stability criteria and that therefore would imply a phase transition. There are two physically interesting procedures that might yield such an equation. The first is the *method of naive calculation*, the second is the *method of empirical curve fitting*.

By the method of naive calculation we mean the following. Suppose that we are presented with a thorough knowledge of the atomic or molecular characteristics of some species of matter. We are to attempt thereby to predict the properties of a macroscopic sample of the material. Our problem is simple in principle, although awesome in detail; we might *assume* first that the macroscopic sample is homogeneous, each molecule being surrounded by the same average environment of nearest neighboring molecules. We then proceed to treat the molecular inter- actions in detail by the methods of the quantum theory of matter, and we subject these detailed quantum mechanical results to the various types of smoothing and averaging dictated by the theory of statistical mechanics. We presumably emerge from our mass of calculation eventually with a theoretical prediction of the fundamental equation of the material. But (and this is the point we wish to stress) our problem is not finished. For our calculation is predicated on the *assumption* that the material is homogeneous. If the predicted fundamental equation everywhere satisfies the criteria of intrinsic stability our assumption is justified a posteriori. But, if the theoretical fundamental equation does not everywhere satisfy the criteria of intrinsic stability, we know that the system would not remain homogeneous but would split up into two or more portions. The true fundamental equation would therefore differ from the originally predicted nonstable theoretical equation. It is clearly of interest to ask how the true stable fundamental equation is related to the hypothetical unstable fundamental equation as originally naively predicted.*

The second procedure, capable of yielding a tentative fundamental equation which may later prove to be unstable, is the *method of empirical curve fitting*. Suppose that we are interested in the properties of H_2O and that we make empirical measurements of its equations of state. Suppose further that these observations, for some reason of convenience, accident, or design, are carried out only in the high-temperature region (above the boiling temperature) and in the low-temperature region (between the boiling and freezing temperature). Although no observations are made in the vicinity of the boiling point, the equations of state for this region are interpolated between the high- and low-temperature regions. The fundamental equation predicted from these interpolated equations of state do not satisfy the conditions of stability in the region of the boiling point.

The very useful van der Waals equation of state illustrates both of the foregoing methods. It can be *derived* on the basis of a highly oversimplified molecular model, but basically it is a result of empirical curve fitting. For many simple substances that undergo liquid-gas transitions the van der

---

* For a discussion of the statistical mechanical aspects of such a calculation see T. L. Hill, *Statistical Mechanics*, McGraw-Hill, New York, 1956, p. 164, or L. van Hove, *Physica* **15,** 951 (1949).

Waals equation of state represents the properties quite well above and below the boiling point. The empirical interpolated equation is

$$P = \frac{NRT}{V - bN} - \frac{N^2 a}{V^2} \tag{9.1}$$

where a and b are constants to be determined empirically for the particular system of interest.

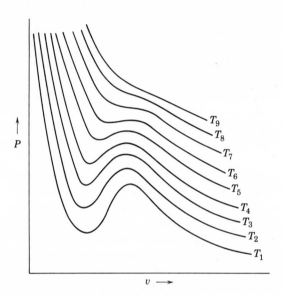

Figure 9.1

In order to investigate the detailed consequences of instability, we assume that we have been given a tentative equation of state of the general form indicated schematically in Figure 9.1. The van der Waals equation has this general form, but we shall not restrict the discussion to any particular analytic equation. In Figure 9.1 we show the pressure P as a function of the molar volume v for various values of temperature $T(T_1 < T_2 < T_3 \cdots)$.

Now we note immediately that the equation of state does not everywhere satisfy the criteria of intrinsic stability. For one of these criteria is that

$$\left(\frac{\partial P}{\partial v}\right)_T < 0 \tag{9.2}$$

and this condition is clearly violated over the portion *FKM* of a typical

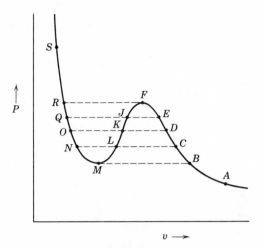

Figure 9.2

isotherm which, for clarity, is shown separately in Figure 9.2. A phase transition consequently must occur in this substance, and we shall see that the characteristics of this transition can be studied on the basis of the equation of state of Figure 9.2.

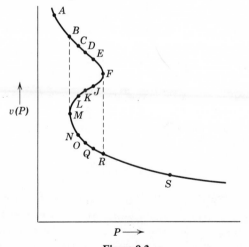

Figure 9.3

An interesting perspective can be obtained by an alternative representation of the given equation of state. From the Gibbs–Duhem relation we have

$$d\mu = -s\,dT + v\,dP \tag{9.3}$$

and integrating at constant temperature

$$\mu = \int v \, dP + \phi(T) \tag{9.4}$$

where $\phi(T)$ is an undetermined function of the temperature, arising as the "constant of integration". The integrand $v(P)$, for constant temperature, is given by Figure 9.2, which is most conveniently represented with P as abscissa and v as ordinate, as shown in Figure 9.3. By arbitrarily assigning a value to the chemical potential at the point A, we can now compute

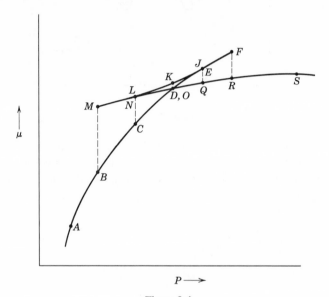

Figure 9.4

the value of μ at any other point on the same isotherm, such as B, for from equation 9.4

$$\mu_B - \mu_A = \int_A^B v(P) \, dP \tag{9.5}$$

In this way we obtain Figure 9.4. This figure, representing μ versus P, may be considered a plane section of a three-dimensional representation of μ versus P and T, as shown in Figure 9.5. Four different constant-temperature sections of the μ-surface, corresponding to four isotherms in Figure 9.1 are shown. It is also noted that the closed loop of the μ versus P curves, which results from the fact that $v(P)$ is triple-valued in P (see Figure 9.3) disappears for high temperatures in accordance with Figure 9.1.

Finally, we note that the relation $\mu = \mu(T, P)$ constitutes a fundamental relation for 1 mole of the material, as the chemical potential μ is the Gibbs function per mole. It would then appear from Figure 9.5 that we have almost succeeded in the construction of a fundamental equation from a single given equation of state, but it should be recalled that although each of the traces of the μ-surface in the various constant temperature

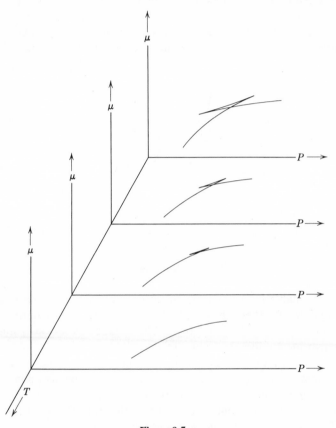

Figure 9.5

planes of Figure 9.5 has the proper form each contains an additive "constant" $\phi(T)$, which varies from one temperature plane to another. Consequently, we do not know the complete form of the $\mu(T, P)$-surface, although we certainly are able to form a rather good mental picture of its essential topological properties.

Having now described in some detail the properties of our hypothetical fundamental equation, we return to consideration of the stability, or lack of stability, of the system to which it refers.

We shall consider a system in the state A of Figure 9.3 or 9.4 and in contact with a temperature and pressure reservoir. The pressure of the reservoir is quasi-statically increased and leads to a corresponding quasi-static increase in the pressure of the system. The temperature is maintained strictly constant. The system proceeds along the isotherm in Figure 9.3 from the point A in the direction of point B. For pressures less than P_B (corresponding to the point B) we see that the volume of the system (for given pressure and temperature) is single-valued and unique. As the pressure increases above P_B, however, three states of equal P and T

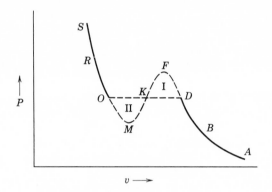

Figure 9.6

become available to the system, as, for example, the states designated by C, L, and N. Of these three states, L is unstable, but at both C and N the equilibrium is stable, and the Gibbs function is a (local) minimum. These two local minimum values of the Gibbs function (or of $\mu = G/N$) are indicated by the points C and N in Figure 9.4. Now, whether the system actually selects the state C or the state N depends upon which of these two local minima of the Gibbs function is the lower, or absolute, minimum. It is clear from Figure 9.4 that the state C is the true physical state for this value of the pressure and temperature.

As the pressure of the reservoir, hence of the system, is further slowly increased, the unique point D is reached. At this point the μ-surface intersects itself, as shown in Figure 9.4, and the absolute minimum of μ or G thereafter comes from the other branch of the curve. Thus at the pressure $P_E = P_Q$, which is greater than P_D, the physical state is Q. Below P_D the right-hand branch of the isotherm in Figure 9.3 is the physically significant branch, whereas above P_D the left-hand branch is physically significant. The physical isotherm thus deduced from the hypothetical isotherm of Figure 9.3 is therefore as shown in Figure 9.6.

The points D and O are determined by the condition that $\mu_D = \mu_O$ or, from equation 9.4,

$$\int_D^O v(P)\, dP = 0 \tag{9.6}$$

where the integral is taken along the hypothetical isotherm. Referring to Figure 9.3, we see that this condition can be given a direct graphical interpretation by breaking the integral into several portions:

$$\int_D^F v\, dP + \int_F^K v\, dP + \int_K^M v\, dP + \int_M^O v\, dP = 0 \tag{9.7}$$

and rearranging as follows:

$$\int_D^F v\, dP - \int_K^F v\, dP = \int_M^K v\, dP - \int_M^O v\, dP \tag{9.8}$$

Now the integral $\int_D^F v\, dP$ is the area under the arc DF in Figure 9.3, and the integral $\int_K^F v\, dP$ is the area under the arc KF. The difference in these integrals is the area in the closed region $DFKD$, or the area marked I in Figure 9.6. Similarly, the right-hand member of equation 9.8 represents the area II in Figure 9.6, and the unique points O and D are therefore determined by the graphical condition

$$\text{area I} = \text{area II} \tag{9.9}$$

For pressures slightly below P_D the molar volume is relatively large, whereas for pressures slightly above P_D the molar volume is relatively small; the molar volume suffers a discontinuous change at the pressure of the phase transition. Similarly, various properties change discontinuously in the transition, and the substance may appear totally different at pressures just below and just above P_D. The two forms of the substance are called *phases*. States on the right-hand branch of the isotherm are said to belong to one phase of the system, and states on the left-hand branch of the isotherm are said to belong to a different phase.

For an isotherm of the form we have been considering we note that the low P-high v phase is one of small slope: that is $-(\partial P/\partial v)_T$ is small in magnitude, and the substance is highly compressible. The high P-low v phase is much denser, and $-(\partial P/\partial v)_T$ is much larger in magnitude, so that this phase is relatively incompressible. Such an isotherm is one that we may expect for a gas–liquid transition, the right-hand portion of the isotherm corresponding to the gaseous phase, and the left-hand portion of the isotherm corresponding to the liquid phase.

Referring again to Figure 9.1, we note that we can select a point on the "gaseous" portion of the T_1 isotherm, heat the system to T_8 at constant volume (a vertical path in the figure), compress the system at constant temperature T_8, and cool the system at constant volume, thereby reaching the "liquid" portion of the T_1 isotherm. In this process no phase transition occurs, and it is impossible to say at what point the system ceased to be gaseous and became liquid. This situation illustrates that the terms gaseous and liquid have more intuitive connotation than strict denotation, and we shall not attempt to give definitions here. The distinction is clearly irrelevant to our general discussion of phase transitions.

If the phase transition occurs between two forms of a solid, as in the transition from the face-centered to the body-centered cubic crystal structure which occurs in iron, the slopes of the left-hand and the right-hand portions of the isotherms in a P-v plot may be expected to be approximately equal. Except for this difference in detail, the form of the isotherms is apt to be substantially the same as shown in Figure 9.1. The formalism which we have described is quite general and applies to gas-liquid, gas-solid, liquid-solid, solid-solid, and other transitions. The crucial feature is simply the re-entrant property of the μ-surface, as shown in Figure 9.5.

Problems—Section 9.1

9.1–1. Find the temperature at which O_2 boils at a pressure of 1 atm and at a pressure of 0.5 atm. Use the van der Waals constants given in Table D.3.

9.2 The Discontinuity in the Volume—The Lever Rule

It is of some interest to examine the details of a phase transition, and we shall first consider the changes in volume associated with the transition. As we have seen, the dependence of volume on pressure is discontinuous along an isotherm, this discontinuity occurring at the pressure of the phase transition.

Consider the isotherm of Figure 9.6 and assume that a system has a pressure precisely equal to that at which the phase transition occurs. Then the system may equally well be in the state D or in the state O, or any arbitrary fraction of the system may be in the state D and the remainder in the state O. Thus at a temperature of 0°C and a pressure of 1 atm we may have water completely in the liquid phase or completely in the solid ice phase, or we may have any fraction of the water solidified and floating in equilibrium in the liquid phase, as cubes of ice float in a tumbler of water.

If a fraction x_D of a system is in the less condensed phase, in equilibrium with a fraction $x_O = 1 - x_D$ in the more condensed phase, the average molar volume v_T of the total system is clearly

$$v_T = x_D v_D + x_O v_O \qquad (9.10)$$

$$= v_O + x_D(v_D - v_O) \qquad (9.11)$$

The state of such a mixture is conventionally represented by a point at the appropriate value of v on the straight line connecting the points O and D, as shown by the state T in Figure 9.7.

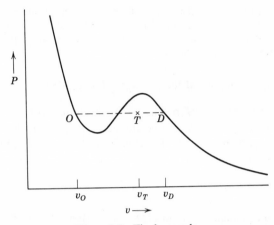

Figure 9.7   The lever rule.

The relationship of such a state, representing a two-phase system, and the mole fractions of each of the phases is conveniently expressed by the *lever rule*. We have

$$(x_D + x_O)v_T = x_D v_D + x_O v_O \qquad (9.12)$$

whence

$$\frac{x_O}{x_D} = \frac{v_D - v_T}{v_T - v_O} \qquad (9.13)$$

The quantity $(v_D - v_T)$ is represented by the distance TD on Figure 9.7, whereas the quantity $(v_T - v_O)$ is represented by the distance OT. Thus the lever rule (equation 9.13) states that the mole fractions of the two phases represented by the point T are in inverse ratio to the distances from T to the points O and D.

Although the volume of a system is a *mathematically* discontinuous function of the pressure along an isotherm, such as that in Figure 9.7, we see that this does not necessitate the occurrence of a *physically* discontinuous process. A system brought along the isotherm from A to S changes its total volume continuously, holding its pressure constant while passing from D to O and taking advantage of the coexistence of two phases, which is possible at that particular pressure.

Problems—Section 9.2

9.2–1. One hundred grams of H_2O are at a temperature of 120°C. If 10 grams are in the vapor phase and 90 grams are in the liquid phase, what is the pressure and what is the total volume of the system? Use the van der Waals constants given in Table D.3.

9.2–2. Let x be the weight-fraction of solid phase in a solid-liquid two-phase system. If the temperature is changed at constant total volume, find the rate of change of x; that is, find dx/dT. Assume that the standard parameters v, α, κ_T, c_P are known for each phase.

9.3   The Discontinuity of the Entropy—Latent Heat

Not only is there a nonzero change in the molar volume at the phase transition, but there are associated nonzero changes in the molar energy and the molar entropy as well. The change in the entropy can be computed by integrating the quantity

$$ds = \left(\frac{\partial s}{\partial v}\right)_T dv \tag{9.14}$$

along the hypothetical isotherm $OMKFD$. Alternatively, by the thermo-dynamic mnemonic diagram, we can write

$$\Delta s = s_D - s_O = \int_{OMKFD} \left(\frac{\partial P}{\partial T}\right)_v dv \tag{9.15}$$

A geometrical interpretation of this entropy difference, in terms of the area between neighboring isotherms, is shown in Figure 9.8.

The change in the molar entropy is associated with a flux of heat between the system and the reservoir. This heat is simply $T\,\Delta s$ and is called the *latent heat per mole*, generally designated by the notation l. To be explicit, we shall indicate the order in which the molar entropies appear on the right by subscripts on l:

$$l_{DO} = T(s_D - s_O) \tag{9.16}$$

Thus l_{DO} is the heat *emitted* by a mole of material making the transition *from D to O*.

If the phase transition is between the liquid and solid phases, the latent heat is called the *heat of fusion*; if between liquid and gaseous phases, the *heat of vaporization*; and if between solid and gaseous phases, the *heat of sublimation*.

In accordance with the underlying quantum statistical significance of the entropy as a measure of the disorder, we expect the more condensed phase to have the smaller entropy. The latent heat l_{DO} consequently is likely to be positive if the subscript O refers to the more condensed phase.

For pure water at 0°C the liquid-solid transition occurs at a pressure of 1 atm. The latent heat or the heat of fusion $l_{\text{liq-solid}}$ is then 80 cal/gram, or 1440 cal/mole. At a temperature of 100°C the liquid-gaseous transition also occurs at a pressure of 1 atm, and the heat of vaporization $l_{\text{gas-liq}}$ is 540 cal/gram, or 9720 cal/mole.

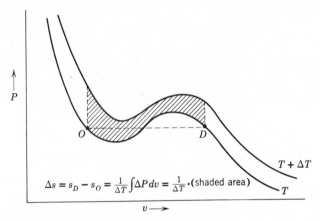

$$\Delta s = s_D - s_O = \frac{1}{\Delta T}\int \Delta P\, dv = \frac{1}{\Delta T}\cdot(\text{shaded area})$$

Figure 9.8

As the system is transformed at fixed temperature and pressure from the pure phase O to the pure phase D, it absorbs an amount of heat per mole equal to $l_{DO} = T\,\Delta s$. The volume change per mole is $\Delta v = v_D - v_O$, and this is associated with a transfer of work equal to $P\,\Delta v$. Consequently, the total change in the molar energy is

$$\Delta u = u_D - u_O = T\,\Delta s - P\,\Delta v \qquad (9.17)$$

Problems—Section 9.3

9.3–1. Find the latent heat per mole of O_2 at a pressure of 1 atm. Use the van der Waals constants given in Table D.3, and recall problem 9.1–1.

9.4   Phase Loci—The Clapeyron Clausius Equation

Returning to Figure 9.6, we have seen that the stability criteria enable us to classify the isotherm shown into three portions. The portion to the left of O is associated with one phase—let us say the liquid phase for definiteness. The portion $OMKFD$ of the hypothetical isotherm is rejected as unstable, whereas the portion of the isotherm to the right of D is associated with a second phase, which we refer to as the gaseous phase. The total P-v diagram of Figure 9.1 may be divided accordingly by drawing a curve through the phase transition points O and D of each isotherm, as indicated in Figure 9.9. Then a system with pressure P and molar volume v in the lower far right portion of Figure 9.9 is in the gaseous

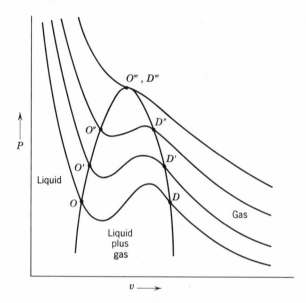

Figure 9.9

phase; in the lower left portion it is in the liquid phase, and within the inverted parabola-like locus it is a mixture of liquid and gaseous phases in accordance with the lever rule. As pointed out in the last several paragraphs of section 9.1, it is not possible to draw a definite boundary between the liquid and gaseous regions, and a system led from the liquid to the gaseous regions by a path that avoids the inverted parabolic area of Figure 9.9 transforms continuously and smoothly without undergoing any discontinuous alteration in its properties.

Another representation of the states corresponding to each of the possible phases of a system derives from Figure 9.5, in which μ is represented as a function of T and P. The μ-surface may be re-entrant, as shown in the figure, and the curve along which the two branches of the surface intersect (as the point D or O of Figure 9.4) determines the locus of states for which a phase transition occurs. Suppose we now project the curve of intersection of the two branches of the μ-surface on to the P-T plane. Or, in each μ-P section, as shown in Figure 9.4, we project the point D or O on the P-axis; the points so projected determine a

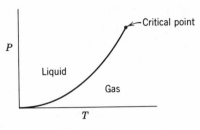

Figure 9.10

curve such as that shown in Figure 9.10, and the labeling of the two regions, corresponding to different phases, is evident.

The termination of the phase curve corresponds to the vertex of the mixture region in Figure 9.10 (above which the isotherms are monotonic) and to the vanishing of the re-entrant characteristic in the μ-surface at

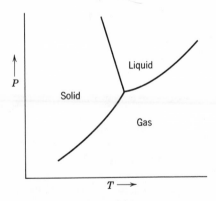

Figure 9.11

high temperature in Figure 9.5. The unique state so determined in each of the figures is the *critical point*. The *critical temperature* and the *critical pressure* are the temperature and pressure at the critical point.

If a system has more than two phases, the phase diagram may appear as that of H_2O, which is illustrated in Figure 9.11. The possible complexity of such diagrams is severely limited by the Gibbs phase rule, described in section 9.6.

The slope of a phase curve in a P-T diagram can be related to the latent heat and to the volume discontinuity by the Clapeyron–Clausius equation. Consider the four states shown in Figure 9.12: states A and A' are coincident but correspond to different phases, and states B and B' are similar. That is, A and B are to be associated with the left-hand region of Figure 9.12, and A' and B', with the right-hand region. The pressure difference $P_B - P_A = P_{B'} - P_{A'}$ is assumed to be infinitesimal ($= dP$), and the temperature difference $T_B - T_A \equiv dT$. The slope of the curve is dP/dT.

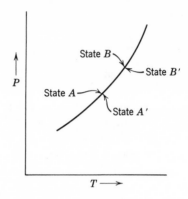

Figure 9.12

Now phase equilibrium requires that

$$\mu_A = \mu_{A'} \tag{9.18}$$

and

$$\mu_B = \mu_{B'} \tag{9.19}$$

whence

$$\mu_B - \mu_A = \mu_{B'} - \mu_{A'} \tag{9.20}$$

But

$$\mu_B - \mu_A = -s\,dT + v\,dP \tag{9.21}$$

and

$$\mu_{B'} - \mu_{A'} = -s'\,dT + v'\,dP \tag{9.22}$$

in which s and s' are the molar entropies and v and v' are the molar volumes in each of the phases. By inserting equations 9.21 and 9.22 in equation 9.20 and rearranging terms, we easily find

$$\frac{dP}{dT} = \frac{s' - s}{v' - v} \tag{9.23}$$

or

$$\frac{dP}{dT} = \frac{\Delta s}{\Delta v} \tag{9.24}$$

in which Δs and Δv are the discontinuities in molar entropy and molar volume associated with the phase transition. According to equation 9.16, the latent heat is

$$l = T \, \Delta s \tag{9.25}$$

whence

$$\boxed{\frac{dP}{dT} = \frac{l}{T \, \Delta v}} \tag{9.26}$$

This is the Clapeyron–Clausius equation.

Consider a solid-liquid transition with a positive latent heat ($s_{liq} > s_{solid}$). The slope of the phase curve will be positive, and an increase in pressure will raise the transition temperature; or, if the system is kept at constant temperature, an increase in pressure will tend to drive the system from the liquid to the solid phase, in accordance with Le Châtelier's principle. In the case of water the slope of the solid-liquid transition curve is negative, as shown in Figure 9.11. This is associated with the rather anomalous fact that the specific volume of the solid phase is larger than that of a liquid, a peculiarity responsible for the fact that ice floats in water and that the ocean has not been frozen solid from bottom to top.

Problems—Section 9.4

9.4–1. A particular liquid boils at 127°C at a pressure of 800 mm Hg. It has a heat of vaporization of 1000 cal/mole. At what temperature will it boil if the pressure is raised to 810 mm Hg?

9.4–2. A long vertical column of a particular liquid is kept isothermal at temperature −5°C. The material below a certain point in the column is found to be solid; that above this point is liquid. The temperature is now changed to −5.2°C, and the solid-liquid interface is observed to shift upward by 40 cm. The latent heat is 2 cal/gram, and the density of the liquid phase is 1 gram/cm³. Find the density of the solid phase.

Hint: Note that the pressure at the original position of the interface remains constant.

Answer: 2.6 grams/cm³.

9.4–3. It is found that a certain liquid boils at a temperature of 95°C at the top of a hill, whereas it boils at a temperature of 105°C at the bottom. The latent heat is 1000 cal/mole. What is the approximate height of the hill?

9.4–4. The following demonstration is often done in elementary physics classes. Two weights are hung on the ends of a wire, which passes over a block of ice. The wire gradually passes through the block of ice, but the block remains intact even after the wire has passed completely through it. Explain this phenomenon of "regelation."

9.4–5. In the vicinity of the triple point the vapor pressure of liquid ammonia (in atmospheres) is represented by

$$\ln P = 15.16 - \frac{3063}{T}$$

This is the equation of the liquid-vapor boundary curve in a *P-T* diagram. Similarly, the vapor pressure of solid ammonia is

$$\ln P = 18.70 - \frac{3754}{T}$$

What are the temperature and pressure at the triple point? What are the latent heats of sublimation and vaporization? What is the latent heat of fusion at the triple point?

9.5   Metastable States in Phase Transitions

We return now to a consideration of the actual mechanism of the phase transition, and we again consider a single-component system at point *A* on the isotherm of Figure 9.2. The system is assumed to be in a cylinder with a movable piston, and the pressure is slowly and continuously increased, the temperature being maintained constant by diathermal contact with a heat reservoir. The system moves slowly to the left along the isotherm to the state *B* and thence to *D*. As we have seen, the system at *D* breaks up into two phases, a portion remaining in the state *D* and a portion appearing at the state *O*. The reason for this transition is that although such states as *E* correspond to local minima of the Gibbs function the state *Q* corresponds to a deeper local minimum. Thus the system brought to the state *E* finds that another state of the same pressure and temperature but of greater density (smaller *v*) is preferable and selects the latter state. But, if the reader will permit us the luxury of an anthropomorphic terminology, we may now inquire about the manner in which the system, slowly brought to the state *D*, becomes aware of the existence and attractiveness of the competing state *O*. We may well visualize that the system at *D*, faced with the unpleasant result of an increasing Gibbs function if it ventures to alter its state slightly, returns from this slight exploratory excursion to the locally preferable state *D*. How then is it to learn that far removed at *O* is an even more attractive state? To answer this question, we must appeal to the perspective afforded by statistical mechanics. According to statistical mechanics, the microstate of a system in equilibrium is not static, but the system perpetually undergoes rapid fluctuations. It is by means of these fluctuations that the system probes and explores to discover the state with the minimum value of the appropriate potential. To be specific, with reference to our particular system brought to the state *D*, the system is not quiescent on the microscopic scale, but rather there are local fluctuations in density from point to point, the average density being that corresponding to the point *D*. Of course, small fluctuations in density are most probable, and large fluctuations, such as that required to take a small portion of the system to the state O, are very rare indeed. So the system may sit for a very long time at D, until eventually a large spontaneous fluctuation occurs, taking a small portion of the system to O. This fluctuation, unlike others, does not decay, for the portion of the system brought to O finds its new state equally satisfactory to its initial state. Such a stabilized fluctuated portion of the system then becomes a *nucleus* for the growth of the second phase. The study of the formation and growth of such phase nuclei is an important branch of modern kinetic theory.

In most practical instances a system brought to the state D does not have to wait for the eventual appearance of a spontaneous fluctuation to take it to O, for artificial fluctuations are often induced by outside mechanisms. Thus a mechanical shock or tap on the system sets up longitudinal waves, with regions of condensation and rarefaction. The region of condensation is a region of small molar volume; it is consequently a region in which the system may be brought into the state O and in which it forms a phase nucleus.

If a system is slowly compressed and if extraneous perturbations are very carefully avoided, the system may remain in the state D for a very long time without the formation of a phase nucleus O. In fact, the system can, with great care, be led along the isotherm past D to E and, in principle, to F. The portion DEF of the isotherm therefore corresponds to metastable states of the system, as does the portion OM. The intermediate segment MKF violates the criteria of intrinsic stability and corresponds to unstable states; no amount of care will induce a system to assume a corresponding homogeneous state.

An example of a metastable state of a system is "supercooled" water. This is water that has been cooled below 0°C at a pressure of 1 atm. A tap on a beaker of water in this condition precipitates a sudden dramatic crystallization of the system.

9.6 First-Order Phase Transitions in Multicomponent Simple Systems— Gibbs Phase Rule

For multicomponent systems the criteria of stability are given in Chapter 8 and are similar in form to the stability criteria for single-component systems. If the stability criteria are not satisfied, a phase transition occurs in a fashion precisely analogous to that which we have studied in detail in the preceding sections. However, the mole numbers generally are in different ratios in each phase, so that the phases differ not only in crystalline form or atomic ordering but also in gross composition. A mixture of H_2O and $NaCl$ brought to the boiling temperature undergoes a phase transition in which the gaseous phase is almost pure H_2O, whereas the coexistent liquid phase contains both constituents—the difference in composition between the two phases in this case is the basis of purification by distillation.

The mechanism of phase transition in multicomponent systems is a straightforward generalization of that in single-component systems, and the geometrical interpretation in terms of Gibbs-function surfaces can be carried over directly. The Gibbs function is a function of T, P, N_1, $N_2 \cdots N_r$, and the surface must be represented in a corresponding multidimensional space. The geometrical concepts are identical to those already developed but are more complex in detail because of the higher dimensionality of the space.

Given the fact that a phase transition does occur, in either a single or multicomponent system, we are faced with the problem of how such a multiphase system can be treated within the framework of our theory. The solution is simple indeed, for we need only consider each separate phase as a separate simple system and the given system as a composite system. The "wall" between the simple systems or phases is then completely nonrestrictive and may be analyzed by the methods appropriate to nonrestrictive walls.

As an example, we consider a container maintained at a temperature T and a pressure P and enclosing a mixture of two components. The system is observed to contain two phases: a liquid phase and a solid phase. We wish to find the composition of each phase.

The chemical potential of the first component in the liquid phase is $\mu_1^{(L)}(T, P, x_1^{(L)})$, and in the solid phase it is $\mu_1^{(S)}(T, P, x_1^{(S)})$, in which x_1 is the mole fraction of the first component. The fact that a different functional form for μ_1 is appropriate to each phase is analogous to the different functional behavior of μ to the left and to the right of the point O or D in Figure 9.4. The condition of equilibrium with respect to the transfer of the first component from phase to phase is

$$\mu_1^{(L)}(T, P, x_1^{(L)}) = \mu_1^{(S)}(T, P, x_1^{(S)}) \qquad (9.27)$$

Similarly, the chemical potentials of the second component are $\mu_2^{(L)}(T, P, x_1^{(L)})$ and $\mu_2^{(S)}(T, P, x_1^{(S)})$; we can write these in terms of x_1 rather than x_2 because $x_1 + x_2$ is unity in each phase. Thus equating $\mu_2^{(L)}$ and $\mu_2^{(S)}$ gives a second equation, which, with equation 9.27, determines $x_1^{(L)}$ and $x_1^{(S)}$.

Let us suppose that three coexistent phases are observed in the foregoing system. Denoting these by I, II, and III, we have, for the first component,

$$\mu_1^{I}(T, P, x_1^{I}) = \mu_1^{II}(T, P, x_1^{II}) = \mu_1^{III}(T, P, x_1^{III}) \qquad (9.28)$$

and a similar pair of equations for the second component. Thus we have four equations and only three composition variables x_1^{I}, x_1^{II}, and x_1^{III}. This means that we are *not* free to specify both T and P a priori, but if T is specified then the four equations determine P, x_1^{I}, x_1^{II}, and x_1^{III}. Although it is possible to select both a temperature and pressure arbitrarily and then to find a two-phase state, a three-phase state can exist only for one particular pressure if the temperature is specified.

In the same system we might inquire about the existence of a state in which four phases coexist. Analogous to equation 9.28, we have three equations for the first component and three for the second. Thus we have six equations involving T, P, x_1^{I}, x_1^{II}, x_1^{III}, and x_1^{IV}. This means that we can have four coexistent phases only for a uniquely defined temperature and pressure, neither of which can be arbitrarily preselected by the experimenter but which are unique properties of the system.

Five phases cannot coexist in a two-component system, for the eight resultant equations would then overdetermine the seven variables (T, P, $x_1^{I} \cdots x_1^{V}$), and no solution would be possible in general.

We can easily repeat the foregoing counting of variables for a multicomponent, multiphase system.

In a system with r components the chemical potentials in the first phase are functions of the variables, T, P, x_1^{I}, $x_2^{I} \cdots x_{r-1}^{I}$. The chemical potentials in the second phase are functions of T, P, x_1^{II}, $x_2^{II} \cdots x_{r-1}^{II}$. If there are M phases, the complete set of independent variables thus consists of T, P and $M(r-1)$ mole fractions; $2 + M(r-1)$ variables in all. There are $M-1$ equations of chemical potential equality for each component, or a total of $r(M-1)$ equations. Therefore the number f of variables, which can be arbitrarily assigned, is $[2 + M(r-1)] - r(M-1)$, or

$$f = r - M + 2 \qquad (9.29)$$

The fact that $r - M + 2$ variables from the set $[T, P, x_1^{I}, x_2^{I} \cdots x_{r-1}^{M}]$ can be assigned arbitrarily in a system with r components and M phases is the *Gibbs phase rule*.

The quantity f can be interpreted alternatively as the number of *thermodynamic degrees of freedom*, previously introduced in section 3.2 and defined as the number of *intensive parameters* capable of independent variation. To justify this interpretation we now count the number of thermodynamic degrees of freedom in a straightforward way, and we show that this number agrees with equation 9.29.

For a single-component system in a single phase there are two degrees of freedom, the Gibbs–Duhem relation eliminating one of the three variables T, P, μ. For a single-component system with two phases there are three intensive parameters (T, P, and μ, each constant from phase to phase), and there are two Gibbs–Duhem relations. There is thus one degree of freedom. In Figure 9.11 pairs of phases accordingly coexist over one-dimensional regions (curves).

If we have three coexistent phases of a single-component system, the three Gibbs–Duhem relations completely determine the three intensive parameters T, P, and μ. The three phases can coexist only in a unique

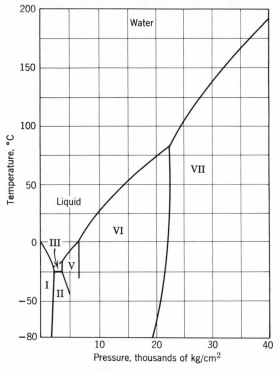

Figure 9.13 The phase-diagram of water. The various crystalline modifications of ice are numbered in roman numerals. By permission, from *American Institute of Physics Handbook*, McGraw-Hill Book Company, Inc., 1957.

zero-dimensional region, or point, as shown in Figure 9.11. This unique state is known as the *triple point*. It may be recalled from section 2.6 that the triple point of water defines the fixed point 273.16°K on the Kelvin scale of temperature.

At high pressures ice undergoes several polymorphic transformations (i.e., solid–solid phase transitions), and several other triple points occur. The P–T diagram for water is illustrated in Figure 9.13. The pressure scale of Figure 9.13 is so severely contracted, in comparison to Figure 9.11, that the gaseous region has been reduced to an invisibly narrow line along the vertical axis. It is seen that at no point do four phases coexist. The four simultaneous Gibbs–Duhem relations would overdetermine the three intensive parameters, and no solution would be possible in general.

For a multicomponent, multiphase system the number of degrees of freedom can be counted easily in similar fashion. If the system has r components, there are $r + 2$ intensive parameters: $T, P, \mu_1, \mu_2 \cdots \mu_r$. Each of these parameters is a constant from phase to phase. But in each of the M phases there is a Gibbs–Duhem relation. These M relations reduce the number of independent parameters to $(r + 2) - M$. The number of degrees of freedom f is therefore $r - M + 2$, as given in equation 9.29.

The Gibbs phase rule therefore may be stated as follows. *In a system with r components and M coexistent phases it is possible arbitrarily to preassign $r - M + 2$ variables from the set $[T, P, x_1^I, x_2^I \cdots x_{r-1}^M]$, or from the set $[T, P, \mu_1, \mu_2 \cdots \mu_r]$.*

It is now a simple matter to corroborate that the Gibbs phase rule gives the same results for single-component and two-component systems as we found in the preceding several paragraphs. For single-component systems $r = 1$ and $f = 0$ if $M = 3$. This agrees with our previous conclusion that the triple point is a unique state for a single-component system. Similarly, for the two-component system we saw that four phases coexist in a unique point ($f = 0$, $r = 2$, $M = 4$); that the temperature could be arbitrarily assigned for the three-phase system ($f = 1$, $r = 2$, $M = 3$), and that both T and P could be arbitrarily assigned for the two-phase system ($f = 2$, $r = 2$, $M = 2$).

9.7 Phase Diagrams for Binary Systems

The Gibbs phase rule (equation 9.29) provides the basis for the study of the possible forms which may be assumed by phase diagrams such as Figure 9.13. These phase diagrams, particularly for binary (two-component) or ternary (three-component) systems, are of great practical importance in metallurgy and physical chemistry, and much work has been done on their classification. To illustrate the application of the phase rule, we shall discuss two typical diagrams for binary systems.

For a single-component system the Gibbs function per mole is a function of temperature and pressure, as in the three-dimensional representation in Figure 9.5. The phase diagram of Figure 9.10 was obtained by projection of the curve of intersection in Figure 9.5 on the two-dimensional subspace of P–T. Now for a binary system the molar Gibbs function $G/(N_1 + N_2)$ is a function of the three variables T, P, and x_1. The analogue of Figure 9.5 is four-dimensional, and that of Figure 9.10 is three-dimensional. They are obtained by projection of the hyper-curve of intersection on the P, T, x_1 hyper-plane.

The three-dimensional phase diagram for a simple but common type of binary gas–liquid system is shown in Figure 9.14. For obvious reasons of graphic convenience the three-dimensional space is represented by a series

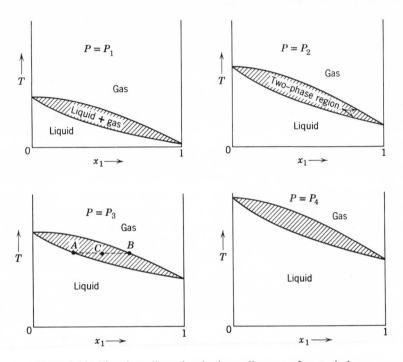

Figure 9.14 The three-dimensional phase diagram of a typical gas-liquid binary system. The two-dimensional sections are constant pressure planes, with $P_1 < P_2 < P_3 < P_4$.

of two-dimensional constant-pressure sections. At a fixed value of the mole fraction x_1 and fixed pressure the gaseous phase is stable at high temperature and the liquid phase is stable at low temperature. At a temperature such as that labeled C in Figure 9.14 the system separates into two phases—a liquid phase at A and a gaseous phase at B. The composition at point C in Figure 9.14 is analogous to the volume at point T in Figure 9.7, and a form of the lever rule is clearly applicable.

The region marked "gas" in Figure 9.14 is a three-dimensional region, and T, P, and x_1 can be independently varied within this region. This is true also for the region marked "liquid." In each case $r = 2$, $M = 1$, and $f = 3$.

The state represented by point C in Figure 9.14 is really a two-phase state, composed of A and B. Thus only A and B are physical points, and the shaded region occupied by point C is a sort of nonphysical "hole" in the diagram. The two-phase region is the surface enclosing the shaded volume in Figure 9.14. This surface is two-dimensional ($r = 2$, $M = 2$, $f = 2$). Specifying T and P determines x_1^A and x_1^B uniquely.

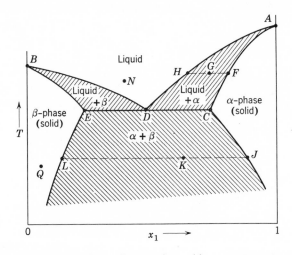

Figure 9.15 Typical phase diagram for a binary system at constant pressure.

If a binary liquid with the mole fraction x_1^A is heated at atmospheric pressure, it will follow a vertical line in the appropriate diagram in Figure 9.14. When it reaches point A, it will begin to boil. The vapor that escapes will have the composition appropriate to point B.

A common type of phase diagram for a liquid–solid, two-component system is indicated schematically in Figure 9.15, in which only a single constant-pressure section is shown. Two distinct solid phases, of different crystal structure, exist: one is labeled α and the other is labeled β. The curve $BDHA$ is called the *liquidus* curve, and the curves BEL and ACJ are called *solidus* curves. Point G corresponds to a two-phase system— some liquid at H and some solid at F. Point K corresponds to α-solid at J plus β-solid at L.

If a liquid with composition x_H is cooled, the first solid to precipitate out has composition x_F. If it is desired to have the solid precipitate with the same composition as the liquid, it is necessary to start with a liquid of composition x_D. A liquid of this composition is called a *eutectic* solution. A eutectic solution freezes sharply and homogeneously, producing good alloy castings in metallurgical practice.

The liquidus and solidus curves are the traces of two-dimensional surfaces in the complete T, x_1, P space.

The eutectic point D is the trace of a curve in the full T, x_1, P space. The eutectic is a three-phase region, in which liquid at D, β-solid at E, and α-solid at C can coexist. The fact that a three-phase system can exist over a one-dimensional curve follows from the phase rule ($r = 2$, $M = 3$, $f = 1$).

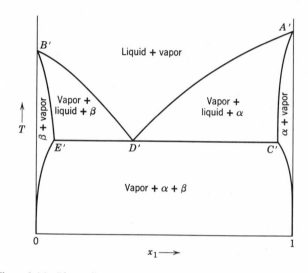

Figure 9.16   Phase diagram for a binary system in equilibrium with its vapor phase.

Suppose we start at a state such as N in the liquid phase. Keeping T and x_1 constant, we decrease the pressure so that we follow a straight line perpendicular to the plane of Figure 9.15 in the T, x_1, P space. We eventually come to a two-phase surface, which represents the liquid–gas phase transition. This phase transition occurs at a particular pressure for the given temperature and the given composition. Similarly, there is another particular pressure which corresponds to the temperature and composition of point Q and for which the solid β is in equilibrium with its own vapor. To each point T, x_1 we can associate a particular pressure P in this way. Then a phase diagram can be drawn, as shown in Figure 9.16. This phase diagram differs from that of Figure 9.15 in that the pressure at each point is different, and each point represents at least a two-phase system (of which one phase is the vapor). The curve $B'D'$ is now a one-dimensional curve ($M = 3, f = 1$), and the eutectic point D' is a unique point ($M = 4, f = 0$). Point B' is the triple point of the pure first component, and point A' is the triple point of the pure second component.

Although Figures 9.15 and 9.16 are very similar in general appearance, they are clearly very different in meaning, and confusion can easily arise from failure to distinguish carefully between these two types of phase diagrams.

The detailed forms of phase diagrams can take on a myriad of differences in detail, but the dimensionality of the intersections of the various multiphase regions is determined entirely by the phase rule.

Problems—Section 9.7

9.7–1. The phase diagram of a solution of A in B, at a pressure of 1 atm, is as shown. The upper bounding curve of the two-phase region can be represented by

$$T = T_0 - (T_0 - T_1)x_A{}^2$$

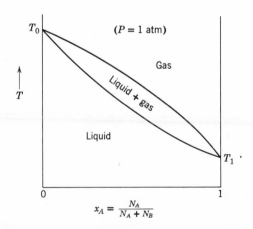

The lower bounding curve can be represented by

$$T = T_0 - (T_0 - T_1)x_A(2 - x_A)$$

A beaker containing equal mole numbers of A and B is brought to its boiling temperature. What is the composition of the vapor as it first begins to boil off? Does boiling tend to increase or decrease the mole fraction of A in the remaining liquid?

Answer: x_A (vapor) $= 0.866$

9.7–2. Show that if a small fraction $(-dN/N)$ of the material is boiled off the system referred to in problem 9.7–1 the change in the mole fraction in the remaining liquid is

$$dx_A = -[(2x_A - x_A{}^2)^{\frac{1}{2}} - x_A]\left(\frac{-dN}{N}\right)$$

9.7–3. The phase diagram of a solution of A in B, at a pressure of 1 atm and in the region of small concentration ($x_A \ll 1$), is as shown. The upper

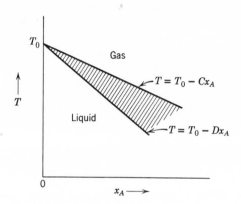

bounding curve of the two-phase region can be represented by

$$T = T_0 - Cx_A$$

and the lower bounding curve by

$$T = T_0 - Dx_A$$

in which C and D are positive constants ($D > C$).

If a liquid of concentration $x_A{}^\circ$ is brought to a boil and kept boiling until only a fraction (N_f/N_i) of the material remains, derive an expression for the final concentration.

Show that if $D = 3C$ and if $N_f/N_i = \frac{1}{2}$, the final concentration is one fourth of the initial concentration of component A.

9.8   Tisza's Theory of Second-Order Phase Transitions

In a first-order phase transition the molar entropy, molar volume, and other molar parameters suffer discontinuous changes. Specifically, the discontinuity in the entropy gives rise to a latent heat. However, other types of transitions are observed as well. In these *higher-order phase transitions* the molar parameters are continuous but their derivatives are noncontinuous.

A classification of phase transitions was suggested by Ehrenfest. According to this classification, a first-order phase transition is one in which the molar Gibbs function g is continuous but its derivatives $(\partial g/\partial T)_P = -s$

and $(\partial g/\partial P)_T = v$ are discontinuous. A second-order phase transition is one in which g and its first derivatives are continuous but its second derivatives are discontinuous. Similarly third- and higher-order transitions can be defined by direct generalization.

When Ehrenfest proposed his classification of higher-order phase transitions, the types of discontinuities he had in mind were finite "jumps," directly analogous to the finite jump in the value of the molar volume in a liquid–gas, first-order phase transition. It has turned out, however, that such a simple type of higher-order phase transition rarely occurs in nature. In most higher-order phase transitions the discontinuities that occur are infinities. Thus in the second-order transition which marks the onset of an ordered ionic arrangement in an alloy the specific heat does not show a finite jump but becomes infinitely large at the transition temperature. At the present time it appears that the onset of super-conductivity in zero magnetic field (Figure 14.7) is the only second-order phase transition that exhibits a simple jump in the derivatives of g.

Two theories of higher-order phase transitions have been given. The first, by Ehrenfest, is applicable to those transitions in which the discontinuities are simple jumps in the values of the derivatives of the molar Gibbs function. The theory of Tisza, in contrast, is applicable to those transitions in which the discontinuities are infinite values of the derivatives. As we have indicated, Tisza's theory is the more generally applicable; it applies to the order-disorder transition in alloys, to the onset of ferroelectricity in such materials as Rochelle salt or barium titanate, to the onset of ferromagnetism or antiferromagnetism, to the onset of superfluidity in liquid helium, and to many others. Tisza's theory is given in this section. In the following section we indicate briefly the nature of Ehrenfest's theory.

The physical basis of the Tisza theory is the conception that a second-order phase transition occurs when a system passes through a critical region, such as that shown in Figure 9.10. Along the phase line in Figure 9.10 the stability criteria are not satisfied, and beyond the critical point the stability criteria are satisfied. The critical point marks the point of separation between definite stability and definite instability. A second-order phase transition may be thought of as corresponding to incipient instability.

In a single-component system a second-order phase transition is a highly specialized phenomenon, occurring only at a particular pair of values of pressure and temperature. But in a multicomponent system the critical region is multidimensional and is readily observed. In fact a two-phase system has r degrees of freedom in an r-component system; the boundary of a two-phase region therefore has $r - 1$ degrees of freedom.

The boundary of a two-phase region constitutes a critical region, so that critical regions are $(r - 1)$-dimensional.

The criteria of stability arise from the requirement that the quadratic form

$$d^2u = \frac{1}{2} \sum_0^{t-1} u_{jk}\, dx_j\, dx_k \qquad (9.30)$$

be positive-definite. That is, in a stable system d^2u is positive for every combination of values of the variables $dx_1, dx_2 \cdots$ (except the trivial set $dx_1 = dx_2 = \cdots = 0$), as indicated schematically in A of Figure 9.17.

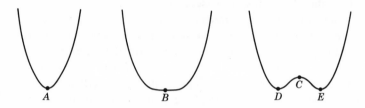

Figure 9.17   Schematic representation of stable, critical, and unstable points. The vertical axis is the molar energy u, and the horizontal axis is a schematic one-dimensional representation of the parameters $x_0, x_1 \cdots$. The state A is a minimum point and is stable. The state C is unstable; a first-order phase transition occurs, with phases at D and E. Intermediate between the foregoing conditions is the critical state B. The second-order terms vanish, and the upward curvature comes only from fourth-order terms.

In an unstable system d^2u can be made negative by some choice of values of $dx_1, dx_2 \cdots$; the quadratic form is *indefinite*, as shown schematically in C of Figure 9.17. The boundary between stability and instability occurs when the quadratic form is *positive-semidefinite*, as represented in B of Figure 9.17. That is, for any combination of values of $dx_1, dx_2 \cdots$ the quadratic form is either positive or zero, but it is never negative. To study second-order phase transitions, we must study the mathematical conditions under which the quadratic form (equation 9.30) is positive-semidefinite.

Returning to equation 8.65, we recall that after s successive completions of the square the quadratic form becomes

$$d^2u = \frac{1}{2} \sum_0^{s-1} \frac{1}{\psi_{kk}^{k-1}} (dP_k^{k-1})^2 + \frac{1}{2} \sum_s^{t-1} \psi_{jk}^{s-1}\, dx_j\, dx_k \qquad (9.31)$$

The next step would consist of writing

$$dP_s^{s-1} = \sum_s^{t-1} \psi_{sk}^{s-1}\, dx_k \qquad (9.32)$$

whence

$$d^2u = \frac{1}{2}\sum_0^s \frac{1}{\psi_{kk}^{k-1}}(dP_k^{k-1})^2 + \frac{1}{2}\sum_{s+1}^{t-1}\left(\psi_{jk}^{s-1} - \frac{\psi_{sj}^{s-1}\psi_{sk}^{s-1}}{\psi_{ss}^{s-1}}\right)dx_j\,dx_k \quad (9.33)$$

However, this step can be carried out only if the quantity ψ_{ss}^{s-1} is nonzero. Let us suppose that ψ_{ss}^{s-1} is zero, so that the step leading from equation 9.31 to 9.33 cannot be carried out. We assume

$$\psi_{ss}^{s-1} \equiv u[P_0 \cdots P_{s-1}]_{ss} = \left(\frac{\partial P_s}{\partial x_s}\right)_{P_0 \cdots P_{s-1},x_{s+1}\cdots x_{t-1}} = 0 \quad (9.34)$$

Then equation 9.31 becomes

$$d^2u = \frac{1}{2}\sum_0^{s-1}\frac{1}{\psi_{kk}^{k-1}}(dP_k^{k-1})^2 + \sum_{s+1}^{t-1}\psi_{sk}^{s-1}\,dx_s\,dx_k + \frac{1}{2}\sum_{s+1}^{t-1}\psi_{jk}^{s-1}\,dx_j\,dx_k \quad (9.35)$$

As the process of completion of the square cannot be carried further, equation 9.35 provides the form which must be analyzed for positive-semidefiniteness.

By assuming that ψ_{ss}^{s-1} is zero, we have insured that d^2u can take the value zero. In fact, if we put $dP_0 = dP_1{}^0 = \cdots = dP_{s-1}^{s-2} = dx_{s+1} = \cdots dx_{t-1} = 0$, leaving only $dx_s \neq 0$, the quadratic form vanishes. We now inquire about conditions which prevent d^2u from taking negative values.

Examination of equation 9.35 makes it readily apparent that in order to have d^2u positive-semidefinite we must demand that

$$\psi_{sk}^{s-1} \equiv u[P_0 \cdots P_s]_{sk} = \frac{\partial P_k}{\partial x_s}$$

$$= \left(\frac{\partial P_s}{\partial x_k}\right)_{P_0 \cdots P_{s-1},x_s \cdots x_{t-1}} = 0 \qquad \text{for all } k > s \quad (9.36)$$

If ψ_{sk}^{s-1} were not to be zero, we could take all the variables except dx_s and dx_k to be zero in equation 9.35; the only nonzero terms would then be $\psi_{kk}^{s-1}(dx_k)^2 + \psi_{sk}^{s-1}\,dx_s\,dx_k$, which could be made negative by appropriate choices of values of dx_s and dx_k.

As far as second-order terms are concerned, then, the criteria of a critical point is that for some value of s equations 9.34 and 9.36 must hold.

The value of s for which equation 9.34 holds will depend upon the ordering of the variables. In order to make s unique, we henceforth assume that the variables have been numbered in a way that makes s as small as possible.

If s is less than $t - 1$ the variables $x_0, x_1 \cdots x_{r-1}$ can be thought of as divided into two classes. The variables $x_0 \cdots x_s$ cooperate to produce the critical point, whereas the variables $x_{s+1} \cdots x_{t-1}$ are really irrelevant to the critical behavior. Furthermore, the two sets of variables are independent in the sense of equation 9.36, which states that in the critical region any of the variables dx_k of the second set can be altered without influencing the intensive parameter P_s, or that x_s can be varied (at constant $P_0 \cdots P_{s-1}$) without influencing any of the intensive parameters P_k of the second set.

As a matter of nomenclature, those second-order transitions in which the molar entropy ds is included among the set of variables cooperating to produce the transition are called *order-disorder transitions*. Those transitions in which the entropy is only among the second set of *irrelevant variables* are called *displacive transitions*.

If we assume that equations 9.34 and 9.36 hold, the quadratic form (equation 9.35) becomes

$$d^2u = \frac{1}{2} \sum_{0}^{s-1} \frac{1}{\psi_{kk}^{k-1}} (dP_k^{k-1})^2 + \frac{1}{2} \sum_{s+1}^{t-1} \psi_{jk}^{s-1} \, dx_j \, dx_k \qquad (9.37)$$

The second sum can now be considered to be positive-definite, as we have already insured that d^2u can take a zero value by equation 9.34. We introduce the new variable

$$d({}_sP_{s+1}^s) = \sum_{s+1}^{t-1} \psi_{s+1,k}^{s-1} \, dx_k \qquad (9.38)$$

representing the differential of P_{s+1} at constant $P_0, P_1 \cdots P_{s-1}, x_s$. Then

$$d^2u = \frac{1}{2} \sum_{0}^{s-1} \frac{1}{\psi_{kk}^{k-1}} (dP_k^{k-1})^2 + \frac{1}{2} \frac{1}{{}_s\psi_{s+1}^s} (d_sP_{s+1}^s)^2 + \sum_{s+2}^{t-1} {}_s\psi_{jk}^{s+1} \, dx_j \, dx_k \qquad (9.39)$$

where

$${}_s\psi^k \equiv u[P_0 \cdots P_{s-1}, P_{s+1} \cdots P_k] = u - \sum_{\substack{j=0 \\ (j \neq s)}}^{k} P_j x_j \qquad (9.40)$$

Continuing the process we finally find

$$d^2u = \frac{1}{2} \sum_{0}^{s-1} \frac{1}{\psi_{kk}^{k-1}} (dP_k^{k-1}) + \frac{1}{2} \sum_{s+1}^{t-1} \frac{1}{{}_s\psi_{kk}^{k-1}} (d_sP_k^{k-1})^2 \qquad (9.41)$$

and, in order that the second sum be positive-definite, we require that

$${}_s\psi_{kk}^{k-1} = \left(\frac{\partial P_k}{\partial x_k} \right)_{P_1 \cdots P_{s-1}, x_s, P_{s+2} \cdots P_{k-1}, x_{k+1} \cdots x_{t-1}} > 0 \qquad (9.42)$$

Summarizing the criteria of positive-semidefiniteness we have found to this point, we have

$$\psi_{kk}^{k-1} \equiv u[P_0 \cdots P_{k-1}]_{kk} > 0, \qquad k < s \qquad (9.43)$$

$${}_s\psi_{kk}^{k-1} \equiv u[P_0 \cdots P_{s-1}, P_{s+1} \cdots P_{k-1}]_{kk} > 0, \qquad k > s \qquad (9.44)$$

and

$$\psi_{sk}^{s-1} \equiv u[P_0 \cdots P_{s-1}]_{sk} = 0, \qquad k \geqslant s \qquad (9.45)$$

The final aspect of the analysis has to do with the higher-order terms that insure stability in the critical region, even though the second-order terms may vanish. As in equations 8.9–8.16 and the general analogue (8.49), we write the expansion of $\Delta U'$ to fourth order:

$$\Delta U' = X_t[d^2u + d^3u + d^4u + \cdots] \tag{9.46}$$

where the linear terms vanish in the usual fashion. The second-order terms are given by equation 9.35, and

$$d^3u = \frac{1}{3!} \sum_0^{t-1} u_{ijk}\, dx_i\, dx_j\, dx_k \tag{9.47}$$

$$d^4u = \frac{1}{4!} \sum_0^{t-1} u_{ijkl}\, dx_i\, dx_j\, dx_k\, dx_l \tag{9.48}$$

In order to discuss the third- and fourth-order terms in a fashion parallel to the discussion of the second-order terms, we should make a coordinate transformation from the variables $dx_0, dx_1 \cdots dx_{s-1}$ to the variables $dP_0, dP_1^\circ \cdots dP_{s-1}^{s-2}$, just as in equation 9.35. The leading third-order term then becomes $\psi_{sss}^{s-1}(dx_s)^3$, and the leading fourth-order term becomes $\psi_{ssss}^{s-1}(dx_s)^4$. As in Figure 9.17(B) we require that the third-order terms vanish and that the fourth-order terms be positive. The necessary (but not sufficient) conditions given by Tisza are then

$$\psi_{sss}^{s-1} = \left(\frac{\partial^2 P_s}{\partial x_s{}^2}\right)_{P_0 \cdots P_{s-1}, x_{s+1} \cdots x_{t-1}} = 0 \tag{9.49}$$

and

$$\psi_{ssss}^{s-1} = \left(\frac{\partial^3 P_s}{\partial x_s{}^3}\right)_{P_0 \cdots P_{s-1}, x_{s+1} \cdots x_{t-1}} > 0 \tag{9.50}$$

In summary, equations 9.43–9.45 and 9.49–9.50 define a critical region.

We now turn our attention to the physical consequences of the critical behavior. In particular, we shall show that various quantities (such as specific heats and compressibilities) become infinite in the critical region.

The infinite behavior of the specific heat c_P for a simple gas–liquid critical point can be anticipated on the basis of Figure 9.7. Consider the point T in Figure 9.7, which represents a mixture of liquid and gas. If heat is added to this two-phase system, some liquid evaporates *at constant temperature*, and the point T simply shifts toward D. Thus the specific heat in this two-phase system appears to be infinite.

Now consider various points within the two-phase region in Figure 9.9. At these points approach the critical point (labeled $O = D$), the difference in the specific volumes of the two phases disappears. At the critical point the two phases become identical, so that no discontinuity in the extensive parameters is observable. But the infinite value of the specific heat remains as a clue to the incipient instability.

To draw the conclusion of infinite values in greater generality, we consider the quantity

$$\psi_{ss}^s = -\left(\frac{\partial x_s}{\partial P_s}\right)_{P_0 \cdots P_{s-1}, x_{s+1} \cdots} = -\left(1 \Big/ \frac{\partial P_s}{\partial x_s}\right)_{P_0 \cdots P_{s+1}, x_{s+1} \cdots} = \frac{-1}{\psi_{ss}^{s-1}} \tag{9.51}$$

By equation 9.45 we see that this quantity becomes infinite.

Consider now the quantity ψ_{sj}^s, with $j < s$. We have

$$\psi_{sj}^s = -\left(\frac{\partial x_j}{\partial P_s}\right)_{P_0 \cdots P_{s-1}, x_{s+1} \cdots}$$

$$= -\left(\frac{\partial x_j}{\partial x_s}\right)_{P_0 \cdots P_{s-1}, x_{s+1}} \Big/ \left(\frac{\partial P_s}{\partial x_s}\right)_{P_0 \cdots P_{s-1}, x_{s+1} \cdots}$$

$$= -\psi_{sj}^{s-1} / \psi_{ss}^{s-1} \qquad (j < s) \tag{9.52}$$

and again this quantity becomes infinite by equation 9.45.

Finally, we consider ψ_{jk}^s, with $j, k, < s$. We can then show (problem 9.8-1) that

$$\psi_{jk}^s = \psi_{jk}^{s-1} - \frac{\psi_{js}^{s-1} \psi_{ks}^{s-1}}{\psi_{ss}^{s-1}} \qquad (j, k < s) \tag{9.53}$$

and this quantity also becomes infinite.

The last three equations can be summarized in the single conclusion that

$$|\psi_{jk}^s| = \left| \left(\frac{\partial x_k}{\partial P_j}\right)_{P_0 \cdots P_s, x_{s+1} \cdots} \right| \to \infty \qquad j, k \leqslant s \tag{9.54}$$

The quantities ψ_{jk}^s are the elements of the *compliance matrix* of Appendix G, and the conclusion equation 9.54 can be obtained more directly by inversion of the singular stiffness matrix there defined.

Equation 9.54 exhibits the most significant physical property of the critical region.

As a simple illustration of a critical point, we consider a single-component system with a critical point such as that indicated in Figure 9.10. Let $dx_0 = ds$ and $dx_1 = dv$. The two significant coefficients are

$$\psi_{00} \equiv u_{00} = \frac{\partial^2 u}{\partial s^2} = \frac{\partial T}{\partial s} = T/c_v \tag{9.55}$$

and

$$\psi_{11}^0 = \frac{\partial^2 f}{\partial v^2} = -\left(\frac{\partial P}{\partial v}\right)_T = \frac{1}{v \kappa_T} \tag{9.56}$$

If the critical point is determined by ψ_{11}^0, so that both ds and dv cooperate in the critical behavior, we have

$$\left(\frac{\partial P}{\partial v}\right)_T = 0 \qquad \text{from equation 9.45} \qquad (9.57)$$

$$\left(\frac{\partial^2 P}{\partial v^2}\right)_T = 0 \qquad \text{from equation 9.49} \qquad (9.58)$$

$$-\left(\frac{\partial^3 P}{\partial v^3}\right)_T > 0 \qquad \text{from equation 9.50} \qquad (9.59)$$

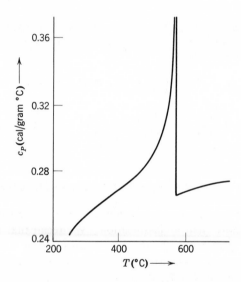

Figure 9.18 Specific heat of quartz near a second-order phase transition.

Also, from equation 9.54,

$$\left| \left(\frac{\partial s}{\partial T}\right)_P \right| = c_P/T \rightarrow \infty \qquad (9.60)$$

$$\left| \left(\frac{\partial v}{\partial T}\right)_P \right| = \left| \left(\frac{\partial s}{\partial P}\right)_T \right| = \alpha \rightarrow \infty \qquad (9.61)$$

and

$$\left| \left(\frac{\partial v}{\partial P}\right)_T \right| = v\kappa_T \rightarrow \infty \qquad (9.62)$$

Observations of c_P, α, and κ_T at the critical point of single-component systems, and at the second-order transitions of the various systems mentioned in the introduction of this section, corroborate the prediction of extraordinary high values of these quantities. The specific heat of quartz in the vicinity of a second-order phase transition is shown in Figure 9.18.

Problems—Section 9.8

9.8-1. Derive equation 9.53 by writing

$$\psi_{jk}^s = \left(\frac{\partial x_j}{\partial P_k}\right)_{P_s} \qquad (j < s)$$

where the variables $P_0 \cdots P_{s-1}, x_{s+1} \cdots$ have been suppressed in the notation of the partial derivative. Now, considering x_j as a function of P_k, x_s (and the suppressed variables), we have

$$dx_j = \left(\frac{\partial x_j}{\partial P_k}\right)_{x_s} dP_k + \left(\frac{\partial x_j}{\partial x_s}\right)_{P_k} dx_s$$

and

$$\left(\frac{\partial x_j}{\partial P_k}\right)_{P_s} = \left(\frac{\partial x_j}{\partial P_k}\right)_{x_s} + \left(\frac{\partial x_j}{\partial x_s}\right)_{P_k}\left(\frac{\partial x_s}{\partial P_k}\right)_{P_s}$$

etc.

9.9   Ehrenfest's Theory of Second-Order Phase Transitions

Ehrenfest's theory of second- and higher-order phase transitions is, in actuality, little more than a classification. We recall that Ehrenfest first pointed out the possibility of nth-order transitions in which the molar Gibbs function and its $(n - 1)$st-order derivatives are continuous, whereas the nth-order derivatives suffer discontinuous jumps.

Ehrenfest also pointed out that if such transitions actually exist certain analogues of the Clapeyron–Clausius equations apply.

We consider a second-order phase transition, and we let the phase line appear as shown in Figure 9.12. Then, since $v_A = v_{A'}$ and $v_B = v_{B'}$, we have

$$v_B - v_A = v_{B'} - v_{A'} \tag{9.63}$$

and

$$\left(\frac{\partial v}{\partial T}\right)_P dT + \left(\frac{\partial v}{\partial P}\right)_T dP = \left(\frac{\partial v'}{\partial T}\right)_P dT + \left(\frac{\partial v'}{\partial P}\right)_T dP \tag{9.64}$$

whence

$$\frac{dP}{dT} = \frac{\Delta\alpha}{\Delta\kappa_T} \tag{9.65}$$

Similarly, from the assumed continuity of the molar entropy,

$$\frac{dP}{dT} = \frac{1}{vT}\frac{\Delta c_P}{\Delta \alpha} \tag{9.66}$$

These analogues of the Clapeyron–Clausius equation are known as *Ehrenfest's equations*.

For a third-order transition of the Ehrenfest type we would not only have g, s, and v continuous, but also c_P, α, and κ_T. The derivatives of c_P, α, and κ_T would have discontinuous jumps. It is easy to corroborate that the resultant Ehrenfest equations are

$$\frac{dP}{dT} = \frac{1}{vT}\frac{\Delta(\partial c_P/\partial T)_P}{\Delta(\partial \alpha/\partial T)_P} \tag{9.67}$$

$$\frac{dP}{dT} = \frac{\Delta(\partial \alpha/\partial T)_P}{\Delta(\partial \kappa_T/\partial T)_P} \tag{9.68}$$

and

$$\frac{dP}{dT} = \frac{\Delta(\partial \alpha/\partial P)_T}{\Delta(\partial \kappa_T/\partial P)_T} \tag{9.69}$$

Unfortunately, no known cases of higher-order transitions of the Ehrenfest type have been found, except for the second-order transition of superconductors in zero magnetic field.

CHAPTER 10

The Nernst Postulate

10.1 Qualitative Statistical Comments

The one remaining aspect of the general principles of classical thermodynamics is the development of the consequences of postulate IV. That postulate refers to the *vanishing of the entropy at zero temperature* and is generally referred to as the Nernst postulate.

The postulate actually formulated by Nernst was somewhat weaker than our postulate IV. Nernst's formulation was that *the entropy change in any isothermal process approaches zero as the temperature at which the process occurs approaches zero*. The stronger statement, which we have adopted, was later suggested by Planck. Nevertheless, even the stronger statement generally is referred to as the Nernst postulate.

It is obvious that the Planck form of the postulate implies Nernst's original statement. Consider two states A and B. If both S_A and S_B approach zero as the temperature approaches zero, as required by Planck, then the change in entropy in a process $A \rightarrow B$ also approaches zero, as required by Nernst. The converse, of course, is not true.

Although we avoid introduction of statistical mechanical considerations in our general theory, we can obtain an insight into the underlying physical significance of the Planck statement by a qualitative reference to statistics. Corresponding to a given thermodynamic (macroscopic) state there generally are many microscopic states. The system undergoes continuous transitions among these microstates during the course of a single macroscopic observation. The entropy is proportional to the logarithm of the number of these microstates. The Planck statement then implies that at zero temperature the macroscopic state includes only a *single* microstate. Or, there exists one particular microstate of lower energy than any other, and this microstate alone is occupied at zero temperature.

The quantum statistical justification of Planck's assertion is less direct than the justification of the other thermodynamic postulates. Its status is more that of a reasonable abstraction from many specific calculations than a theorem subject to a rigorous general proof. That is, many calculations of specific models yield unique (i.e., "nondegenerate") states of lowest energy. Thus the lowest energy configuration of every alloy is found to be either a particular ordered state or a state separated into two pure phases, in either case a single unique configuration.

In some cases, however, quantum mechanical calculations *have* yielded results in which several states have equal energy and are simultaneously the states of lowest energy. Such systems would violate Planck's statement. But it has generally been found on closer examination that these theoretical calculations are based on simplified models, and it is generally possible to find some small, previously ignored interaction that conspires to make one microstate have slightly lower energy than the others. Thus it is only an extremely small interaction between the nuclei in a crystal, transmitted indirectly from nucleus to electrons to nucleus, that insures that the directions of the nuclear spins are ordered in the lowest state. If this very small interaction is ignored, all configurations of nuclear spin directions have equal energy, and the Planck assertion then appears to be violated.

There are certain notable cases in which calculations persist in giving nonunique lowest energy states. Thus an alloy with two types of atoms, A and B, may order $ABAB \cdot \cdot \cdot$. It can equally well order $BABA \cdot \cdot \cdot$. That is, there are two equivalent lowest states. Similarly, a ferromagnetic material has its electronic spins aligned, but they can equally well align in one direction as in another. That is, we can interchange the north and south poles of a permanent magnet without altering its energy. Cases such as these are the most difficult to reconcile with Planck's assertion. However, two facts should be noted in such cases. The first is that the inevitable interactions between the given system and other systems in the universe have been ignored; it is reasonable to expect that if the extremely small interaction of a permanent magnet with other magnets in the universe were included one particular direction of the magnet would turn out to be the lowest in energy. And the second fact to be noted is that the transitions among the equivalent states in these cases involve large macroscopic changes. Transitions among these equivalent states do not occur during a macroscopic measurement, so that the *effective* number of underlying microstates is only unity after all. Thus the north and south poles of a magnet do not interchange in the course of a physical measurement. Effectively, only a single microstate contributes to the macroscopic observation, and the Planck assertion is effectively valid.

Another possible source of doubt of the validity of the Planck statement lies in our ignorance of intranuclear coordinates. For even if we have corroborated that the positions of ions are ordered in an alloy, and if the electron spins also are ordered, there are still other microscopic parameters unavailable to observation. We do not know what coordinates may adequately describe the internal structure of nuclei, and it certainly has not been experimentally corroborated that these coordinates are completely ordered at zero temperature. Nevertheless, every reasonable expectation favors the absolute validity of the Planck statement. Furthermore, statistical calculations reveal that all contributions to the entropy from the ionic coordinates, from the spin coordinates, and from the intranuclear coordinates are additive. Thus each contribution approaches zero separately. If, in a statistical calculation, the intranuclear coordinates (or any other subtle coordinates) are completely ignored, the Planck statement retains its validity with respect to all the explicitly included coordinates; and, if, in a thermodynamic measurement, the contribution to the entropy of some subtle coordinates is not observed, the Planck statement retains its validity with respect to the observed entropy contributions. This is the key consideration that justifies the adoption of the Planck statement.

With this advocation, we forthwith adopt the postulate that the entropy of every system in equilibrium approaches zero as $T \to 0$, and we proceed to investigate the consequences of this postulate.

10.2 Specific Heats and Other Derivatives at Low Temperature

A number of derivatives vanish at zero temperature as a consequence of the Nernst postulate. Among these quantities are the specific heats, as we now demonstrate.

Consider the two states A and B on the T–V diagram of Figure 10.1. The state B is at zero temperature and its entropy consequently vanishes. The entropy at point A can be related to that at B by an integral carried along the vertical line in Figure 10.1:

$$S_A = S_B + \int_0^{T_A} \left(\frac{\partial S}{\partial T} \right)_{V, N_1, N_2 \cdots} dT \tag{10.1}$$

$$S_A = S_B + \int_0^{T_A} \frac{N c_v}{T} \, dT \tag{10.2}$$

The entropy S_A must be finite. But, in order that the integral in equation 10.2 may converge at the lower limit, it is clearly necessary that

$$c_v \to 0 \qquad \text{as} \qquad T \to 0 \tag{10.3}$$

In reaching this conclusion, we should recognize that the assignment of a particular value to S_B is irrelevant; the vanishing of the specific heat depends only on the fact that the entropy is *finite* at $T = 0$.

If, in the argument presented, the pressure is substituted for the volume, the conclusion clearly becomes

$$c_P \to 0 \quad \text{as} \quad T \to 0 \quad\quad\quad (10.4)$$

All specific heats vanish at zero temperature.

We now consider the derivative $(\partial S/\partial P)_T$, the change in entropy per unit isothermal change in pressure. According to the Nernst postulate,

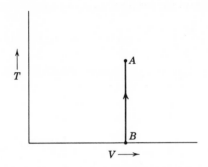

Figure 10.1   The path of integration of equation 10.1.

the change in entropy in an isothermal pressure increase (or any other isothermal process) vanishes at zero temperature. The immediate consequence is

$$\left(\frac{\partial S}{\partial P}\right)_T \to 0 \quad \text{as} \quad T \to 0 \quad\quad\quad (10.5)$$

According to the mnemonic diagram, this is equivalent to the statement

$$\left(\frac{\partial V}{\partial T}\right)_P \to 0 \quad \text{as} \quad T \to 0 \quad\quad\quad (10.6)$$

or

$$\alpha \to 0 \quad \text{as} \quad T \to 0 \quad\quad\quad (10.7)$$

The coefficient of thermal expansion vanishes at zero temperature.

Again we repeat the logic, interchanging the roles of volume and pressure. The change in entropy in an isothermal expansion vanishes at zero temperature, whence

$$\left(\frac{\partial S}{\partial V}\right)_T \to 0 \quad \text{as} \quad T \to 0 \quad\quad\quad (10.8)$$

and, by the mnemonic diagram,

$$\left(\frac{\partial P}{\partial T}\right)_V \to 0 \quad \text{as} \quad T \to 0 \tag{10.9}$$

To develop the general analogues of equations 10.5–10.9, we let X_k be the volume or any of the mole numbers in the fundamental equation $U = U(S, X_1, X_2 \cdots)$. Then, as in equation 10.8,

$$\left(\frac{\partial S}{\partial X_k}\right)_{T,X_1,X_2\cdots X_{k-1},X_{k+1}\cdots} \to 0 \quad \text{as} \quad T \to 0 \tag{10.10}$$

and, by the appropriate Maxwell relation,

$$\left(\frac{\partial P_k}{\partial T}\right)_{X_1,X_2\cdots} \to 0 \quad \text{as} \quad T \to 0 \tag{10.11}$$

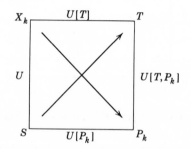

Also, as in equation 10.5,

$$\left(\frac{\partial S}{\partial P_k}\right)_{T,X_1,X_2\cdots X_{k-1},X_{k+1}\cdots} \to 0 \quad \text{as} \quad T \to 0 \tag{10.12}$$

and again, by an appropriate Maxwell relation,

$$\left(\frac{\partial X_k}{\partial T}\right)_{X_1,X_2\cdots X_{k-1},P_k,X_{k+1}\cdots} \to 0 \quad \text{as} \quad T \to 0 \tag{10.13}$$

Equations 10.10–10.13 constitute the general result, of which equations 10.5–10.9 are special cases.

10.3 Thomsen and Berthelot's Principle

The *principle of Thomsen and Berthelot* is an empirical rule for the prediction of the equilibrium states in certain types of processes. It was in connection with his attempt to find the underlying theoretical rationale of this empirical principle that Nernst was led to his postulate. The

Thomsen–Berthelot principle still furnishes a useful rule in chemistry, and it now provides us with an instructive application of the Nernst postulate.

Consider a system maintained at constant temperature and pressure by contact with appropriate reservoirs and released from some initial state by the removal of constraints. According to the empirical principle of Thomsen and Berthelot, the equilibrium state to which the system proceeds is that which evolves the greatest efflux of heat, or, in the more usual language, "that process is realized which is most exothermic." We stress that the term process is used here in the static sense of classical thermodynamics, characterizing only initial and final states rather than the intermediate dynamics.

The formal statement of the principle of Thomsen and Berthelot is most conveniently put in terms of the enthalpy. We recall that in isobaric processes the enthalpy acts as a potential for heat, so that the total heat efflux is

$$\text{heat efflux} = H_{\text{initial}} - H_{\text{final}} \qquad (10.14)$$

The statement of Thomsen and Berthelot therefore is equivalent to the statement that the equilibrium state is that which maximizes $H_{\text{initial}} - H_{\text{final}}$ or that which minimizes H_{final}. On the other hand, we know that the *proper* thermodynamic criterion for the equilibrium state reached at constant T and P is that the Gibbs function be minimum. The problem which faced Nernst was this. Why should minimum enthalpy so commonly predict the same equilibrium states as minimum Gibbs function?

Empirically, the principle of Thomsen and Berthelot is found to be reliable only if the temperature is not too high. For many systems it is quite reliable at room temperature, but it definitely fails at elevated temperatures. The key to the principle then lies in an examination of the situation at low temperature.

Since $G = H - TS$ for both the initial and final states, the changes in enthalpy, Gibbs function, and entropy in the process are related by

$$\Delta G = \Delta H - T\,\Delta S \qquad (10.15)$$

Therefore, the mere fact that ΔS is bounded at zero temperature implies that ΔG and ΔH become identical at zero temperature. But, of course, the Thomsen and Berthelot principle is not generally applied at zero temperature. The question is why ΔG and ΔH remain so nearly equal for a considerable range of temperature above $T = 0$.

By dividing through equation 10.15 by T, we have

$$\frac{\Delta H - \Delta G}{T} = \Delta S \qquad (10.16)$$

Both the numerator and the denominator approach zero as T approaches zero, and the ratio approaches the value of ΔS at zero temperature. To evaluate the limit of the indeterminate form, we employ L'Hospital's rule, differentiating numerator and denominator, whence

$$\left(\frac{d\,\Delta H}{dT}\right)_{T=0} - \left(\frac{d\,\Delta G}{dT}\right)_{T=0} = \lim_{T\to 0} \Delta S \qquad (10.17)$$

The Nernst postulate therefore implies that

$$\left(\frac{d\,\Delta H}{dT}\right)_{T=0} = \left(\frac{d\,\Delta G}{dT}\right)_{T=0} \qquad (10.18)$$

If ΔG and ΔH are plotted as a function of T, the Nernst postulate

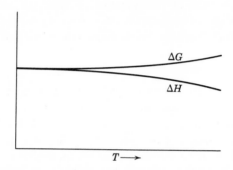

Figure 10.2   Illustrating the principle of Thomsen and Berthelot.

insures not only that the values are equal at $T = 0$, but that the slopes are also equal, as indicated in Figure 10.2. The changes in Gibbs function and enthalpy are consequently very nearly equal over a considerable range in temperatures, justifying the approximate validity of the Thomsen and Berthelot principle over these temperatures.

It will be noted that the slopes of both ΔH and ΔG are zero in Figure 10.2. This follows from the fact that

$$\left(\frac{d\,\Delta H}{dT}\right)_P = \Delta\left(\frac{dH}{dT}\right)_P = \Delta C_P \qquad (10.19)$$

and the specific heat vanishes at zero temperature, as demonstrated in equation 10.4.

10.4   The "Unattainability" of Zero Temperature

Sweeping statements to the effect that the absolute zero of temperature can never be reached by *any* physically realizable process are sometimes made. Temperatures of $0.001°K$ have been attained in the laboratory, and there is no suggestion that temperatures of 10^{-6}°K, 10^{-10}°K, or any other nonzero temperature, may not be obtained. Whether the state of *precisely* zero temperature is physically realizable by any conceivable

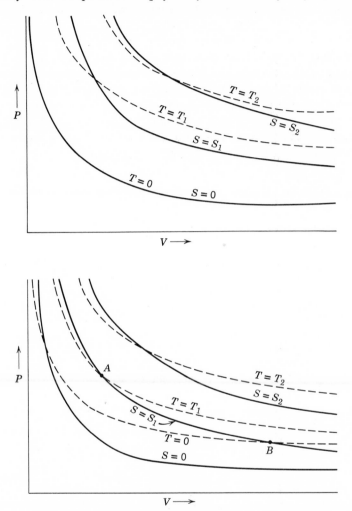

Figure 10.3 Isotherms and adiabats near zero temperature.

process seems to be a nonphysical question. However, the Nernst postulate does imply that no simple adiabatic process can lead from a nonzero to a zero temperature. The Nernst postulate identifies the isotherm $T = 0$ as being coincident with the adiabat $S = 0$, although other isotherms and adiabats are distinct. As no two adiabats can intersect, it therefore follows that no adiabat (other than $S = 0$) can intersect the $T = 0$ isotherm. Therefore, no adiabatic process initiated at nonzero temperature can lead to zero temperature.

The situation described is indicated schematically in Figure 10.3*a*. In Figure 10.3*b* the isotherms and adiabats are shown in violation of the Nernst postulate. An adiabatic process initiated at temperature T_1, carried along the path *A–B*, would then lead to zero temperature.

Various subtle and ingenious suggestions have been advanced for other processes leading to zero temperature, such as separation of the super-fluid component of liquid helium by means of fine capillary tubes. In each case some objection of principle or practice has been found. The attempt to invent a method successful in principle is an academic game at best, intellectually challenging but of no great physical import.

CHAPTER 11

Summary of Principles
for General Systems

11.1 General Systems

Throughout the first ten chapters the principles of thermodynamics have been so stated for simple systems that their generalization is virtually self-evident. And, in a number of cases, such as the discussion of stability, we have actually used verbatim the statements appropriate to general systems.

The pattern of generalization is simple and direct. The fundamental equation of a simple system is of the form

$$U = U(S, V, N_1, N_2 \cdots N_r) \qquad (11.1)$$

The volume and the mole numbers play symmetrical roles throughout, and we can rewrite equation 11.1 in the symmetrical form

$$U = U(X_0, X_1, X_2, X_3 \cdots X_t) \qquad (11.2)$$

where X_0 signifies the entropy, X_1 the volume, and the remaining X_k are the mole numbers. To generalize to nonsimple systems, we adopt all the previous formalism with respect to equation 11.2, merely reinterpreting the parameters X_k. For general systems the extensive parameters X_k include various magnetic, electric, and elastic parameters in addition to the entropy, volume, and mole numbers. We shall not attempt to enumerate specifically the various new extensive parameters appropriate to general systems. These are introduced in the following chapters as various specific types of systems are considered individually. We now merely anticipate the existence of additional extensive parameters, and we recognize that these new parameters play roles in the theory completely symmetric

191

with, and analogous to, the roles of the volume and mole numbers of simple systems.

For the convenience of the reader we recapitulate briefly the main theorems of the first ten chapters, using a language appropriate to general systems.

11.2 The Postulates

Postulate I. *There exist particular states (called equilibrium states) which, macroscopically, are characterized completely by the specification of the internal energy U and a set of extensive parameters $X_1, X_2 \cdots X_t$ later to be specifically enumerated.*

Postulate II. *There exists a function (called the entropy) of the extensive parameters, defined for all equilibrium states, and having the following property. The values assumed by the extensive parameters in the absence of a constraint are those which maximize the entropy over the manifold of constrained equilibrium states.*

Postulate III. *The entropy of a composite system is additive over the constituent subsystems (whence the entropy of each constituent system is a homogeneous first-order function of the extensive parameters). The entropy is continuous and differentiable and is a monotonically increasing function of the energy.*

Postulate IV. *The entropy of any system vanishes in the state for which* $T \equiv (\partial U/\partial S)_{X_1, X_2} \ldots = 0.$

11.3 The Intensive Parameters

The differential form of the fundamental equation is

$$dU = T\, dS + \sum_1^t P_k\, dX_k = \sum_0^t P_k\, dX_k \qquad (11.3)$$

in which

$$P_k = \frac{\partial U}{\partial X_k} \qquad (11.4)$$

The term $T\, dS$ is the flux of heat and $\sum_1^t P_k\, dX_k$ is the work. The intensive parameters are functions of the extensive parameters, the functional relations being the equations of state. Furthermore, the conditions of equilibrium with respect to a transfer of X_k between two subsystems is the equality of the intensive parameters P_k.

The Euler relation, which follows from the homogeneous first-order property, is

$$U = \sum_0^t P_k X_k \qquad (11.5)$$

and the Gibbs–Duhem relation is

$$\sum_0^t X_k \, dP_k = 0 \qquad (11.6)$$

Similar relations hold in the entropy representation.

11.4 Legendre Transforms

A partial Legendre transformation can be made by replacing the variables $X_0, X_1, X_2 \cdots X_s$ by $P_0, P_1 \cdots P_s$. The Legendre transformed function is

$$U[P_0, P_1 \cdots P_s] = U - \sum_0^s P_k X_k \qquad (11.7)$$

The natural variables of this function are $P_0 \cdots P_s, X_{s+1} \cdots X_t$, and the natural derivatives are

$$\frac{\partial U[P_0 \cdots P_s]}{\partial P_k} = -X_k, \qquad k = 0, 1 \cdots s \qquad (11.8)$$

$$\frac{\partial U[P_0 \cdots P_s]}{\partial X_k} = P_k \qquad k = s + 1 \cdots t \qquad (11.9)$$

and consequently

$$dU[P_0 \cdots P_s] = \sum_0^s (-X_k) \, dP_k + \sum_{s+1}^t P_k \, dX_k \qquad (11.10)$$

The equilibrium values of any unconstrained extensive parameters in a system in contact with reservoirs of constant $P_0, P_1 \cdots P_s$ minimize $U[P_0 \cdots P_s]$ at constant $P_0 \cdots P_s$.

11.5 Maxwell Relations

The mixed partial derivatives of the potential $U[P_0 \cdots P_s]$ are equal, whence, from equation 11.10,

$$\frac{\partial X_j}{\partial P_k} = \frac{\partial X_k}{\partial P_j} \qquad \text{if} \qquad j, k \leqslant s \qquad (11.11)$$

$$\frac{\partial X_j}{\partial X_k} = \frac{-\partial P_k}{\partial P_j} \qquad \text{if} \qquad j \leqslant s \qquad \text{and} \qquad k > s \qquad (11.12)$$

and

$$\frac{\partial P_j}{\partial X_k} = \frac{\partial P_k}{\partial X_j} \quad \text{if} \quad j, k > s \qquad (11.13)$$

In each of these partial derivatives the variables to be held constant are all those of the set $P_0 \cdots P_s$, $X_{s+1} \cdots X_t$, except the variable with respect to which the derivative is taken.

These relations can be read from the mnemonic diagram of Figure 11.1.

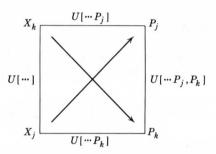

Figure 11.1 The general thermodynamic mnemonic diagram. The potential $U[\cdots]$ is a general Legendre transform of U. The potential $U[\cdots P_j]$ is $U[\cdots] - P_j X_j$. That is, $U[\cdots P_j]$ is transformed with respect to P_j in addition to all the variables of $U[\cdots]$. The other functions are similarly defined.

11.6   Stability and Phase Transitions

The criteria of stability are

$$\left(\frac{\partial P_j}{\partial x_j}\right)_{P_0 \cdots P_{j-1}, x_{j+1} \cdots x_{t-1}} > 0 \quad . \quad \text{for all } j \qquad (11.14)$$

where $x_j = X_j / X_t$.

If the criteria of stability are not satisfied, a system breaks up into two or more portions called phases. Analogues of the Gibbs phase rule can be derived for particular types of nonsimple systems, but the general form is not of practical utility.

The critical phases that form the boundary between full stability and instability are determined by the conditions (equation 9.45)

$$\left(\frac{\partial P_k}{\partial x_s}\right)_{P_0 \cdots P_{s-1}, x_{s+1} \cdots x_{t-1}} = 0 \quad \text{for all} \quad k \geqslant s \qquad (11.15)$$

and (from equations 9.49 and 9.50),

$$\left(\frac{\partial^2 P_s}{\partial x_s^2}\right)_{P_0 \cdots P_{s-1}, x_{s+1} \cdots x_{t-1}} = 0 \qquad (11.16)$$

$$\left(\frac{\partial^3 P_s}{\partial x_s^3}\right)_{P_0 \cdots P_{s-1}, x_{s+1} \cdots x_{t-1}} > 0 \qquad (11.17)$$

At such a critical "point" a number of observable parameters become unbounded. In particular (from equations 9.54),

$$\left(\frac{\partial x_k}{\partial P_j}\right)_{P_0 \cdots P_s, x_{s+1} \cdots x_{t-1}} \to \infty \qquad j, k \leqslant s \qquad (11.18)$$

11.7 Properties at Zero Temperature

Finally, for a general system the specific heats vanish at zero temperature.

$$c_{x_1, x_2} \cdots \equiv T\left(\frac{\partial s}{\partial T}\right)_{x_1, x_2 \cdots} \to 0 \qquad \text{as} \qquad T \to 0 \qquad (11.19)$$

and

$$c_{x_1 \cdots x_{k-1}, P_k, x_{k+1} \cdots} \to 0 \qquad \text{as} \qquad T \to 0 \qquad (11.20)$$

Furthermore, the four following types of derivatives vanish at zero temperature.

$$\left(\frac{\partial s}{\partial x_k}\right)_{T, x_1 \cdots x_{k-1}, x_{k+1} \cdots} \to 0 \qquad \text{as} \qquad T \to 0 \qquad (11.21)$$

$$\left(\frac{\partial P_k}{\partial T}\right)_{x_1, x_2 \cdots} \to 0 \qquad \text{as} \qquad T \to 0 \qquad (11.22)$$

$$\left(\frac{\partial s}{\partial P_k}\right)_{T, x_1 \cdots x_{k-1}, x_{k+1} \cdots} \to 0 \qquad \text{as} \qquad T \to 0 \qquad (11.23)$$

and

$$\left(\frac{\partial x_k}{\partial T}\right)_{x_1 \cdots x_{k-1}, P_k, x_{k+1} \cdots} \to 0 \qquad \text{as} \qquad T \to 0 \qquad (11.24)$$

The applications of thermodynamics follow from the specific interpretations of these theorems when the x_k are suitably identified for particular systems.

PART II

Representative Applications

CHAPTER 12

Chemical Thermodynamics

12.1 Chemical Reactions

In the second part of this book we turn our attention to nonsimple systems. By specific examples, we shall demonstrate the manner in which the simple formalism heretofore developed can be generalized to new types of processes and to new types of extensive parameters.

The first generalization is to chemical reactions. The extensive parameters of the systems to be discussed are precisely those with which we are familiar—energy, entropy, volume, and the mole numbers of each of the chemical components. However, we shall consider a new type of process; a chemical reaction.

A chemical reaction is a process in which the various mole numbers of a system change, some increasing at the expense of a decrease in others. The relationships among the changing mole numbers are governed by the basic laws of chemistry and are described by *chemical equations*. Representative chemical equations are

$$2H_2 + O_2 \rightleftharpoons 2H_2O \tag{12.1}$$

$$2O \rightleftharpoons O_2 \tag{12.2}$$

$$3H_2 + SO_2 \rightleftharpoons H_2S + 2H_2O \tag{12.3}$$

The meaning of the first of these equations is that the changes in the mole numbers of H_2, O_2, and H_2O stand in the ratio of $-2 : -1 : +2$. The three chemical equations accordingly are equivalent to the following three statements,

$$dN_{\text{H}_2} : dN_{\text{O}_2} : dN_{\text{H}_2\text{O}} = -2 : -1 : +2 \qquad (12.4)$$

$$dN_{\text{O}} : dN_{\text{O}_2} = -2 : +1 \qquad (12.5)$$

$$dN_{\text{H}_2} : dN_{\text{SO}_2} : dN_{\text{H}_2\text{S}} : dN_{\text{H}_2\text{O}} = -3 : -1 : +1 : +2 \qquad (12.6)$$

We define a factor of proportionality $d\tilde{N}$, so that equation 12.1 or 12.4 implies

$$dN_{\text{H}_2} = -2d\tilde{N}, \qquad dN_{\text{O}_2} = -d\tilde{N}, \qquad dN_{\text{H}_2\text{O}} = +2d\tilde{N} \qquad (12.7)$$

Similarly equation 12.2 or 12.5 implies

$$dN_{\text{O}} = -2d\tilde{N}, \qquad dN_{\text{O}_2} = d\tilde{N} \qquad (12.8)$$

In general, a chemical equation can be written in the form

$$v_1'A_1 + v_2'A_2 + \cdots + v_{k-1}'A_{k-1} \rightleftharpoons v_k'A_k + v_{k+1}'A_{k+1} + \cdots \qquad (12.9)$$

where the quantities A_k are symbols for the chemical constituents and the quantities v_k' are small positive integers called *stoichiometric coefficients*. Such a chemical equation is the chemist's notation for the set of equations

$$dN_j = -v_j' \, d\tilde{N} \quad \text{if} \quad j < k \qquad (12.10)$$

and

$$dN_j = +v_j' \, d\tilde{N} \quad \text{if} \quad j \geqslant k \qquad (12.11)$$

It is convenient to define another set of stoichiometric coefficients by

$$v_j = -v_j' \quad \text{if} \quad j < k \qquad (12.12)$$

and

$$v_j = +v_j' \quad \text{if} \quad j \geqslant k \qquad (12.13)$$

The stoichiometric coefficients v_j are negative for the "reactants" and positive for the "products" in equation 12.9. By transferring all terms to the right of equation 12.9, we can then write

$$0 \rightleftharpoons \sum_j v_j A_j \qquad (12.14)$$

and

$$dN_j = v_j \, d\tilde{N} \qquad (12.15)$$

The identification of the reactants and products in a chemical equation is not unique, for the reaction may proceed in either direction. The assignment of a conventional direction is purely arbitrary, and the absolute signs of the v_j have no physical significance (although the relative sign of two coefficients is definite, of course). A common convention is to take the direction of the reaction as that in which it is exothermic, in accordance with the principle of Thomsen and Berthelot (section 10.3).

In section 12.5 we discuss further the matter of absorption or evolution of heat in the course of a chemical reaction.

12.2   Chemical Equilibrium

The thermodynamic treatment of chemical processes is completely analogous to the treatment of processes in simple systems. Consider a system with r chemical components, among which the chemical reaction

$$0 \rightleftharpoons \sum_1^r \nu_j A_j \tag{12.16}$$

can occur. If some of the components are not involved in the reaction, the corresponding stoichiometric coefficients are zero, so that the summation formally goes over all components. The change in Gibbs function associated with a virtual change in the mole numbers is

$$dG = \sum_1^r \mu_j \, dN_j \tag{12.17}$$

But the changes in the mole numbers are related by the stoichiometric coefficients, whence

$$dG = \left(\sum_1^r \mu_j \nu_j \right) d\tilde{N} \tag{12.18}$$

If the system is in contact with temperature and pressure reservoirs (the ambient atmosphere), the condition of equilibrium is that dG vanish for arbitrary $d\tilde{N}$, so that

$$\sum_1^r \nu_j \mu_j = 0 \tag{12.19}$$

This is the condition of chemical equilibrium. It is analogous to the condition of temperature equality for heat-flow processes, of pressure equality for volume transfers, or of chemical-potential equality for matter flow.

If the system originally contains N_1° moles of the first component, N_2° moles of the second component, etc., the chemical reaction proceeds to some extent and the final mole numbers are $N_1, N_2 \cdots N_r$. The chemical equation requires that for each value of j

$$N_j = N_j^\circ + \int dN_j = N_j^\circ + \nu_j \, \Delta \tilde{N} \tag{12.20}$$

Consequently there is only one quantity to be found; the single parameter $\Delta \tilde{N}$. Each of the chemical potentials in equation 12.19 can be expressed as a function of T, P, and the mole numbers. If T and P are known, equation 12.19 is a single equation in the single unknown $\Delta \tilde{N}$ and consequently permits explicit solution of the problem.

12.3   Degree of Reaction

If $\Delta \tilde{N}$ were to increase sufficiently, one of the mole numbers N_j would eventually become negative. That is, if the reaction were to proceed, one of the reactants would eventually be exhausted. The maximum value of $\Delta \tilde{N}$ for which all N_j remain positive consequently defines the greatest conceivable extent of reaction. Similarly, the algebraically minimum value of $\Delta \tilde{N}$ for which all N_j remain positive defines the greatest conceivable extent of the reverse reaction. The actual value of $\Delta \tilde{N}$ in equilibrium may be anywhere between these two extremes. The *degree of reaction* ϵ is defined as

$$\epsilon = \frac{\Delta \tilde{N} - \Delta \tilde{N}_{min}}{\Delta \tilde{N}_{max} - \Delta \tilde{N}_{min}} \tag{12.21}$$

It is possible that a straightforward solution of the equation of chemical equilibrium (12.19) may yield a value of $\Delta \tilde{N}$ which is larger than $\Delta \tilde{N}_{max}$ or smaller than $\Delta \tilde{N}_{min}$. In such a case the process is terminated by the exhaustion of one of the components. The condition equation 12.19 is not attained by the system, but the system attains the smallest value of $|\Sigma \nu_k \mu_k|$ consistent with nonnegative values of the N_j. The degree of reaction is then zero or unity, and the reaction is said to "go to completion."

As a specific example, we suppose that $\frac{1}{2}$ mole of H_2S, $\frac{3}{4}$ mole of H_2O, 2 moles of H_2, and 1 mole of SO_2 are introduced into a vessel. The system is maintained at a temperature of 30°C and a pressure of 1 atm. The chemical constituents can undergo the chemical reaction of equation 12.3. Then the condition of equilibrium is

$$-3\mu_{H_2} - \mu_{SO_2} + \mu_{H_2S} + 2\mu_{H_2O} = 0 \tag{12.22}$$

and

$$N_{H_2} = 2 - 3\Delta \tilde{N} \qquad \Delta \tilde{N} = \tfrac{2}{3} \ max \tag{12.23}$$

$$N_{SO_2} = 1 - \Delta \tilde{N} \qquad \Delta \tilde{N} = 1 \tag{12.24}$$

$$N_{H_2S} = \tfrac{1}{2} + \Delta \tilde{N} \qquad \Delta \tilde{N} = -\tfrac{1}{2} \tag{12.25}$$

$$N_{H_2O} = \tfrac{3}{4} + 2\Delta \tilde{N} \qquad \Delta \tilde{N} = -\tfrac{3}{8} \ min \tag{12.26}$$

If each of the chemical potentials were known as functions of T, P, and the N_j's, we would insert equations 12.23–12.26 into equation 12.22 and solve for $\Delta \tilde{N}$. Let us suppose that the solution is $\Delta \tilde{N} = \tfrac{1}{4}$, and we then compute the degree of reaction. If $\Delta \tilde{N} = \tfrac{2}{3}$, then N_{H_2} becomes zero by equation 12.23; this is $\Delta \tilde{N}_{max}$. If $\Delta \tilde{N} = -\tfrac{3}{8}$, then N_{H_2O} becomes zero; this is $\Delta \tilde{N}_{min}$. The degree of reaction consequently is $\tfrac{3}{5}$.

Let us suppose, however, that the temperature is lowered, and that solution of equation 12.22 then yields the value of $\Delta \tilde{N} = 0.8$. This value is greater than $\Delta \tilde{N}_{max}$. The true solution is $\Delta \tilde{N} = \Delta \tilde{N}_{max} = \frac{2}{3}$, and the degree of reaction is unity.

12.4 Simultaneous Reactions

If two or more chemical reactions are possible among the constituents of a system, each reaction gives rise to an equilibrium condition similar to that of equation 12.19. To demonstrate that this is so, we consider two reactions

$$0 \rightleftharpoons \sum_1^r \nu_j^{(1)} A_j \tag{12.27}$$

and

$$0 \rightleftharpoons \sum_1^r \nu_j^{(2)} A_j \tag{12.28}$$

In each case certain of the stochiometric coefficients may be zero, corresponding to those constituents that are not involved in the particular reaction. Corresponding to the first reaction, we define a factor of proportionality $d\tilde{N}^{(1)}$, and corresponding to the second reaction we define $d\tilde{N}^{(2)}$.

Then

$$dN_j^{(1)} = \nu_j^{(1)} \, d\tilde{N}^{(1)} \tag{12.29}$$

and

$$dN_j^{(2)} = \nu_j^{(2)} \, d\tilde{N}^{(2)} \tag{12.30}$$

The total change dN_j is the sum of the partial changes due to each reaction

$$dN_j = dN_j^{(1)} + dN_j^{(2)} \tag{12.31}$$

The virtual change of the Gibbs function is

$$dG = \sum_1^r \mu_j \, dN_j \tag{12.32}$$

or

$$dG = \left(\sum_j \nu_j^{(1)} \mu_j \right) d\tilde{N}^{(1)} + \left(\sum_j \nu_j^{(2)} \mu_j \right) d\tilde{N}^{(2)} \tag{12.33}$$

As dG must vanish for arbitrary $d\tilde{N}^{(1)}$ and $d\tilde{N}^{(2)}$, we conclude that

$$\sum_1^r \nu_j^{(1)} \mu_j = 0 \tag{12.34}$$

and

$$\sum_1^r \nu_j^{(2)} \mu_j = 0 \tag{12.35}$$

These two simultaneous equations permit evaluation of the two unknowns

$\Delta \tilde{N}^{(1)}$ and $\Delta \tilde{N}^{(2)}$, which, in turn, determine all the mole numbers in equilibrium by the equations

$$N_j = N_j^\circ + \nu_j^{(1)} \, \Delta \tilde{N}^{(1)} + \nu_j^{(2)} \, \Delta \tilde{N}^{(2)} \tag{12.36}$$

The concept of degree of reaction is not a useful one if more than one reaction is permissible, and we shall not attempt to extend its definition to this case.

12.5 Heat of Reaction

As a chemical reaction occurs at constant temperature and pressure, heat may be evolved or absorbed. To investigate this phenomenon, we recall that the enthalpy acts as a "potential for heat flux" at constant pressure (section 6.3), so that the evolution of heat is associated with a change in enthalpy. The relationship between the enthalpy and the Gibbs function is

$$H = G + TS \tag{12.37}$$

or

$$H = G - T \left(\frac{\partial G}{\partial T} \right)_{P, N_1, N_2 \cdots} \tag{12.38}$$

If an infinitesimal chemical reaction $d\tilde{N}$ occurs, both H and G change and

$$dH = \frac{dH}{d\tilde{N}} d\tilde{N} = \frac{dG}{d\tilde{N}} d\tilde{N} - T \frac{\partial}{\partial T} \left(\frac{dG}{d\tilde{N}} \right)_{P, N_1, N_2 \cdots} d\tilde{N} \tag{12.39}$$

But the change in Gibbs function is

$$dG = \sum_1^r \mu_j \, dN_j = \left(\sum_1^r \nu_j \mu_j \right) d\tilde{N} \tag{12.40}$$

whence

$$\frac{dG}{d\tilde{N}} = \sum_1^r \nu_j \mu_j \tag{12.41}$$

At equilibrium $dG/d\tilde{N}$ vanishes, but the temperature derivative of $dG/d\tilde{N}$ does not, so that in the vicinity of the equilibrium state equation 12.39 becomes

$$\frac{dH}{d\tilde{N}} = -T \frac{\partial}{\partial T} \left(\sum_1^r \nu_j \mu_j \right)_{P, N_1, N_2 \cdots} \tag{12.42}$$

The quantity $dH/d\tilde{N}$ is known as the *heat of reaction*; it is the heat absorbed per unit reaction in the vicinity of the equilibrium state. It is positive for *endothermic* reactions and negative for *exothermic* reactions.

We have assumed that the reaction considered is not one that goes to completion. If the reaction does go to completion, the summation in equation 12.41 does not vanish in the equilibrium state, and this summation appears as an additional term in equation 12.42.

As the summation in equation 12.42 vanishes at the equilibrium composition, it is intuitively evident that the temperature derivative of this quantity is related to the temperature dependence of the equilibrium concentrations. We shall find it convenient to develop this connection explicitly only in the special case of ideal gases, in section 12.9. However, it is of interest here to note the plausibility of the relationship and to recognize that such a relationship permits the heat of reaction to be measured by determinations of equilibrium compositions at various temperatures rather than by relatively difficult calorimetric experiments.

12.6 Stability and the Le Châtelier Principle

The stability criteria in the presence of chemical reactions follow from the requirement that the Gibbs function be a minimum or that in the equilibrium state

$$\frac{d^2G}{d\tilde{N}^2} > 0 \tag{12.43}$$

Thus

$$\frac{d}{d\tilde{N}} \sum_1^r v_k \mu_k > 0 \tag{12.44}$$

Perhaps the most interesting inference that can be drawn from the stability criterion is the form of Le Châtelier's principle for chemical systems. We first consider the effect of a change of temperature at constant pressure, and we show that an increase in temperature shifts the chemical equilibrium in that direction in which heat is absorbed.

The shift in equilibrium is described by the change in $\Delta\tilde{N}$ produced by the given change in temperature. We specify constant pressure, and, since we are interested in chemical equilibrium, the quantity $\Sigma v_j \mu_j$ is also constant (in fact, zero). Thus we are interested in the quantity

$$\left(\frac{\partial \tilde{N}}{\partial T}\right)_{P,\Sigma v_j \mu_j} = -\frac{(\partial \Sigma v_j \mu_j/\partial T)_{P,\Delta\tilde{N}}}{(\partial \Sigma v_j \mu_j/\partial \tilde{N})_{P,T}} \tag{12.45}$$

The numerator is related to the heat of reaction by equation 12.42, so that

$$\left(\frac{\partial \tilde{N}}{\partial T}\right)_{P,\Sigma v_j \mu_j} = \frac{1}{T}\left(\frac{\partial \Sigma v_j \mu_j}{\partial \tilde{N}}\right)^{-1}\frac{dH}{d\tilde{N}} \tag{12.46}$$

The second factor is positive by the stability criterion, so that the sign of $(\partial \tilde{N}/\partial T)_P$ is the same as the sign of the heat of reaction $dH/d\tilde{N}$. For endothermic reactions an increase in temperature increases $\Delta \tilde{N}$, and for an exothermic reaction an increase in temperature decreases $\Delta \tilde{N}$. To summarize, *if the temperature is increased at constant pressure, the chemical equilibrium shifts in that direction in which heat is absorbed.*

A similar result attends a change in pressure at constant temperature. We have

$$\left(\frac{\partial \tilde{N}}{\partial P}\right)_{T,\Sigma \nu_j \mu_j} = -\left(\frac{\partial \Sigma \nu_j \mu_j}{\partial P}\right)_{T,\Delta \tilde{N}} \Big/ \left(\frac{\partial \Sigma \nu_j \mu_j}{\partial \tilde{N}}\right)_{T,P} \qquad (12.47)$$

The significance of the numerator follows from the fact that

$$\Sigma \nu_j \mu_j = \frac{\partial G}{\partial \tilde{N}}$$

whence

$$\left(\frac{\partial \Sigma \nu_j \mu_j}{\partial P}\right)_{T,\Delta \tilde{N}} = \frac{\partial^2 G}{\partial P \, \partial \tilde{N}} = \frac{\partial^2 G}{\partial \tilde{N} \, \partial P} = \frac{\partial V}{\partial \tilde{N}} \qquad (12.48)$$

Alternatively we can write

$$\left(\frac{\partial \Sigma \nu_j \mu_j}{\partial P}\right)_{T,\Delta \tilde{N}} = \Sigma \nu_j \left(\frac{\partial \mu_j}{\partial P}\right)_{T,N_1,N_2 \cdots} = \Sigma \nu_j v_j \qquad (12.49)$$

and again we see that this quantity is $\partial V/\partial \tilde{N}$, or the change of volume per unit reaction. Equation 12.47 therefore shows that the sign of $\partial \tilde{N}/\partial P$ is opposite to the sign of $\partial V/\partial \tilde{N}$. It follows that *an increase in pressure at constant temperature shifts the chemical equilibrium in that direction which decreases the total volume.*

12.7   Gibbs Phase Rule for Chemical Systems

The Gibbs phase rule is altered in a simple way by the possibility of chemical reactions.

We consider a system with r components and M phases, and we repeat the counting of the number of degrees of freedom, as in section 9.6. However, we assume that c chemical reactions are possible among the components. The $(r + 2)$ intensive parameters T, P, μ_1, $\mu_2 \cdots \mu_r$ are equal from phase to phase by the conditions of equilibrium for transfer of heat, volume, or material. Among these $(r + 2)$ parameters there are M Gibbs–Duhem equations, and there are c equations of chemical equilibrium (of the form 12.27 or 12.28). Consequently the number of degrees of freedom is

$$\boxed{f = (r + 2) - M - c}$$ (12.50)

The maximum possible number of coexisting phases is $r - c + 2$.

The special case of chemical reactions which go to completion is of interest. One component is exhausted and does not actually appear in the system. If we ignore the existence of this component and also ignore the associated chemical equation, both r and c in equation 12.50 are reduced by one. The number of degrees of freedom is unchanged, and all physical predictions are unaffected as long as the chemical reaction remains at completion. This fortunate fact is responsible for the simplicity of thermodynamics, which would be completely intractable if every conceivable chemical reaction had to be considered explicitly.

As an example, consider a chemical experiment involving aqueous solutions of various acids and salts. In principle, the water could dissociate into hydrogen and oxygen by the reaction 12.1, but this reaction goes to completion with the exhaustion of hydrogen. Rather than H_2, O_2, and water as components (in addition to the various dissolved acids and salts), only water and O_2, generally, are considered explicitly, and the reaction 12.1 is ignored. In fact, we realize that explicit consideration of every conceivable reaction for this system would demand that we consider not only reaction 12.1 but also 12.2, similar reactions for the dissociation of hydrogen, and an enormous number of other reactions which describe the formation of myriad outlandish chemical complexes.

12.8 Chemical Reactions in Ideal Gases

In order that the chemist may obtain specific numerical answers for the equilibrium composition in a particular system, he must know the explicit form of the equation of state $\mu = \mu(T, P, N_1, N_2 \cdots)$. At high temperatures, when all the components are in the gaseous phase, the equation of state of an ideal gas provides a convenient approximate description of the system. The results of the preceding sections then become explicit and detailed. These results are of considerable practical importance and are interesting also as concrete illustrations of the general principles. In the remainder of this chapter we shall particularize the general results to the specific case of ideal gas reactions.

The chemical potential of the kth component in a mixture of ideal gases is (by equations D.46 and D.47)

$$\mu_k = RT\phi_k(T) + RT \ln P + RT \ln x_k$$ (12.51)

where x_k denotes the molar concentration $N_k/\Sigma N_j$. The equation of chemical equilibrium for a reaction with stoichiometric coefficients $\nu_1, \nu_2 \cdots$ is

$$\sum_1^r \nu_k \mu_k = 0 \tag{12.52}$$

whence

$$\sum_k \nu_k \ln x_k = -\sum_k \nu_k \ln P - \sum_k \nu_k \phi_k(T) \tag{12.53}$$

Writing

$$\ln K(T) = -\sum_k \nu_k \phi_k(T) \tag{12.54}$$

we have

$$\prod_k x_k^{\nu_k} = P^{-\Sigma \nu_k} K(T) \tag{12.55}$$

This equation is the *mass action law*. The quantity $K(T)$ is called the *equilibrium constant* for the reaction considered. If $K(T)$ is known explicitly as a function of T for a particular reaction, the equilibrium concentrations can be computed by the mass action law.

Returning to the illustrative example of equations 12.22–12.26, if the temperature is high enough that each of the components is well represented as an ideal gas, we have

$$N = \Sigma N_j = 4.25 - \Delta \tilde{N} \tag{12.56}$$

and

$$x_{H_2S} = \frac{0.5 + \Delta \tilde{N}}{4.25 - \Delta \tilde{N}} \tag{12.57}$$

and similarly for the other components. The mass action law then becomes

$$\frac{(0.5 + \Delta \tilde{N})(0.75 + 2\Delta \tilde{N})^2(4.25 - \Delta \tilde{N})}{(2 - 3\Delta \tilde{N})^3(1 - \Delta \tilde{N})} = PK(T) \tag{12.58}$$

Problems—Section 12.8

12.8–1. At temperatures above $200°C$ phosphorus pentachloride dissociates according to the reaction

$$PCl_5 \rightleftharpoons PCl_3 + Cl_2$$

A PCl_5 sample weighing 1.9 grams is at a temperature of $320°C$ and has a pressure of 0.31 atm. After the reaction has come to equilibrium, the system is found to have a volume of 2.4 liters. Determine the degree of dissociation and the equilibrium constant.

12.8–2. The equilibrium constant of the reaction $SO_3 \rightleftharpoons SO_2 + \frac{1}{2}O_2$ has the value 0.540 $(atm)^{\frac{1}{2}}$ at $T = 1000°K$. If 1 mole of SO_2 and 2 moles of O_2 are introduced into a vessel and maintained at a pressure of 4 atm, find the number of moles of SO_3 present in equilibrium. The equation for N_{SO_3} should be solved roughly by graphical means to 20 per cent accuracy.

12.8–3. Twenty grams of CO and 20 grams of O_2 are put in a cylinder. The temperature is kept at 5400°R (absolute Fahrenheit) and the pressure at 2 atm. At this temperature the equilibrium constant for the reaction

$$2CO + O_2 \rightleftharpoons 2CO_2$$

is

$$K = 10^{0.94} \text{ atm}$$

How many grams of CO_2 are in the cylinder in equilibrium? It is sufficient to give a completely numerical set of simultaneous equations. Explicit solution is not required.

12.8–4. Show that the stability criterion 12.44 is satisfied if each of the chemical components is an ideal gas.

12.9 Temperature Dependence of the Equilibrium Constant

The equilibrium constant is defined by equation 12.54 in terms of the functions ϕ_k. These functions, in turn, are defined in terms of integrals of the specific heats $c_{P_k}(T)$ by equation D.45, or

$$RT\phi_k = h_{0k} - T(s_{0k} + R \ln P_0) - T \int_{T_0}^{T} \frac{dT'}{T'^2} \int_{T_0'}^{T'} c_{P_k}(T'') \, dT'' \quad (12.59)$$

where P_0, T_0 are the pressure and temperature of the fiducial state, and h_{0k} and s_{0k} are the molar enthalpy and molar entropy of the kth ideal gas component in the fiducial state. Finally, we recall that the specific heats $c_{P_k}(T)$ can be represented as power series in the temperature, as in equation D.33 or Table D.2. Putting all these facts together, we clearly can write $K(T)$ explicitly as a series in T, with the coefficients related to the coefficients of the expansion of the specific heats c_{P_k}.

Insertion of the power series for c_{P_k} into equation 12.59 and that equation into $K(T)$ clearly gives a result of the form

$$\ln K(T) = \left(\frac{1}{R}\frac{dH}{d\tilde{N}}\right)_0 \frac{1}{T} + A \ln T + B + CT + DT^2 + \cdots \quad (12.60)$$

The relation of the coefficients in this equation to those in Table D.2 is left to the reader. By adopting the notation $(1/R \, dH/d\tilde{N})_0$ for the coefficient of the $1/T$ term, we have anticipated a physical significance of this coefficient as *the heat of reaction at zero temperature*. This significance follows directly by insertion of equation 12.60 into the van't Hoff relation, to be derived in the following section.

Values of the coefficients in equation 12.60 are given for several representative chemical reactions in Table 12.1.

Table 12.1

TEMPERATURE DEPENDENCE OF EQUILIBRIUM CONSTANTS

$\frac{1}{R}\left(\frac{dH}{d\tilde{N}}\right)_0$	A	B	C	D	E
$2H_2O \rightleftharpoons 2H_2 + O_2$	-24900	1.335	-1.08	-0.965×10^{-4}	0.139×10^{-6}	-0.665×10^{-10}
$N_2O_4 \rightleftharpoons 2NO_2$	-2692	1.75	5.943	48.3×10^{-4}	-7.144×10^{-6}	
$2HI \rightleftharpoons H_2 + I_2$	-540.4	0.503	-2.350			
$2HBr \rightleftharpoons H_2 + Br_2$	-5223	0.553	-2.72			
$I_2 \rightleftharpoons 2I$	-7550	$+0.75$	-0.440	-4.09×10^{-4}	0.04726×10^{-6}	

The coefficients in the table are defined by

$$\log_{10} K(T) = \frac{1}{RT}\left(\frac{dH}{d\tilde{N}}\right)_0 + A \log_{10} T + B + CT + DT^2$$

The logarithms are to the base 10, the dimensions of $K(T)$ are (atmospheres)$^{\Sigma \nu_k}$, and T is measured in $°K$.

Problems—Section 12.9

12.9–1. To what extent is I_2 dissociated at $0°C$ and 1 atm pressure? At what rate does the percentage dissociation change as the temperature is raised?

12.10 Heat of Reaction of Ideal Gas Reactions

Continuing with the particularization of the general results to the special case of ideal gas reactions, we consider the heat of reaction. From equation 12.42 we have

$$\frac{dH}{d\tilde{N}} = -T\frac{\partial}{\partial T}(\Sigma \nu_j \mu_j)_{P,N_1,N_2} \cdots \tag{12.61}$$

and, inserting equation 12.51,

$$\frac{dH}{d\tilde{N}} = -T\frac{\partial}{\partial T}(RT\Sigma \nu_j \phi_j + RT\Sigma \nu_j \ln P + RT\Sigma \nu_j \ln x_j) \tag{12.62}$$

$$\frac{dH}{d\tilde{N}} = -\Sigma \nu_j \mu_j - RT^2 \frac{d}{dT}\Sigma \nu_j \phi_j \tag{12.63}$$

Recognizing that $\Sigma \nu_j \mu_j$ vanishes at equilibrium and recalling the definition (equation 12.54) of the equilibrium constant, we find the *van't Hoff relation*

$$\frac{dH}{d\tilde{N}} = RT^2 \frac{d}{dT} \ln K(T)$$ (12.64)

At the end of section 12.1 we referred to the relation between the heat of reaction and the temperature dependence of the equilibrium composition. This relation is made explicit for ideal gases by the van't Hoff relation. Measurements of the equilibrium constant at various temperatures enable calculation of the heat of reaction without calorimetric methods; the equilibrium constant is measured by direct determination of the concentrations x_k.

Problems—Section 12.10

12.10–1. What is the heat of reaction for the dissociation of N_2O_4 into $2NO_2$ at 0°C? $3239\ R$

12.10–2. A hypothetical material A_1 undergoes a dissociation reaction of the form

$$3A_1 \rightleftharpoons A_2 + A_3$$

All three materials A_1, A_2, and A_3 are ideal gases. It is observed that at a pressure of 1 atm and a temperature of 300°K the material A_1 is 40 per cent dissociated. Raising the temperature by 10°K increases the percentage dissociation to 41 per cent. What is the heat of reaction? $10,500\ R$

12.11 Additivity of Reactions

A chemical reaction sometimes can be considered as the sum of two other chemical reactions. As an example, consider the reactions

$$2H_2 + O_2 \rightleftharpoons 2H_2O$$ (12.65)

and

$$2CO + O_2 \rightleftharpoons 2CO_2$$ (12.66)

Subtracting these two equations in algebraic fashion gives

$$2H_2 - 2CO \rightleftharpoons 2H_2O - 2CO_2$$ (12.67)

or

$$2[H_2 + CO_2 \rightleftharpoons H_2O + CO]$$ (12.68)

We now show that the quantities $\ln K(T)$ of the various reactions can be subtracted in a corresponding fashion.

Consider two reactions

$$0 \rightleftharpoons \Sigma \nu_j^{(1)} A_j \tag{12.69}$$

and

$$0 \rightleftharpoons \Sigma \nu_j^{(2)} A_j \tag{12.70}$$

and a third reaction obtained by multiplying the first reaction by a constant B_1, the second reaction by B_2, and adding

$$0 \rightleftharpoons \Sigma \nu_j^{(3)} A_j \equiv \Sigma (B_1 \nu_j^{(1)} + B_2 \nu_j^{(2)}) A_j \tag{12.71}$$

Assume that the equilibrium constant of the first reaction is $K_1(T)$ and that of the second reaction is $K_2(T)$, so that by definition,

$$\ln K_1(T) = -\Sigma \nu_j^{(1)} \phi_j(T) \tag{12.72}$$

and

$$\ln K_2(T) = -\Sigma \nu_j^{(2)} \phi_j(T) \tag{12.73}$$

The equilibrium constant for the *resultant reaction* equation 12.71 is defined by an analogous equation, from which it follows that

$$\ln K_3(T) = B_1 \ln K_1(T) + B_2 \ln K_2(T) \tag{12.74}$$

Because of this additivity, a table of coefficients, such as Table 12.1, can be extended to additional reactions which are sums of listed reactions.

Problems—Section 12.11

12.11–1.   Find the heat of reaction, at $0°C$, for the reaction

$$2HI \rightleftharpoons H_2 + 2I$$

12.11–2.   From equations 12.54 and 12.59 we can write

$$R \ln K(T) = -\frac{\Delta H_0}{T} + \Delta S_0 + \int_{T_0}^{T} \frac{dT'}{T'^2} \int_{T_0'}^{T'} \sum_k \nu_k c_{Pk}(T'') \, dT''$$

For the reaction

$$H_2 + \tfrac{1}{2}O_2 \rightleftharpoons H_2O$$

we are given that $\Delta H_0 = -57{,}100$ cal, and $\Delta S_0 = -3.50$. For the reaction

$$CO + \tfrac{1}{2}O_2 \rightleftharpoons CO_2$$

we are given that $\Delta H_0 = -66{,}800$ cal and $\Delta S_0 = -4.46$. The specific heats of each of the components is given in Table D.2. Find the degree of reaction for the reaction

$$CO + H_2O \rightleftharpoons CO_2 + H_2$$

at a temperature of $400°K$ if 1 mole each of CO and H_2O are initially present.

CHAPTER 13

Solid Systems— Elasticity

13.1 Elastic Strain

An adequate description of the mechanical state of a solid is more exacting than that of a fluid. Although the volume is the only mechanical extensive parameter necessary for the description of a fluid system, several additional mechanical variables are required for the description of a solid.

The essential aspect that distinguishes a solid from a fluid is the definite geometrical relation among the various portions of matter in the solid. These relations are described in terms of the *elastic strain components*.

Consider a system in a fiducial state and select two points within it, labeled P and Q in Figure 13.1. Let the (infinitesimal) vector distance from P to Q be $d\mathbf{r}$. Point P is at the position $\mathbf{r}$ relative to some origin O, and point Q is at $\mathbf{r} + d\mathbf{r}$.

Consider the system in a different mechanical state, with a new geometrical relationship existing among the points O, P, and Q. The new positions of P and Q are denoted by P' and Q' in Figure 13.1.

Let the vectorial displacement suffered by point P (i.e., the vector $\mathbf{PP'}$) be denoted by $\mathbf{s}(\mathbf{r})$. The displacement of point Q is $\mathbf{s}(\mathbf{r} + d\mathbf{r})$. Then the vector $\mathbf{P'Q'}$, denoted by $d\mathbf{r'}$ is obtained by noting that in Figure 13.1

$$\mathbf{s}(\mathbf{r}) + d\mathbf{r'} = d\mathbf{r} + \mathbf{s}(\mathbf{r} + d\mathbf{r}) \qquad (13.1)$$

or

$$d\mathbf{r'} = d\mathbf{r} + \mathbf{s}(\mathbf{r} + d\mathbf{r}) - \mathbf{s}(\mathbf{r}) \qquad (13.2)$$

If we expand $\mathbf{s}(\mathbf{r} + d\mathbf{r})$ in a Taylor series in $d\mathbf{r}$, we find

$$\mathbf{s}(\mathbf{r} + d\mathbf{r}) = \mathbf{s}(\mathbf{r}) + d\mathbf{r} \cdot \nabla \mathbf{s}(\mathbf{r}) + \cdots \qquad (13.3)$$

213

For small continuous deformations the higher-order terms in this equation can be neglected. The more general case of finite deformations, in which the higher-order terms must be kept or in which the expansion in equation 13.3 may not even be possible, has been extensively studied in recent years. But we shall restrict our attention, for convenience, to the classical theory of elasticity, predicated on the assumption of a slowly varying and mathematically continuous strain function $s(\mathbf{r})$, for which the truncated form of equation 13.3 is sufficient. We thereby find

$$d\mathbf{r}' = d\mathbf{r} + d\mathbf{r} \cdot \nabla s(\mathbf{r}) \tag{13.4}$$

The foregoing equation can be written in a very convenient tensor form.

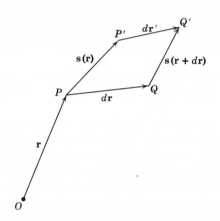

Figure 13.1

As the reader can corroborate by expanding according to the row-by-column rule of tensor multiplication and by comparison with equation 13.4,

$$d\mathbf{r}' = d\mathbf{r} + d\mathbf{r} \cdot \mathscr{S}(\mathbf{r}) \tag{13.5}$$

where $\mathscr{S}(\mathbf{r})$ is the "derived tensor of $s(\mathbf{r})$," which in Cartesian coordinates takes the explicit form

$$\mathscr{S}(\mathbf{r}) = \begin{bmatrix} \dfrac{\partial s_x(\mathbf{r})}{\partial x} & \dfrac{\partial s_y(\mathbf{r})}{\partial x} & \dfrac{\partial s_z(\mathbf{r})}{\partial x} \\[2ex] \dfrac{\partial s_x(\mathbf{r})}{\partial y} & \dfrac{\partial s_y(\mathbf{r})}{\partial y} & \dfrac{\partial s_z(\mathbf{r})}{\partial y} \\[2ex] \dfrac{\partial s_x(\mathbf{r})}{\partial z} & \dfrac{\partial s_y(\mathbf{r})}{\partial z} & \dfrac{\partial s_z(\mathbf{r})}{\partial z} \end{bmatrix} \tag{13.6}$$

Equation 13.5 gives the relative position $(d\mathbf{r}')$ of two points $(P'Q')$ in any state of the system in terms of their relative position $(d\mathbf{r})$ in the fiducial state. The tensor $\mathscr{S}$ effects this transformation, and we might expect the components of this tensor to be the parameters which properly describe the deformation of the solid. Although this is essentially true, certain refinements must be noted.

First, suppose that the final state of the system is obtained from the fiducial state merely by a translation of the system, that is, by a bodily parallel displacement of the system in space. Then $s(r)$ is independent of r, the tensor $\mathscr{S}$ is identically zero, and dr' is equal to dr. It is appropriate that the thermodynamic parameters should vanish in this case, for the bodily translation of the entire system clearly is irrelevant to its thermodynamic description.

Alternatively, suppose that the final state is obtained from the fiducial state by a rigid rotation in space. Clearly, this transformation should also be irrelevant to the thermodynamic description, as it really does not alter the internal relationships of the various points that make up the system. But $\mathscr{S}(r)$ does not vanish in this case.

As an example, let the final state result from an infinitesimal rotation around the z-axis by an angle $d\phi$. Then, if k is a unit vector in the z-direction, we can write

$$s(r) = (k \times r)\, d\phi \tag{13.7}$$

and

$$\mathscr{S} = \begin{bmatrix} 0 & d\phi & 0 \\ -d\phi & 0 & 0 \\ 0 & 0 & 0 \end{bmatrix} \tag{13.8}$$

Now, it will be noted that the tensor 13.8 is antisymmetric. That is, the xy component is the negative of the yx component, or, more generally, the ij component is the negative of the ji component. It is left to the problems to show that every rotation leads to an antisymmetric $\mathscr{S}$ tensor. And, conversely, every antisymmetric $\mathscr{S}$ tensor describes a pure rotation.

If a given tensor $\mathscr{S}$ is written as the sum of an antisymmetric and a symmetric tensor, the antisymmetric part describes a rigid rotation, whereas the symmetric part describes a true internal strain or rearrangement. We thus conclude that only the symmetric part of $\mathscr{S}$ is relevant to a thermodynamic description.

The decomposition of $\mathscr{S}$ into a symmetric and an antisymmetric part is unique and easily obtained. Let $\mathscr{S}^t$ denote the "transpose" of $\mathscr{S}$; that is, $\mathscr{S}^t$ is the tensor obtained by reflecting $\mathscr{S}$ around its principal diagonal or by interchanging the ij and the ji components. Then write the identity

$$\mathscr{S} = \tfrac{1}{2}(\mathscr{S} + \mathscr{S}^t) + \tfrac{1}{2}(\mathscr{S} - \mathscr{S}^t) \tag{13.9}$$

symm.   antisym.

The first parenthesis is clearly a symmetric tensor, and the second is an antisymmetric tensor. Equation 13.9 therefore exhibits explicitly the decomposition of $\mathscr{S}$ into symmetric and antisymmetric parts.

The symmetric tensor $\mathbf{\Sigma}$ defined by

$$\mathbf{\Sigma} = \tfrac{1}{2}(\mathscr{S} + \mathscr{S}^t) \tag{13.10}$$

is called the *strain tensor*. Its components are the thermodynamically relevant parameters for the description of the mechanical state of a solid system.

In Cartesian coordinates the strain tensor has the explicit form

$$
\mathbf{\Sigma} =
\begin{bmatrix}
\Sigma_{xx} & \Sigma_{xy} & \Sigma_{xz} \\
\Sigma_{xy} & \Sigma_{yy} & \Sigma_{yz} \\
\Sigma_{xz} & \Sigma_{yz} & \Sigma_{zz}
\end{bmatrix}
=
\begin{bmatrix}
\dfrac{\partial s_x}{\partial x} & \dfrac{1}{2}\left(\dfrac{\partial s_x}{\partial y} + \dfrac{\partial s_y}{\partial x}\right) & \dfrac{1}{2}\left(\dfrac{\partial s_x}{\partial z} + \dfrac{\partial s_z}{\partial x}\right) \\[2ex]
\dfrac{1}{2}\left(\dfrac{\partial s_x}{\partial y} + \dfrac{\partial s_y}{\partial x}\right) & \dfrac{\partial s_y}{\partial y} & \dfrac{1}{2}\left(\dfrac{\partial s_y}{\partial z} + \dfrac{\partial s_z}{\partial y}\right) \\[2ex]
\dfrac{1}{2}\left(\dfrac{\partial s_x}{\partial z} + \dfrac{\partial s_z}{\partial x}\right) & \dfrac{1}{2}\left(\dfrac{\partial s_y}{\partial z} + \dfrac{\partial s_z}{\partial y}\right) & \dfrac{\partial s_z}{\partial z}
\end{bmatrix}
\tag{13.11}
$$

Each of the components of this tensor can be given a simple pictorial significance. We note that if we ignore the antisymmetric part of $\mathscr{S}$ in equation 13.5, that equation becomes

$$d\mathbf{r}' = d\mathbf{r} + d\mathbf{r} \cdot \mathbf{\Sigma} \tag{13.12}$$

This equation is given a precise meaning by adopting a coordinate system that is rotated with the system; in such a coordinate system the antisymmetric portion of $\mathscr{S}$ vanishes and equation 13.12 is valid. In our discussion henceforth we adopt implicitly a locally rotated coordinate system.

The pictorial significance of the diagonal components of $\mathbf{\Sigma}$ is clarified by choosing $d\mathbf{r}$ in equation 13.12 to be of length dl and along the x-axis.

$$d\mathbf{r} = dl\mathbf{i} \tag{13.13}$$

Then, as shown in Figure 13.2, the vector $d\mathbf{r}'$ is

$$
\begin{aligned}
d\mathbf{r}' &= dl\mathbf{i} + dl\mathbf{i} \cdot \mathbf{\Sigma} \\
&= dl(1 + \Sigma_{xx})\mathbf{i} + dl\Sigma_{xy}\mathbf{j} + dl\Sigma_{xz}\mathbf{k}
\end{aligned}
\tag{13.14}
$$

The length of $d\mathbf{r}'$ is $\sqrt{d\mathbf{r}' \cdot d\mathbf{r}'}$, or

$$\ast \quad |d\mathbf{r}'| = dl\sqrt{(1 + \Sigma_{xx})^2 + \Sigma_{xy}^2 + \Sigma_{xz}^2} = dl(1 + \Sigma_{xx}) \tag{13.15}$$

in which the square root has been expanded to first order in the small quantities Σ_{xx}, Σ_{xy}, and Σ_{xz}. Thus *the tensor component Σ_{xx} is the fractional increase in length of an element initially parallel to the x-direction.* Similarly, the other diagonal elements of $\boldsymbol{\Sigma}$ measure the fractional stretching of elements along the y- and z-axes. These elements are called *linear dilatations.*

The off-diagonal elements of $\boldsymbol{\Sigma}$ are called *angular dilatations.* Consider the two elements $dl\mathbf{i}$ and $dl\mathbf{j}$ along the x- and y-axes in the fiducial state,

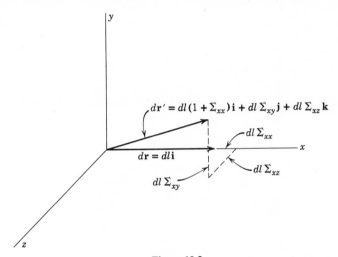

Figure 13.2

as shown in Figure 13.3. In the strained state the element $dl\mathbf{i}$ is transformed to

$$dl\mathbf{i} \rightarrow dl\mathbf{i} + dl\mathbf{i} \cdot \boldsymbol{\Sigma} = dl(1 + \Sigma_{xx})\mathbf{i} + dl\Sigma_{xy}\mathbf{j} + dl\Sigma_{xz}\mathbf{k} \quad (13.16)$$

and the element $dl\mathbf{j}$ is transformed to

$$dl\mathbf{j} \rightarrow dl\Sigma_{xy}\mathbf{i} + dl(1 + \Sigma_{yy})\mathbf{j} + dl\Sigma_{yz}\mathbf{k} \quad (13.17)$$

The cosine of the angle Θ_{xy} between these two elements is the scalar product divided by $(dl)^2$, or

$$\cos\Theta_{xy} = \Sigma_{xy}(1 + \Sigma_{xx}) + \Sigma_{xy}(1 + \Sigma_{yy}) + \Sigma_{xz}\Sigma_{yz} \quad (13.18)$$

or, to first order in the Σ's.

$$\cos\Theta_{xy} = 2\Sigma_{xy} \quad (13.19)$$

Now Θ_{xy} is very close to $\pi/2$, so that we introduce the small angle θ_{xy}, defined by

$$\theta_{xy} = \pi/2 - \Theta_{xy} \quad (13.20)$$

and, to first order in θ_{xy},

$$\cos \Theta_{xy} = \cos \left(\frac{\pi}{2} - \theta_{xy} \right) = \sin \theta_{xy} \simeq \theta_{xy}$$

whence

$$\gamma_{xy} = \theta_{xy} = 2\Sigma_{xy} \tag{13.21}$$

The off-diagonal element Σ_{xy} thereby is identified as half the decrease in the angle between two elements initially along the x- and y-axes. The other off-diagonal elements, Σ_{xz} and Σ_{yz}, have analogous interpretations.

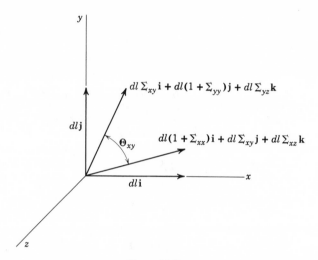

Figure 13.3

For convenience the following notation is generally introduced:

$$\Sigma_1 \equiv \Sigma_{xx} \tag{13.22}$$

$$\Sigma_2 \equiv \Sigma_{yy} \tag{13.23}$$

$$\Sigma_3 \equiv \Sigma_{zz} \tag{13.24}$$

$$\Sigma_4 \equiv 2\Sigma_{yz} \tag{13.25}$$

$$\Sigma_5 \equiv 2\Sigma_{xz} \tag{13.26}$$

$$\Sigma_6 \equiv 2\Sigma_{xy} \tag{13.27}$$

Thus Σ_1, Σ_2, and Σ_3 are fractional increases in x, y, and z directed elements respectively. And Σ_4, Σ_5, and Σ_6 are angular decreases in the yz-, the xz-, and the xy-angles, respectively. The six quantities Σ_i are referred to as *strain components*. Because of the factors of 2 introduced in equations

13.25–13.27, care must be taken to distinguish the strain components from the components of the strain tensor.

The strain components provide a complete description of the internal configuration in a solid system. However, the thermodynamic formalism requires that the basic parameters be extensive, and clearly the strain components are not. This difficulty is remedied in a trivial way by multiplying each strain component by the constant volume V_0 of the system in the fiducial state. Thus the six quantities $V_0\Sigma_i$ are extensive parameters of a solid system.

The thermodynamics of solid systems is completely analogous to that of fluid systems, with the six quantities $V_0\Sigma_i$ replacing the volume V.

In a general case the strain components are functions of position, varying from point to point within the solid. For our thermodynamic purposes we are interested only in homogeneous systems, for which the strain components are independent of position. We henceforth assume homogeneity without further comment.

In order to appreciate the relationship of elastic to fluid systems, it is interesting to compute the volume of a strained system. This is most easily done by considering a cube with edges $dl\mathbf{i}$, $dl\mathbf{j}$, and $dl\mathbf{k}$ in the fiducial state. This cube is distorted to a parallelepiped with edges such as those shown in Figure 13.3. It is left to a problem to show that the volume of this parallelepiped is, to first order in the Σ's,

$$\text{volume of parallelepiped} = (dl)^3(1 + \Sigma_1 + \Sigma_2 + \Sigma_3) \quad (13.28)$$

Thus the quantity $(\Sigma_1 + \Sigma_2 + \Sigma_3)$ is the fractional increase in any volume element in the system; it is called the *volume dilatation*. The actual volume of the strained sample is $\quad$ or $\quad \Delta V = V_0 \left(\varepsilon_{11} + \varepsilon_{22} + \varepsilon_{33} \right)$

$$V = V_0 + V_0\Sigma_1 + V_0\Sigma_2 + V_0\Sigma_3 \quad (13.29)$$

Thus the volume is simply related to the strain components, and equation 13.29 establishes a relation between the thermodynamics of strained solids and the simpler thermodynamics of fluids.

13.2 The Fundamental Equation

The fundamental equation of a homogeneously strained system is

$$S = S(U, V_0\Sigma_1, V_0\Sigma_2, V_0\Sigma_3, V_0\Sigma_4, V_0\Sigma_5, V_0\Sigma_6, N_1, N_2 \cdots) \quad (13.30)$$

or, in the energy representation,

$$U = U(S, V_0\Sigma_1, V_0\Sigma_2, V_0\Sigma_3, V_0\Sigma_4, V_0\Sigma_5, V_0\Sigma_6, N_1, N_2 \cdots) \quad (13.31)$$

The intensive parameters associated with the quantities $V_0 \Sigma_i$ are called *stress components* and are defined by

$$T_i \equiv \frac{1}{V_0}\left(\frac{\partial U}{\partial \Sigma_i}\right)_{S,\{\Sigma\}}$$ (13.32)

in which the subscript $\{\Sigma\}$ denotes constancy of all Σ_j other than Σ_i, and in which the subscripts denoting constancy of all the mole numbers have been omitted for simplicity.

The differential of the energy is

$$dU = T\,dS + T_1 d(V_0 \Sigma_1) + T_2 d(V_0 \Sigma_2) + T_3 d(V_0 \Sigma_3) + T_4 d(V_0 \Sigma_4)$$
$$+ T_5 d(V_0 \Sigma_5) + T_6 d(V_0 \Sigma_6) + \mu_1\,dN_1 + \mu_2\,dN_2 + \cdots \quad (13.33)$$

Before investigating the Maxwell relations and other consequences of the thermodynamic formalism, we shall develop the pictorial significance of the stress components in the next section.

13.3 The Stress Components

Among the various portions of material within a strained system there are mutual forces. These internal forces are associated with the strains just as the pressure is associated with the volume in a fluid system. We shall now develop a mathematical description of these internal forces, and we shall then show their relation to the stress components.

Consider a small tetrahedral figure arbitrarily located within the volume of the system, as shown in Figure 13.4. Three faces of this tetrahedron are assumed to be in coordinate planes. The area of the face that lies in the yz-plane is denoted by dA_x, and similarly for dA_y and dA_z. The fourth face has a normal in some arbitrary direction, characterized by the unit vector $\mathbf{v}$. We choose $\mathbf{v}$ as the inward-directed normal, so that $-\mathbf{v}$ is the outward-directed normal shown in Figure 13.4. The area of this face is denoted by dA_v.

The remainder of the system, outside the small tetrahedron, exerts forces on the tetrahedral subsystem. We assume that these forces are of two kinds—short range forces which act on the surfaces of the tetrahedron and long range forces which act directly on the body of the tetrahedron.

Let the force per unit area exerted on the x-face of the tetrahedron be $\mathbf{T}_x$, so that the actual force is $\mathbf{T}_x\,dA_x$. Similarly, the forces exerted on the other faces of the tetrahedron are $\mathbf{T}_y\,dA_y$, $\mathbf{T}_z\,dA_z$, and $\mathbf{T}_v\,dA_v$.

The force per unit area acting on the x-directed face, $\mathbf{T}_x$, has components T_{xx}, T_{xy}, and T_{xz}. The components T_{xx}, T_{yy}, and T_{zz} are normal forces per unit area, whereas T_{xy}, T_{xz}, T_{yx}, T_{yz}, T_{zx}, and T_{zy} are tangential forces per unit area.

The three components of $\mathbf{T}_\nu$ are $T_{\nu x}$, $T_{\nu y}$, and $T_{\nu z}$, but these are neither simply normal nor tangential forces per unit area.

A relation exists among all these components, so that $\mathbf{T}_\nu$ can be computed if $\mathbf{T}_x$, $\mathbf{T}_y$, and $\mathbf{T}_z$ are known. To find this relation, we write the condition of mechanical equilibrium: that the sum of all the forces acting on the system equals zero.

$$\mathbf{T}_x \, dA_x + \mathbf{T}_y \, dA_y + \mathbf{T}_z \, dA_z + \mathbf{T}_\nu \, dA_\nu = 0 \qquad (13.34)$$

In writing this equation we have taken account only of the short-range

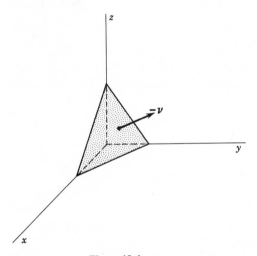

Figure 13.4

forces acting on the faces of the tetrahedron. The long-range forces, acting directly on the volume, are neglected because for a sufficiently small tetrahedron the volume-to-surface ratio becomes negligible.

It is clear from Figure 13.4 that dA_x is the projection of dA_ν on the yz-plane, whence

$$dA_x = (-\nu_x) \, dA_\nu \qquad (13.35)$$

in which ν_x is the x-component of the unit vector $\mathbf{\nu}$, and similarly for dA_y and dA_z. Thus

$$[-\mathbf{T}_x \nu_x - \mathbf{T}_y \nu_y - \mathbf{T}_z \nu_z + \mathbf{T}_\nu] \, dA_\nu = 0 \qquad (13.36)$$

or

$$\mathbf{T}_\nu = \mathbf{T}_x \nu_x + \mathbf{T}_y \nu_y + \mathbf{T}_z \nu_z \qquad (13.37)$$

By writing out the three scalar equations for the components of this equation and by comparison with the results of the row-by-column rule of matrix multiplication, the reader can corroborate that this equation can be written in the alternative form

$$\mathbf{T}_\nu = \mathbf{v} \cdot \mathscr{T} \tag{13.38}$$

in which $\mathbf{v}$ is a row-vector and $\mathscr{T}$ is the tensor with components T_{xx}, T_{xy}, T_{xz}, etc.

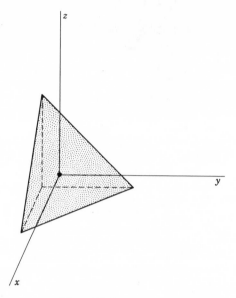

Figure 13.5

The quantity T_{xy} is the y-component of the force $\mathbf{T}_x$ which acts on a unit x-directed surface. The quantity T_{yx} is the x-component of the force $\mathbf{T}_y$ which acts on a unit y-directed surface. We now show that these quantities are equal, so that the tensor $\mathscr{T}$ is symmetric.

To show this symmetry property, it is convenient to select a particularly symmetric tetrahedron, with $(-\mathbf{v})$ along the body diagonal direction $[1/\sqrt{3},\, 1/\sqrt{3},\, 1/\sqrt{3}]$. Then $dA_x = dA_y = dA_z$. We select the point in the center of the $\mathbf{v}$-directed face as an origin, as shown in Figure 13.5. We compute the moments of all the forces around this point. As the tetrahedron is in rotational equilibrium, the sum of the moments must vanish. To the first order all the forces act at the centers of the respective faces. By the symmetry of the figure, all the moment arms are equal and may be omitted from the equations. The sum of the moments around the z-axis is

$$-T_{xy} + T_{yx} = 0 \tag{13.39}$$

Similarly, the sum of the moments around the x-axis is

$$T_{zy} - T_{yz} = 0 \tag{13.40}$$

and around the y-axis it is

$$-T_{zx} + T_{xz} = 0 \tag{13.41}$$

Thus the requirement of rotational equilibrium implies the symmetry of the tensor $\mathscr{T}$.

We now consider the work done in a small change in configuration. Again consider the symmetric tetrahedron, with the origin shifted to the center of the $\mathbf{v}$-directed face, as shown in Figure 13.5. Let the length of each of the edges parallel to the coordinate axes be dl, so that the volume of the tetrahedron is $\frac{1}{6}(dl)^3$. The center of the x-directed face is at the point $[-(dl/3), 0, 0]$. This face is displaced to the position given by equation 13.14. Or, if Σ_{xx} is changed by an amount $d\Sigma_{xx}$, etc, the displacement of the face is

$$\tfrac{1}{3}dl(d\Sigma_{xx}\mathbf{i} + d\Sigma_{xy}\mathbf{j} + d\Sigma_{xz}\mathbf{k}) = \tfrac{1}{3}dl(d\Sigma_1\mathbf{i} + \tfrac{1}{2}d\Sigma_6\mathbf{j} + \tfrac{1}{2}d\Sigma_5\mathbf{k}) \tag{13.42}$$

We have already seen that the force on the face is

$$\tfrac{1}{2}(dl)^2(T_{xx}\mathbf{i} + T_{xy}\mathbf{j} + T_{xz}\mathbf{k}) \tag{13.43}$$

so that the work done is

$$d(\text{work}) = \tfrac{1}{6}(dl)^3(T_{xx}\,d\Sigma_1 + \tfrac{1}{2}T_{xy}\,d\Sigma_6 + \tfrac{1}{2}T_{xz}\,d\Sigma_5) \tag{13.44}$$

The work done on all three faces of the tetrahedron (the displacements are taken relative to the origin so that no work is done on the $\mathbf{v}$-directed face) is then

$$d(\text{work}) = V_0(T_{xx}\,d\Sigma_1 + T_{yy}\,d\Sigma_2 + T_{zz}\,d\Sigma_3$$
$$+ T_{yz}\,d\Sigma_4 + T_{xz}\,d\Sigma_5 + T_{xy}\,d\Sigma_6) \tag{13.45}$$

Comparison of this equation with equation 13.33 identifies the stress components as being identical to the force components per unit area. In particular,

$$T_1 = T_{xx} \tag{13.46}$$

$$T_2 = T_{yy} \tag{13.47}$$

$$T_3 = T_{zz} \tag{13.48}$$

$$T_4 = T_{yz} \tag{13.49}$$

$$T_5 = T_{xz} \tag{13.50}$$

$$T_6 = T_{xy} \tag{13.51}$$

With this pictorial interpretation of the intensive parameters as force components per unit area, we return to the thermodynamic formalism.

13.4 Maxwell Relations

We recall that the fundamental equation of an elastic system is

$$U = U(S, V_0\Sigma_1 \cdots V_0\Sigma_6, N_1, N_2 \cdots) \tag{13.52}$$

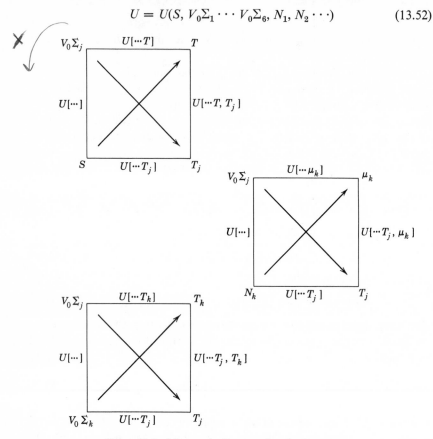

Figure 13.6 Mnemonic diagrams for elastic systems.

and the energy differential is

$$dU = T\,dS + V_0 T_1\,d\Sigma_1 + \cdots + V_0 T_6\,d\Sigma_6$$
$$+ \mu_1\,dN_1 + \mu_2\,dN_2 + \cdots \tag{13.53}$$

The equations of state are

$$T = T(S, V_0\Sigma_1 \cdots V_0\Sigma_6, N_1, N_2 \cdots) \tag{13.54}$$
$$T_i = T_i(S, V_0\Sigma_1 \cdots V_0\Sigma_6, N_1, N_2 \cdots) \tag{13.55}$$
$$\mu_j = \mu_j(S, V_0\Sigma_1 \cdots V_0\Sigma_6, N_1, N_2 \cdots) \tag{13.56}$$

$$U = TS * V_0 \left(\sigma_{ij}\, \epsilon_{ij} \right) + \mu_i N_i$$

As U is a homogeneous first-order function of the extensive parameters, the Euler relation implies that

✳ $U = TS + T_1 V_0 \Sigma_1 + \cdots + T_6 V_0 \Sigma_6 + \mu_1 N_1 + \mu_2 N_2 + \cdots$ (13.57)

The Gibbs–Duhem relation, which implies a relation among the intensive parameters, follows from a comparison of equation 13.53 with the differential of equation 13.57.

✳ $S\, dT + V_0 \Sigma_1\, dT_1 + \cdots + V_0 \Sigma_6\, dT_6 + N_1\, d\mu_1 + \cdots = 0$ (13.58)

Various Legendre transforms of U can be defined. A typical transform, arbitrarily selected, is

$$U[T, T_2, T_5] \equiv U - TS - T_2 V_0 \Sigma_2 - T_5 V_0 \Sigma_5 \qquad (13.59)$$

The natural variables of this function are T, $V_0 \Sigma_1$, T_2, $V_0 \Sigma_3$, $V_0 \Sigma_4$, T_5, $V_0 \Sigma_6$, N_1, $N_2 \cdots$. Obviously, a huge number of such transforms can be defined, and each can be a useful function in some particular situation. The Maxwell relations follow from the equality of the mixed partial derivatives of U and of its various Legendre transforms. These relations can be read from the mnemonic diagrams of Figure 13.6. In those diagrams $U[\cdots]$ indicates some Legendre transform of U, and $U[\cdots T_j]$ is $U[\cdots] - T_j V_0 \Sigma_j$. It is assumed that $U[\cdots]$ has not already been transformed with respect to T_j.

The first mnemonic diagram in Figure 13.6 exhibits the interaction of strain and entropy or of stress and temperature. It yields the relations

$$\frac{1}{V_0} \left(\frac{\partial T}{\partial \Sigma_j} \right)_S = \left(\frac{\partial T_j}{\partial S} \right)_{\Sigma_j} \qquad (13.60)$$

$$V_0 \left(\frac{\partial \Sigma_j}{\partial T} \right)_{T_j} = \left(\frac{\partial S}{\partial T_j} \right)_T \qquad (13.61)$$

$$V_0 \left(\frac{\partial \Sigma_j}{\partial S} \right)_{T_j} = - \left(\frac{\partial T}{\partial T_j} \right)_S \qquad (13.62)$$

and

$$\frac{1}{V_0} \left(\frac{\partial S}{\partial \Sigma_j} \right)_T = - \left(\frac{\partial T_j}{\partial T} \right)_{\Sigma_j} \qquad (13.63)$$

In these derivatives the variables which are held constant are those which are explicitly indicated as subscripts plus all the remaining natural variables of $U[\cdots]$.

The second diagram in Figure 13.6 exhibits the interaction of strains and mole numbers or of stresses and electrochemical potentials. It yields relations similar to equations 13.60–13.63, with T replaced by μ_k and S

replaced by N_k. These relations are useful in the analysis of the effect of elastic strains on diffusion in solid systems.

The third diagram in Figure 13.6 exhibits the interaction of two strain components or of two stress components. One of the four relations obtained from this diagram is

$$\left(\frac{\partial T_k}{\partial \Sigma_j}\right)_{\Sigma_k} = \left(\frac{\partial T_j}{\partial \Sigma_k}\right)_{\Sigma_j} \tag{13.64}$$

and, according to the choice of $U[\cdots]$, this relation may be either at constant S or at constant T.

The importance of this equality becomes evident in the next section.

We now proceed to define the analogues of the quantities κ_T, α, c_v, and c_P.

13.5   The Elastic Coefficients

The *isothermal elastic stiffness coefficients* are defined by

$$c_{ij} = \left(\frac{\partial T_i}{\partial \Sigma_j}\right)_{T,\{\Sigma\}} \tag{13.65}$$

where again the subscript $\{\Sigma\}$ denotes constancy of all Σ_k other than Σ_j, and where constant mole numbers are to be understood implicitly. These coefficients are the analogues of the isothermal bulk modulus $-V(\partial P/\partial V)_T$ of a fluid system.

According to the Maxwell relation (equation 13.64), we find that c_{ij} is symmetric in its indices.

$$c_{ij} = c_{ji} \tag{13.66}$$

Since both i and j can take six values, there are nominally thirty-six stiffness coefficients, but the symmetry relations 13.66 reduces the number of independent coefficients to twenty-one.

The *isothermal elastic compliance coefficients* are defined by

$$\kappa_{ji} = \left(\frac{\partial \Sigma_j}{\partial T_i}\right)_{T,\{T\}} \tag{13.67}$$

The subscript $\{T\}$ now denotes constancy of all T_j other than T_i. The appropriate Maxwell relation from Figure 13.6 gives

$$\kappa_{ji} = \kappa_{ij} \tag{13.68}$$

and again there are twenty-one independent compliance coefficients.

The isothermal elastic compliance coefficients are analogues of the isothermal compressibility κ_T for a fluid system.

The bulk modulus and the isothermal compressibility of a fluid system are simply the reciprocals of each other. Similarly the 6×6 matrix of the stiffness coefficients and the 6×6 matrix of the compliance coefficients are reciprocals. That is, multiplication of these two matrices by the row-by-column rule gives a unit matrix, with zeros as off-diagonal elements and unity as each diagonal element.

A simple algebraic statement of the relation between the stiffness and compliance coefficients, which makes no reference to matrix theory, is obtained as follows. We consider a stress component as a function of temperature, strains, and mole numbers; such an equation results from elimination of S between two equations of state (13.54) and (13.55).

$$T_i = T_i(T, V_0 \Sigma_1 \cdots V_0 \Sigma_6, N_1, N_2 \cdots) \tag{13.69}$$

The differential of this equation at constant temperature and mole numbers is

$$dT_i = \sum_{k=1}^{6} c_{ik} \, d\Sigma_k \qquad (T, N_1, N_2 \cdots \text{constant}) \tag{13.70}$$

The inverse equations are, by definition of the isothermal compliance coefficients,

$$d\Sigma_k = \sum_{i=1}^{6} \kappa_{ki} \, dT_i \qquad (T, N_1, N_2 \cdots \text{constant}) \tag{13.71}$$

Therefore we need only solve the simultaneous linear equations (13.70) for $d\Sigma_k$ and compare with equation 13.71 to obtain the relationship of the c_{ik} and κ_{ki} coefficients. It is a standard result of the algebra of linear equations that

$$\kappa_{ki} = \frac{\text{cofactor of } c_{ik}}{\text{determinant of the } c\text{'s}} \tag{13.72}$$

Here the cofactor and determinant refer to the 6×6 matrix of the stiffness coefficients.

The thermodynamic stability criteria, as discussed in Chapter 7, clearly require that the determinant of the elastic coefficients be positive and nonzero. We return to a more explicit investigation of this requirement at the end of section 13.6.

13.6 Consequences of Physical Symmetry—Cubic and Isotropic Systems

Although there are generally twenty-one independent elastic coefficients, any physical symmetry in the system reduces this number further. As an example, we consider a system with cubic symmetry; the alkali halides

Na(Cl, KBr, etc.), many simple oxides (MnO, Fe_3O_4, etc.), several metals (Cu, Al, Pb, Fe, etc.), and a very large number of other common substances crystallize in the cubic system. For such a system any cyclic permutation $x \rightarrow y \rightarrow z \rightarrow x$ leaves the system invariant. The system is also invariant under reflections in the coordinate planes or under the transformations $x \rightarrow -x$, $y \rightarrow -y$, or $z \rightarrow -z$. And finally the system is invariant under the interchange of two coordinates, such as $x \rightleftharpoons y$, $x \rightleftharpoons z$, or $y \rightleftharpoons z$. These transformations completely describe the symmetry of a cubic system and enable us to find all the relations among the stiffness coefficients in a cubic system.

The most obvious consequence of cubic symmetry is

$$c_{11} \equiv \frac{\partial T_{xx}}{\partial \Sigma_{xx}} = \frac{\partial T_{yy}}{\partial \Sigma_{yy}} = c_{22} \tag{13.73}$$

which results from the transformation $x \rightarrow y \rightarrow z \rightarrow x$. Similarly, we have

$$c_{11} = c_{22} = c_{33} \tag{13.74}$$

Consider now the coefficient c_{61} and make the transformation $y \rightarrow -y$.

$$c_{61} \equiv \frac{\partial T_{xy}}{\partial \Sigma_{xx}} = \frac{\partial T_{x-y}}{\partial \Sigma_{xx}} = -\frac{\partial T_{xy}}{\partial \Sigma_{xx}} = -c_{61} \tag{13.75}$$

In this equation we use the fact that T_{x-y} is the component of $\mathbf{T}_x$ along the $-y$-direction, which is clearly $-T_{xy}$. Equation 13.75 immediately implies that

$$c_{61} = 0 \tag{13.76}$$

By similar transformations it is found that the 6×6 matrix of elastic stiffness coefficients reduces to a matrix with only three independent components. The stiffness matrix for a cubic system is

$$\begin{bmatrix} c_{11} & c_{12} & c_{12} & 0 & 0 & 0 \\ c_{12} & c_{11} & c_{12} & 0 & 0 & 0 \\ c_{12} & c_{12} & c_{11} & 0 & 0 & 0 \\ 0 & 0 & 0 & c_{44} & 0 & 0 \\ 0 & 0 & 0 & 0 & c_{44} & 0 \\ 0 & 0 & 0 & 0 & 0 & c_{44} \end{bmatrix} \tag{13.77}$$

Values of c_{11}, c_{12}, and c_{44} for several common cubic substances are listed in Table 13.1.

Although cubic symmetry is the highest form of symmetry any crystalline solid can have, a noncrystalline amorphous solid can be completely isotropic.

An isotropic system is invariant under any rotational transformation of the coordinate system. It is left to a problem to show that the stiffness matrix then has only two independent parameters. These parameters are conventionally taken as the *Lamé constants* λ_L and μ_L, in terms of which the stiffness matrix is

$$
\begin{bmatrix}
2\mu_L + \lambda_L & \lambda_L & \lambda_L & 0 & 0 & 0 \\
\lambda_L & 2\mu_L + \lambda_L & \lambda_L & 0 & 0 & 0 \\
\lambda_L & \lambda_L & 2\mu_L + \lambda_L & 0 & 0 & 0 \\
0 & 0 & 0 & \mu_L & 0 & 0 \\
0 & 0 & 0 & 0 & \mu_L & 0 \\
0 & 0 & 0 & 0 & 0 & \mu_L
\end{bmatrix}
\tag{13.78}
$$

Table 13.1

ISOTHERMAL ELASTIC STIFFNESS COEFFICIENTS OF CUBIC CRYSTALS
(At room temperature unless otherwise stated)
Stiffness Coefficient in 10^{12}dynes/cm^2

Crystal	c_{11}	c_{12}	c_{44}
Na (210°K)	0.055	0.042	0.049
K	0.046	0.037	0.026
Fe	2.37	1.41	1.16
Ni (demag)	2.50	1.60	1.185
W	5.01	1.98	1.15
Cu	1.684	1.214	0.754
Cu (10°K)	1.762	1.249	0.818
Diamond	9.2	3.9	4.3
Si	1.66	0.64	0.79
Ge	1.29	0.48	0.67
Al	1.08	0.62	0.28
Pb	0.48	0.41	0.14
LiF	1.19	0.54	0.53
NaCl	0.486	0.127	0.128
KCl	0.40	0.062	0.062
NaBr	0.33	0.13	0.13
KBr	0.35	0.058	0.050
KI	0.27	0.043	0.042
AgCl	0.60	0.36	0.062
AgBr	0.56	0.33	0.073

From *Introduction to Solid State Physics*, by C. Kittel, 2nd Edition, John Wiley and Sons, New York, 1956.

By inversion of this matrix the compliance matrix can be written in the form

$$
\left\{
\begin{array}{cccccc}
\dfrac{1}{E_Y} & -\dfrac{\sigma_Y}{E_Y} & -\dfrac{\sigma_Y}{E_Y} & 0 & 0 & 0 \\[2ex]
-\dfrac{\sigma_Y}{E_Y} & \dfrac{1}{E_Y} & -\dfrac{\sigma_Y}{E_Y} & 0 & 0 & 0 \\[2ex]
-\dfrac{\sigma_Y}{E_Y} & -\dfrac{\sigma_Y}{E_Y} & \dfrac{1}{E_Y} & 0 & 0 & 0 \\[2ex]
0 & 0 & 0 & 2\dfrac{1+\sigma_Y}{E_Y} & 0 & 0 \\[2ex]
0 & 0 & 0 & 0 & 2\dfrac{1+\sigma_Y}{E_Y} & 0 \\[2ex]
0 & 0 & 0 & 0 & 0 & 2\dfrac{1+\sigma_Y}{E_Y}
\end{array}
\right\} \qquad (13.79)
$$

The quantities E_Y and σ_Y are called *Young's modulus* and *Poisson's ratio*, respectively, and the inversion of matrix 13.78 to matrix 13.79 shows that

$$
E_Y = \frac{\mu_L(3\lambda_L + 2\mu_L)}{\lambda_L + \mu_L} \qquad (13.80)
$$

and

$$
\sigma_Y = \frac{\lambda_L}{2(\lambda_L + \mu_L)} \qquad (13.81)
$$

Conversely

$$
\lambda_L = \frac{\sigma_Y E_Y}{(1 + \sigma_Y)(1 - 2\sigma_Y)} \qquad (13.82)
$$

$$
\mu_L = \frac{E_Y}{2(1 + \sigma_Y)} \qquad (13.83)
$$

The pictorial significance of Young's modulus and of Poisson's ratio follows directly from equation 13.71 and matrix 13.79. Consider that a stress increment dT_1 is applied along the x-axis and that all other stresses vanish. Then in an isotropic system the resultant strain increments are

$$
d\Sigma_1 = \frac{1}{E_Y} dT_1 \qquad (13.84)
$$

$$
d\Sigma_2 = d\Sigma_3 = -\frac{\sigma_Y}{E_Y} dT_1 \qquad (13.85)
$$

and

$$d\Sigma_4 = d\Sigma_5 = d\Sigma_6 = 0 \qquad (13.86)$$

Thus $1/E_Y$ is the fractional stretch per unit stress, parallel to that stress, and σ_Y is the ratio of the lateral contraction to the longitudinal stretch (i.e.: $\sigma_Y = -d\Sigma_2/d\Sigma_1$).

The stability criteria require that each of the principal minors of the determinant of elastic coefficients be positive (equation G.30). For cubic systems we thereby obtain the stability conditions

$$c_{11} > 0 \qquad (13.87)$$

$$c_{44} > 0 \qquad (13.88)$$

$$c_{11}{}^2 > c_{12}{}^2 \qquad (13.89)$$

and

$$c_{11} + 2c_{12} > 0 \qquad (13.90)$$

Problems—Section 13.6

13.6–1. Show that the stiffness matrix of a cubic system has the form given in equation 13.77.

13.6–2. By inverting the stiffness matrix of a cubic system, show that the compliance matrix has a similar form and that

$$\kappa_{11} = \frac{c_{11} + c_{12}}{(c_{11} - c_{12})(c_{11} + 2c_{12})}$$

$$\kappa_{12} = -\frac{c_{12}}{(c_{11} - c_{12})(c_{11} + 2c_{12})}$$

$$\kappa_{44} = \frac{1}{c_{44}}$$

13.6–3. Show that for a cubic system

$$c_{11} = \frac{\kappa_{11} + \kappa_{12}}{(\kappa_{11} - \kappa_{12})(\kappa_{11} + 2\kappa_{12})}$$

$$c_{12} = -\frac{\kappa_{12}}{(\kappa_{11} - \kappa_{12})(\kappa_{11} + 2\kappa_{12})}$$

$$c_{44} = \frac{1}{\kappa_{44}}$$

13.6–4. Show that the isothermal compressibility

$$\kappa_T \equiv -\frac{1}{V}\left(\frac{\partial V}{\partial P}\right)_T$$

of a cubic crystal is

$$\kappa_T = \frac{3}{c_{11} + 2c_{12}}$$

13.6-5. Express the isothermal compressibility κ_T of an isotropic solid in terms of Young's modulus and Poisson's ratio.

13.6-6. By applying equation G.30 to the determinant 13.77, prove equations 13.87–13.90.

13.6-7. What restrictions are imposed on the Lamé constants by the stability criteria? What restrictions are imposed on Young's modulus and Poisson's ratio?

13.7 Coefficients of Thermal Strain and Stress

The analogues of the coefficient of thermal expansion α are the six coefficients of thermal strain, defined by

$$\alpha_i \equiv \left(\frac{\partial \Sigma_i}{\partial T}\right)_{\{T\}} \tag{13.91}$$

Similarly the analogues of the quantity $(\partial P/\partial T)_V$ are the six coefficients of thermal stress.

$$\beta_i \equiv \left(\frac{\partial T_i}{\partial T}\right)_{\{\Sigma\}} \tag{13.92}$$

For a simple fluid system we have

$$\left(\frac{\partial P}{\partial T}\right)_V = -\left(\frac{\partial V}{\partial T}\right)_P \bigg/ \left(\frac{\partial V}{\partial P}\right)_T = \frac{\alpha}{\kappa_T} \tag{13.93}$$

or

$$\alpha = \kappa_T \left(\frac{\partial P}{\partial T}\right)_V \tag{13.94}$$

This suggests a similar relationship among the α_i, the κ_i, and the β_i. Consider the relation

$$\Sigma_i = \Sigma_i(T, T_1 \cdots T_6, N_1, N_2 \cdots) \tag{13.95}$$

obtained by eliminating S and five of the strain components from the seven equations of state 13.54 and 13.55. The first differential of equation 13.95, at constant mole numbers, is

$$d\Sigma_i = \left(\frac{\partial \Sigma_i}{\partial T}\right)_{\{T\}} dT + \sum_j \left(\frac{\partial \Sigma_i}{\partial T_j}\right)_{T,\{T\}} dT_j = \alpha_i\, dT + \sum_j \kappa_{ij}\, dT_j \tag{13.96}$$

Dividing by dT, at constant strains, gives

$$\alpha_i = -\sum_j \kappa_{ij}\beta_j \tag{13.97}$$

which is completely analogous to equation 13.92.
It is left to the reader to show also that

$$\beta_j = -\sum_i c_{ji}\alpha_i \tag{13.98}$$

The low temperature behavior of the coefficients of thermal strain and stress are determined by the Nernst postulate. The entropy must vanish at zero temperature, for all states of stress, so that ✓   How does th

$$\left(\frac{\partial S}{\partial T_k}\right)_{T,\{T\}} \to 0 \qquad \text{as} \qquad T \to 0 \tag{13.99}$$

or, by the appropriate Maxwell relation (Figure 13.6),

$$\alpha_k = \left(\frac{\partial \Sigma_k}{\partial T}\right)_{\{T\}} \to 0 \qquad \text{as} \qquad T \to 0 \tag{13.100}$$

Similarly,

$$\left(\frac{\partial S}{\partial \Sigma_k}\right)_{T,\{\Sigma\}} \to 0 \qquad \text{as} \qquad T \to 0 \tag{13.101}$$

whence

$$\beta_k = \left(\frac{\partial T_k}{\partial T}\right)_{\{\Sigma\}} \to 0 \qquad \text{as} \qquad T \to 0 \tag{13.102}$$

This type of reasoning can be extended to apply to the elastic coefficients. Since S must vanish for all Σ's at $T = 0$, we have

$$\left(\frac{\partial^2 S}{\partial \Sigma_j \, \partial \Sigma_k}\right)_{T,\{\Sigma\}} \to 0 \qquad \text{as} \qquad T \to 0 \tag{13.103}$$

whence

$$\frac{\partial}{\partial \Sigma_j}\left(\frac{\partial T_k}{\partial T}\right)_{\{\Sigma\}} = \frac{\partial}{\partial T}\left(\frac{\partial T_k}{\partial \Sigma_j}\right)_{T,\{\Sigma\}} \to 0 \qquad \text{as} \qquad T \to 0 \tag{13.104}$$

and

$$\frac{\partial c_{kj}}{\partial T} \to 0 \qquad \text{as} \qquad T \to 0 \tag{13.105}$$

The elastic constants consequently approach constant values, with vanishing slope on a plot of c_{kj} versus T.

Problems—Section 13.7

13.7–1. Discuss the behavior of the compliance coefficients near zero temperature.

13.8   Specific Heats

The analogue of the specific heat at constant volume is the *specific heat at constant strain.*

$$c_{\{\Sigma\}} \equiv \frac{T}{N}\left(\frac{\partial S}{\partial T}\right)_{\{\Sigma\}} \tag{13.106}$$

Similarly the analogue of the specific heat at constant pressure is the *specific heat at constant stress.*

$$c_{\{T\}} \equiv \frac{T}{N}\left(\frac{\partial S}{\partial T}\right)_{\{T\}} \tag{13.107}$$

Various other specific heats with constant mixed combinations of strain and stress components can also be defined, but equations 13.106 and 13.107 are by far the most important.

For a fluid system we have the relation

$$c_P = c_v + \frac{TV\alpha^2}{N\kappa_T} \tag{13.108}$$

and we may expect a similar relation for elastic systems. To obtain this equation, we consider the entropy as a function of the temperature, strains, and mole numbers; an equation obtained by inversion of the equation of state (13.54).

$$S = S(T, V_0\Sigma_1 \cdots V_0\Sigma_6, N_1, N_2 \cdots) \tag{13.109}$$

The differential at constant mole numbers is

$$dS = \frac{N}{T} c_{\{\Sigma\}} \, dT + \sum_i \left(\frac{\partial S}{\partial \Sigma_i}\right)_{T,\{\Sigma\}} d\Sigma_i \tag{13.110}$$

and dividing through by dT, at constant stresses,

$$c_{\{T\}} = c_{\{\Sigma\}} - \frac{T}{N}\sum_i \left(\frac{\partial S}{\partial \Sigma_i}\right)_{T,\{\Sigma\}} \alpha_i \tag{13.111}$$

By the Maxwell relation 13.63, this becomes

$$c_{\{T\}} = c_{\{\Sigma\}} - Tv\sum_i \beta_i\alpha_i \tag{13.112}$$

Either the α's or the β's can be eliminated from this equation by equation 13.97 or 13.98.

By reasoning strictly analogous to that in equations 10.1–10.4, we find that both specific heats $c_{\{\Sigma\}}$ and $c_{\{T\}}$ approach zero as T approaches zero.

$$c_{\{\Sigma\}} \to 0 \quad \text{as} \quad T \to 0 \tag{13.113}$$

$$c_{\{T\}} \to 0 \quad \text{as} \quad T \to 0 \tag{13.114}$$

Furthermore, by equation 13.112, the difference of the specific heats approaches zero very rapidly.

13.9 Other Coefficients

We have now seen how analogues of κ_T, α, c_v, and c_P are defined for elastic systems, and we have seen that the relations among such coefficients for fluid systems have their counterparts for elastic systems.

As a final illustration of the strict analogy, we consider the *adiabatic stiffness coefficients.*

$$c_{ij}^{(S)} \equiv \left(\frac{\partial T_i}{\partial \Sigma_j}\right)_{S,\{\Sigma\}} \tag{13.115}$$

These coefficients are the analogues of the adiabatic bulk modulus $-V(\partial P/\partial V)_{S,N}$ of a fluid system.

When an elastic wave propagates in an elastic solid, the restoring forces are determined by the stiffness coefficients. At low frequencies the appropriate coefficients are the isothermal stiffness coefficients, but at higher frequencies the adiabatic coefficients become appropriate. This shift produces a dispersion of elastic waves, or a dependence of velocity on frequency. It is clear that the application of the stiffness coefficients to the propagation of elastic waves is not properly a subject of equilibrium thermodynamics, and we merely note this application in passing.

For a fluid system the adiabatic bulk modulus is related to the isothermal bulk modulus by the relation

$$-V\left(\frac{\partial P}{\partial V}\right)_{S,N} = -V\left(\frac{\partial P}{\partial V}\right)_{T,N} + \frac{VT}{Nc_v}\left[\left(\frac{\partial P}{\partial T}\right)_{V,N}\right]^2 \tag{13.116}$$

The analogous equation can be obtained by considering T_i as a function of temperature, strains, and mole numbers

$$T_i = T_i(T, V_0\Sigma_1 \cdots V_0\Sigma_6, N_1, N_2 \cdots) \tag{13.117}$$

The differential at constant mole numbers is

$$dT_i = \left(\frac{\partial T_i}{\partial T}\right)_{\{\Sigma\}} dT + \sum_j \left(\frac{\partial T_i}{\partial \Sigma_j}\right)_{T,\{\Sigma\}} d\Sigma_j \tag{13.118}$$

Dividing through by $d\Sigma_k$ and keeping the entropy and all other strains constant gives

$$\left(\frac{\partial T_i}{\partial \Sigma_k}\right)_{S,\{\Sigma\}} = \left(\frac{\partial T_i}{\partial T}\right)_{\{\Sigma\}}\left(\frac{\partial T}{\partial \Sigma_k}\right)_{S,\{\Sigma\}} + \left(\frac{\partial T_i}{\partial \Sigma_k}\right)_{T,\{\Sigma\}} \tag{13.119}$$

or

$$c_{ik}^{(S)} = \beta_i\left(\frac{\partial T}{\partial \Sigma_k}\right)_{S,\{\Sigma\}} + c_{ik} \tag{13.120}$$

whence, using the standard manipulation of partial derivatives,

$$c_{ik}^{(S)} = c_{ik} - \beta_i\frac{(\partial S/\partial \Sigma_k)_{T,\{\Sigma\}}}{(\partial S/\partial T)_{\{\Sigma\}}} \tag{13.121}$$

Now, by employing the Maxwell relation 13.63, we obtain

$C_{ij}k\ell$
$$c_{ik}^{(S)} = c_{ik} + \frac{Tv_0\beta_i\beta_k}{c_{\{\Sigma\}}}$$ (13.122)

The procedure we have followed in this derivation will be recognized as precisely that outlined in section 7.3. The entropies are brought to the numerators (in equation 13.121) and eliminated by the Maxwell relations or as specific heats in the standard fashion. The reader should recognize at this point that the formalism for elastic systems has many more variables than the formalism for fluid systems but that the procedures nevertheless are completely parallel. Because of the large number of variables, the Jacobian techniques described in section 7.5 are particularly convenient. The application of Jacobians to elastic systems has been described by Ting and Li [*Phys. Rev.* **106**, 1165 (1957)].

Problems—Section 13.9

13.9-1. Show that

$$\frac{c_{\{T\}}}{c_{\{\Sigma\}}} = \frac{\text{determinant of the } c^{(S)}\text{'s}}{\text{determinant of the } c\text{'s}}$$

in which the numerator is the determinant of the 6 × 6 matrix of adiabatic stiffness coefficients and the denominator is the determinant of the 6 × 6 matrix of isothermal stiffness coefficients.

13.10   Hooke's Equation of State

The stress components, being intensive parameters, are functions of the entropy, the strain components, and the mole numbers. It is more convenient to consider the Helmholtz potential representation in which the stress components are functions of the temperature, the strain components, and the mole numbers.

Suppressing the mole numbers in the notation,

$$F = U - TS = F(T, V_0\Sigma_1, V_0\Sigma_2 \cdots V_0\Sigma_6)$$ (13.123)

and

$$T_j = \left(\frac{\partial F}{\partial(V_0\Sigma_j)}\right)_{T,\{\Sigma\}} = T_j(T, V_0\Sigma_1, V_0\Sigma_2 \cdots V_0\Sigma_6)$$ (13.124)

Consider the series expansion of T_j in powers of the strain components Σ_k. The constant term vanishes because the stresses have been so defined as to vanish in the unstrained state. *For the magnitudes of strains that are usually of practical interest all terms of higher order than linear in the expansion are negligibly small.* Thus we can write

$$T_j = \sum_{k=1}^{6} c_{jk} \Sigma_k \qquad (13.125)$$

and the isothermal elastic coefficients c_{jk} can be considered as functions of the temperature only, independent of the strain. This equation is known as Hooke's law, or the Hooke equation of state.

The differential of the Helmholtz potential (again at constant mole numbers) is

$$dF = -S\,dT + V_0 \sum_{1}^{6} T_j\,d\Sigma_j \qquad (13.126)$$

The entropy is frequently independent of the strain, although this is by no means a universal rule. Assuming that this is true, and integrating, gives

$$F = F_0(T) + \tfrac{1}{2} V_0 \sum_{i,j=1}^{6} c_{ij} \Sigma_i \Sigma_j \qquad (13.127)$$

Here $F_0(T)$ is the entropy in the unstrained state—it is a function of T only. Equation 13.127 is the basic equation commonly used for the analysis of "normal" elastic systems.

We have introduced the Hooke law only at the conclusion of this chapter in order to stress that the general thermodynamics of elasticity is quite independent of this particular form of equation of state.

Problems—Section 13.10

13.10–1. Show that for a cubic system obeying Hooke's law, and with a strain-independent entropy,

$$F = F_0(T) + \tfrac{1}{2} c_{11}[\Sigma_1{}^2 + \Sigma_2{}^2 + \Sigma_3{}^2] + \tfrac{1}{2} c_{44}[\Sigma_4{}^2 + \Sigma_5{}^2 + \Sigma_6{}^2] + c_{12}[\Sigma_1\Sigma_2 + \Sigma_2\Sigma_3 + \Sigma_3\Sigma_1]$$

CHAPTER 14

Magnetic
and Electric Systems

14.1 Magnetic Extensive and Intensive Parameters

If matter is acted on by a magnetic field, it generally develops a magnetic moment. A description of this magnetic property, and of its interaction with thermal and mechanical properties, requires the adoption of an additional extensive parameter. This additional extensive parameter X and its corresponding intensive parameter P are to be chosen so that the *magnetic work* dW_{mag} is

$$dW_{\mathrm{mag}} = P\,dX \tag{14.1}$$

where

$$dU = dQ + dW_M + dW_c + dW_{\mathrm{mag}} \tag{14.2}$$

Here dQ is the heat $T\,dS$, dW_M is the mechanical work (e.g., $-P\,dV$), and dW_c is the chemical work $\Sigma \mu_j\,dN_j$. We now consider a specific situation which clearly indicates the appropriate choice of parameters X and P.

Consider a solenoid, or coil, as shown in Figure 14.1. The wire of which the solenoid is wound is assumed to have zero electrical resistance (superconducting). A battery is connected to the solenoid, and the electromotive force (emf) of the battery is adjustable at will. The thermodynamic system is inside the solenoid, and the solenoid is enclosed within an adiabatic wall.

If no changes occur within the system, and if the current I is constant, the battery need supply no emf because of the perfect conductivity of the wire.

Let the current be I and let the local magnetization of the thermodynamic system be $\mathbf{M(r)}$. The current I can be altered at will by controlling the battery emf. The magnetization $\mathbf{M(r)}$ then will change also. We assume that the magnetization at any position $\mathbf{r}$ is a single-valued function of the current

$$\mathbf{M(r)} = \mathbf{M}(\mathbf{r}; I) \tag{14.3}$$

Systems for which $\mathbf{M}(\mathbf{r}; I)$ is not single valued in I are said to exhibit

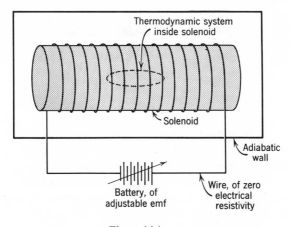

Figure 14.1

hysteresis; most ferromagnetic systems have this property. Hysteresis generally is associated with a magnetic heterogeneity of the sample, the separate regions being known as domains. The analysis we shall develop is generally applicable *within* a ferromagnetic domain, but for simplicity we explicitly exclude all hysteretic systems. Paramagnetic, diamagnetic, and antiferromagnetic systems satisfy the requirement that $\mathbf{M}(\mathbf{r}; I)$ is single-valued in I.

If the thermodynamic system were *not* within the solenoid, the current I would produce a magnetic field $\mathbf{H}_e(I)$. This *external field* may be a function of position within the solenoid, but it is linear in I. That is

$$\mathbf{H}_e = \mathbf{h}I \tag{14.4}$$

where $\mathbf{h}$ is a vector function of position.

We suppose that the current is increased, thereby increasing the external field H_e. The magnetic moment changes in response. In order to accomplish these changes, the battery must deliver work, and we seek the relationship between the work done and the changes in H_e and M.

The rate at which work is done by the battery is given by

$$\frac{dW_{\text{mag}}}{dt} = I \times (\text{voltage}) \tag{14.5}$$

in which (voltage) denotes the back emf induced in the solenoid windings by the changes that occur within the coil.

The induced emf in the solenoid arises from two sources. One source is independent of the thermodynamic system and results from a change in the flux associated with the field H_e. Rather than compute this flux and voltage, we can write the resultant contribution to dW_{mag} directly. For an empty solenoid the work is just the change in the energy of the magnetic field, or

$$dW_{\text{mag}} = d\left(\frac{\mu_o}{8\pi} \int H_e^2 \, dV\right) \tag{14.6}$$

in which μ_o is the permittivity of free space and in which the integral is taken over the entire volume of the solenoid.

The second contribution to dW_{mag} results from the thermodynamic system itself and consequently is of more direct interest to us.

To compute the contribution of the thermodynamic system to the induced voltage, and thence to dW_{mag}/dt, we follow a discussion given by Pippard.*

We know that the induced voltage arises from changes in the magnetic moment of the system. Two principles are then invoked: first, that the change of magnetic moment of each infinitesimal element of the system contributes separately and additively to the total induced emf; and, second, that the induced emf produced by any change in dipole moment depends not on the nature of the dipole but only on the rate of change of its moment and on its position in the solenoid. Consider then a particular model of an elementary dipole at the position r; a small current loop of area a and current i, with a magnetic moment of $m = ia$. If the current in the solenoid is I, the field produced by the solenoid at the point r is $H_e(r) = h(r)I$. This field produces a flux linkage through the small current loop of magnitude $\mu_o h(r) \cdot aI$, where μ_o is the permittivity of free space. Thus the mutual inductance between solenoid and current

---

* A. B. Pippard, *The Elements of Classical Thermodynamics*, Cambridge University Press, 1957.

loop is $\mu_o \mathbf{h}(\mathbf{r}) \cdot \mathbf{a}$. If the current in the current loop changes, it consequently induces a voltage in the solenoid given by

$$(\text{voltage}) = (\mu_o \mathbf{h}(\mathbf{r}) \cdot \mathbf{a}) \frac{di}{dt} \tag{14.7}$$

$$= \mu_o \mathbf{h}(\mathbf{r}) \cdot \frac{d\mathbf{m}}{dt} \tag{14.8}$$

$$= \mu_o \frac{1}{I} \mathbf{H}_e(\mathbf{r}) \cdot \frac{d\mathbf{m}}{dt} \tag{14.9}$$

Thus the work done by the battery is

$$\frac{dW_{\text{mag}}}{dt} = \mu_o \mathbf{H}_e(\mathbf{r}) \cdot \frac{d\mathbf{m}}{dt} \tag{14.10}$$

Although this result has been obtained for a particular model of an elementary dipole, it holds for any change in elementary dipole moment. In particular, if $\mathbf{M}(\mathbf{r})$ is the *magnetization*, or the dipole moment per unit volume in the system, at the point $\mathbf{r}$, we set

$$\mathbf{m} = \mathbf{M}(\mathbf{r}) \, dV \tag{14.11}$$

To obtain the total work, we sum over all elementary dipoles, or integrate over the volume of the sample.

$$\frac{dW_{\text{mag}}}{dt} = \mu_o \int \mathbf{H}_e \cdot \frac{d\mathbf{M}}{dt} \, dV \tag{14.12}$$

Adding the two contributions to the magnetic work, we find

$$dW_{\text{mag}} = d\left(\frac{\mu_o}{8\pi} \int H_e^2 \, dV \right) + \mu_o \int (\mathbf{H}_e \cdot d\mathbf{M}) \, dV \tag{14.13}$$

This is the fundamental result on which the thermodynamics of magnetic systems is based.

Two alternative ways of writing the magnetic work are of interest. The two terms in equation 14.13 can be consolidated in the form

$$dW_{\text{mag}} = \frac{1}{4\pi} \int \mathbf{H}_e \cdot d\mathbf{B}_e \, dV \tag{14.14}$$

where

$$\mathbf{B}_e = \mu_o \mathbf{H}_e + 4\pi\mu_o \mathbf{M} \tag{14.15}$$

The quantity $\mathbf{B}_e$ is a rather peculiar hybrid quantity: the sum of the *external* field $\mathbf{H}_e$ (*not* the local field $\mathbf{H}$) and of the local magnetization, each multiplied by appropriate factors.

The *local* field $\mathbf{H}$ may be introduced in place of the *external* field $\mathbf{H}_e$

by noting that the difference $\mathbf{H} - \mathbf{H}_e$ is just the field produced by the magnetization $\mathbf{M}(\mathbf{r})$ acting as a magnetostatic source. In this way it can be shown* that

$$dW_{\text{mag}} = \frac{1}{4\pi} \int \mathbf{H} \cdot d\mathbf{B} \, dV \tag{14.16}$$

where $\mathbf{H}$ and $\mathbf{B}$ are the *local* values of field and induction, respectively.

The form of the magnetic work expression we shall find most convenient is the first derived (equation 14.13) which expresses dW_{mag} in terms of the external field and the magnetization.

In the general case the magnetization $\mathbf{M}(\mathbf{r})$ will vary from point to point within the system, even if the external field $\mathbf{H}_e$ is constant. This variation may arise from inherent inhomogeneities in the properties of the system, or it may result from demagnetization effects of the boundaries of the system. We wish to develop the theory for homogeneous systems. We therefore assume that $\mathbf{H}_e$ is constant and that the intrinsic properties of the system are homogeneous. We further assume that the system is ellipsoidal in shape. For such a system the magnetization $\mathbf{M}$ is independent of position, as shown in any text on magnetostatics.

The magnetic work equation can now be written as

$$dW_{\text{mag}} = d\left(\frac{\mu_o}{8\pi} \int H_e^2 \, dV\right) + \mu_o \mathbf{H}_e \cdot d\mathbf{I} \tag{14.17}$$

where $\mathbf{I}$ is the total magnetic dipole moment of the system

$$\mathbf{I} = \int \mathbf{M} \, dV = \mathbf{M}V \tag{14.18}$$

The energy differential is

$$dU = T \, dS - P \, dV + d\left(\frac{\mu_o}{8\pi} \int H_e^2 \, dV\right) + \mu_o \mathbf{H}_e \cdot d\mathbf{I} + \sum_1^r \mu_j \, dN_j \tag{14.19}$$

The third term on the right of the foregoing equation does not involve the thermodynamic system itself but arises only from the magnetostatic energy of the empty solenoid. Consequently it is convenient to absorb this term into the definition of the energy. We define a new energy,

$$U' = U - \frac{\mu_o}{8\pi} \int H_e^2 \, dV \tag{14.20}$$

so that U' is the total energy contained within the solenoid relative to the state in which the system is removed to its field free fiducial state and the solenoid is left with the field $\mathbf{H}_e$. This redefinition of the internal

---

* See V. Heine, *Proc. Cambridge Phil. Soc.*, **52**, 546 (1956).

energy does not alter any of the formalism of thermodynamics, and we shall reinterpret all of our previous results in this fashion. Thus we write

$$dU' = T\,dS - P\,dV + \mu_o H_e\,dI_H + \sum_1^r \mu_j\,dN_j \qquad (14.21)$$

where I_H is the component of **I** parallel to $\mathbf{H}_e$.

The extensive parameter descriptive of the magnetic properties of a system is I_H, the component of the total magnetic moment parallel to the external field. The intensive parameter in the energy representation is $\mu_o H_e$.

The fundamental equation is

$$U' = U'(S, V, I_H, N_1 \cdots N_r) \qquad (14.22)$$

and

$$\left(\frac{\partial U'}{\partial I_H}\right)_{S,V,N_1\cdots N_r} = \mu_o H_e \qquad (14.23)$$

14.2 Electric Extensive and Intensive Parameters

If a system is subjected to an external electric field, it generally develops an electric moment. To obtain the extensive and intensive parameters appropriate for the characterization of the electric properties, we consider a system between the plates of a capacitor, as shown in Figure 14.2.

We may consider the capacitor connected to a variable battery, as in Figure 14.2a, or permanently charged, with mechanically movable plates, as in Figure 14.2b. In order to change the field, we may then alter the emf of the battery or move the plates. In either case work must be done, and it is this work which we shall calculate. It is recommended that the student recast the argument in a form appropriate for each of the situations in Figure 14.2, thereby observing the equivalence of considerations based on the work done by a battery and the work done by a mechanical agent.

By considerations similar to those used in the magnetic case, we find that the work is composed of two terms. The first applies to the empty capacitor, and the second arises from the interaction of the electric polarization $\mathbf{P}(\mathbf{r})$ with the external field $\mathbf{E}_e(\mathbf{r})$.

$$dW_{\text{elect.}} = d\left(\frac{\epsilon_0}{8\pi}\int E_e^2\,dV\right) + \int \mathbf{E}_e \cdot d\mathbf{P}\,dV \qquad (14.24)$$

Assuming constant external field, homogeneity, and ellipsoidal sample shape gives

$$dW_{\text{elect.}} = d\left(\frac{\epsilon_0}{8\pi}\int E_e^2\,dV\right) + \mathbf{E}_e \cdot d\mathscr{P} \qquad (14.25)$$

where $\mathscr{P}$ is the total electric dipole moment of the system

$$\mathscr{P} = \int \mathbf{P}\, dV = \mathbf{P}V \tag{14.26}$$

Again we redefine the energy

$$U' = U - \frac{\epsilon_0}{8\pi} \int E_e^2\, dV \tag{14.27}$$

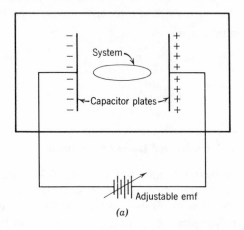

(a)

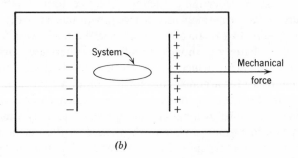

(b)

Figure 14.2

and we obtain

$$dU' = T\, dS - P\, dV + E_e\, d\mathscr{P}_E + \sum_1^r \mu_j\, dN_j \tag{14.28}$$

where $\mathscr{P}_E$ is the component of $\mathscr{P}$ parallel to $\mathbf{E}_e$.

The extensive parameter descriptive of the electrical properties of a system is $\mathscr{P}_E$, *the component of the total electric moment parallel to the external field. The intensive parameter in the energy representation is the external field* E_e.

The fundamental equation is

$$U' = U'(S, V, \mathscr{P}_E, N_1 \cdots N_r) \tag{14.29}$$

and

$$\left(\frac{\partial U'}{\partial \mathscr{P}_E}\right)_{S,V,N_1 \cdots N_r} = E_e \tag{14.30}$$

Because of the close analogy between electric and magnetic systems, we discuss only magnetic systems in further detail.

14.3 Magnetic Free Energies and Maxwell Relations

For a simple nonmagnetic system we recall the thermodynamic criteria of equilibrium; if the system is closed, the energy is minimum, whereas if the system is in contact with a pressure reservoir the enthalpy is minimum. What are the magnetic analogues of these equilibrium criteria?

Consider the system of Figure 14.2. Let us suppose that when the current is I the battery is short-circuited inside the adiabatic wall, and the battery is disconnected. The adiabatic wall can then be considered as completely restrictive, and the entire system is closed. The criterion of equilibrium is the minimization of the energy.

To find the analogue of an open system, we again consider Figure 14.1, and we introduce a device which automatically adjusts the battery to maintain the current in the solenoid constant. This device might be a simple feed-back system from an ammeter in the circuit to the control knob of the battery. The thermodynamic system then finds itself at constant intensive parameter $\mu_o H_e$, which is analogous to constant pressure for the simple system. We may say that the system is in contact with a *magnetic field reservoir*.

We define the *magnetic enthalpy* $U'[H_e]$ by

$$U'[H_e] \equiv U' - \mu_o H_e I_H \tag{14.31}$$

Then *the magnetic enthalpy is minimum in equilibrium for a system in contact with a magnetic field reservoir (i.e., in constant external field).*

Various other Legendre transforms can be defined in a straightforward fashion. As a particular example, consider the combined transform to pressure and field $U'[P, H_e]$

$$U'[P, H_e] = U' + PV - \mu_o H_e I_H \tag{14.32}$$

For this function we have, analogous to equation 6.41,

$$dU'[P, H_e] = T \, dS = dQ, \quad \text{at constant } P, H_e \text{ and mole numbers} \tag{14.33}$$

Consequently, $U'[P, H_e]$ is the "heat function," which acts as a potential for heat flow. It is the analogue of the enthalpy for simple systems.

As in equations 6.43–6.46, we can find the heat input in any process at constant P and H_e by computing the difference in $U'[P, H_e]$. Consider a system in constant magnetic field and constant pressure. We ask how much heat must be put into the system to decrease its magnetic moment from the initial value I_{Hi} to the final value I_{Hf}. The function $U'[P, H_e]$ is a function of S, P, H_e and the mole numbers:

$$U'[P, H_e] = \psi(S, P, H_e, N_1 \cdots N_r) \tag{14.34}$$

The magnetic moment is also a function of these parameters

$$I_H = \frac{\partial U'[P, H_e]}{\partial H_e} = I_H(S, P, H_e, N_1 \cdots N_r) \tag{14.35}$$

Elimination of S between these two equations permits us to replace S by I_H as independent variable.

$$U'[P, H_e] = \phi(I_H, P, H_e, N_1 \cdots N_r) \tag{14.36}$$

The total heat input required in the process is

$$\int dQ = \phi(I_{Hf}, P, H_e, N_1 \cdots N_r) - \phi(I_{Hi}, P, H_e, N_1 \cdots N_r) \tag{14.37}$$

The equality of the mixed second derivatives of the various Legendre transforms gives rise to many Maxwell relations, analogous to those discussed in Chapter 5.

Some relevant forms of the thermodynamic mnemonic diagram are given below.

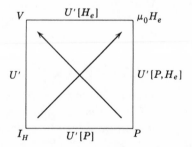

Transforms with respect to P and H_e:

$$\left(\frac{\partial V}{\partial I_H}\right)_{S,P} = \mu_o \left(\frac{\partial H_e}{\partial P}\right)_{S,I_H} \tag{14.38}$$

$$\left(\frac{\partial I_H}{\partial P}\right)_{S,H_e} = \frac{-1}{\mu_o} \left(\frac{\partial V}{\partial H_e}\right)_{S,P} \tag{14.39}$$

etc.

If each of the potentials in the above diagram is further transformed with respect to T, we obtain a very similar diagram, but the Maxwell relations are then at constant temperature rather than at constant entropy.

$$\left(\frac{\partial V}{\partial I_H}\right)_{T,P} = \mu_o \left(\frac{\partial H_e}{\partial P}\right)_{T,I_H} \tag{14.40}$$

$$\left(\frac{\partial I_H}{\partial P}\right)_{T,H_e} = \frac{-1}{\mu_o} \left(\frac{\partial V}{\partial H_e}\right)_{T,P} \tag{14.41}$$

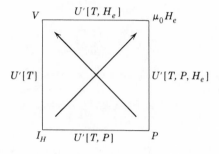

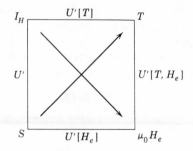

Transforms with respect to T and H_e:

$$\left(\frac{\partial S}{\partial I_H}\right)_{V,T} = - \mu_o \left(\frac{\partial H_e}{\partial T}\right)_{V,I_H} \tag{14.42}$$

$$\left(\frac{\partial T}{\partial I_H}\right)_{V,S} = \mu_o \left(\frac{\partial H_e}{\partial S}\right)_{V,I_H} \tag{14.43}$$

Various other diagrams can be written, and the corresponding Maxwell relations can be read off in straightforward fashion.

14.4 Specific Heats—Magnetic Susceptibility

The various differential coefficients which are the magnetic analogues of c_P, c_v, α, and κ_T are of considerable interest. We shall also be interested in the relations among these quantities, analogous to the now familiar relation

$$c_P - c_v = Tv\alpha^2/\kappa_T \qquad (14.44)$$

The specific heat of a magnetic material can be measured with constant values of any two of the four variables P, V, H_e, I_H. The two specific heats of greatest interest are

$$c_{P,I_H} \equiv T\left(\frac{\partial s}{\partial T}\right)_{P,I_H} \qquad (14.45)$$

and

$$c_{P,H_e} \equiv T\left(\frac{\partial s}{\partial T}\right)_{P,H_e} \qquad (14.46)$$

The magnetic analogue of the isothermal compressibility is the *isothermal susceptance*

$$\kappa_{T,P} \equiv \frac{1}{V}\left(\frac{\partial I_H}{\partial H_e}\right)_{T,P} = \left(\frac{\partial M_H}{\partial H_e}\right)_{T,P} \qquad (14.47)$$

Two points should be noted carefully. First, we have *not* assumed that M_H is linearly related to H_e; on the contrary, the susceptance is an arbitrary function of H_e, T, and P. The simplification of linearity, in which $\kappa_{T,P}$ is assumed to be independent of H_e, is discussed later in connection with approximate equations of state. The second point to be noted is that the susceptance $\kappa_{T,P}$ is different from the susceptibility $\chi_{T,P}$, which is defined in terms of the *local* field.

$$\chi_{T,P} = \left(\frac{\partial M_H}{\partial H}\right)_{T,P} \qquad (14.48)$$

In an ellipsoidal sample the local field is given in terms of the *demagnetization coefficients* N_x, N_y, and N_z, which depend on the ratios of the lengths of the ellipsoidal axes. If the x-, y-, and z-axes are parallel to the ellipsoidal axes, the components of the external and local fields are related by the equations

$$H_x = H_{ex} - N_x M_x, \qquad H_y = H_{ey} - N_y M_y, \qquad H_z = H_{ez} - N_z M_z \qquad (14.49)$$

Then, if H_e is parallel to the x-axis,

$$\frac{1}{\kappa_{T,P}} = \frac{1}{\chi_{T,P}} + N_x \qquad (14.50)$$

Finally, the analogue of the coefficient of thermal expansion is the derivative $(\partial I_H/\partial T)_{P,H_e}$. No special symbol is commonly associated with this derivative, and we shall not adopt one here.

As in equations 7.61–7.65, the reader should derive the analogue of equation 14.44:

$$c_{P,I_H} - c_{P,H_e} = -\frac{T\mu_o}{NV\kappa_{T,P}}\left(\frac{\partial I_H}{\partial T}\right)^2_{P,H_e} \tag{14.51}$$

In addition to the foregoing differential coefficients, there are various others which are of frequent interest but which need not be discussed explicitly. Selection of the proper quantity to characterize a given experimental situation sometimes is fairly delicate. We illustrate this in one case.

Measurement of the susceptance is conveniently accomplished by varying the external field sinusoidally and detecting the sinusoidal variation in I_H by a pick-up coil around the sample. If the system is in contact with a temperature reservoir, the isothermal susceptance $\kappa_{T,P}$ is observed. If, however, the frequency of the sinusoidal variation is increased, we may arrive at a situation in which the flow of heat between system and reservoir cannot occur rapidly enough to maintain the temperature constant. In fact, at extremely high frequency the observed susceptance approaches the adiabatic susceptance $\kappa_{P,S}$. The ratio of these two susceptibilities is easily shown to be equal to the ratio of the specific heats

$$\frac{\kappa_{P,T}}{\kappa_{P,S}} = \frac{c_{P,H_e}}{c_{P,I_H}} \tag{14.52}$$

The Nernst theorem requires that each of the specific heats approach zero as the temperature approaches zero. Also $\partial\kappa_{P,T}/\partial T$ must approach zero, or $\kappa_{P,T}$ must become independent of T.

Problems—Section 14.4

14.4–1. Prove equation 14.50. Find the relation between $\kappa_{T,P}$ and $\chi_{T,P}$ if the external field has an arbitrary direction relative to the ellipsoidal axes of the sample.

14.4–2. Prove equation 14.51.

14.4–3. Prove equation 14.52.

14.5 Magnetic Equations of State

The magnetic properties of real systems are most commonly described in terms of the dependence of the susceptibility $\chi_{T,P}$ on temperature, pressure, and external field (we suppress the mole numbers throughout).

$$\chi_{T,P} = \chi_{T,P}(T, P, H_e) \tag{14.53}$$

Equation 14.50 permits this information to be transcribed into the functional dependence of $\kappa_{T,P}$:

$$\kappa_{T,P} = \kappa_{T,P}(T, P, H_e) \equiv \left(\frac{\partial M_H}{\partial H_e}\right)_{T,P} \tag{14.54}$$

Integration of this equation would yield

$$M_H = M_H(T, P, H_e) \tag{14.55}$$

Thus knowledge of $\chi_{T,P}(T, P, H_e)$ is essentially equivalent to knowledge of an equation of state.

We shall describe the functional dependence of $\chi_{T,P}$ as it is observed for various common magnetic materials.

Materials can be classified magnetically into two classes.

1. Diamagnetic Materials

Examples: Alkali halides (e.g., LiBr, NaCl); aromatic crystals (e.g., benzene, anthracene); certain metals (e.g., bismuth, gamma-brass).

The susceptibility $\chi_{T,P}$ of the nonmetallic diamagnetics is negative, small ($\simeq 10^{-6}$/mole), and almost independent of the magnetic field. It depends on temperature and pressure only in that it is proportional to the density (or inversely proportional to the molar volume). Thus, by equation E.6,

$$\chi_{T,P} \simeq \frac{\chi^{\circ}_{T,P}}{1 - \alpha(T - T_0) + \kappa_T P} \simeq \chi^{\circ}_{T,P}(1 + \alpha(T - T_0) - \kappa_T P) \tag{14.56}$$

The metallic diamagnetics display similar behavior at ordinary temperatures, but in the low-temperature region $\chi_{T,P}$ varies strongly with temperature and oscillates violently with small changes in magnetic field. This dramatic low-temperature phenomenon is called the deHaas-van Alphen effect.

2. Paramagnetic Materials

Examples: Salts of transition and rare earth elements (e.g., $CoCl_2$, $FeSO_4$, Gd_2O_3); most metals (e.g., Na, Mo, W, Pt); and, at sufficiently high temperatures, any material which is not diamagnetic.

The susceptibility $\chi_{T,P}$ of the nonmetallic paramagnetics is positive, of the order of 10^{-2}–10^{-3}/mole, and is almost independent of the field except at very high values of field. The dependence on temperature and pressure frequently can be expressed by the equation

$$\chi_{T,P} = \frac{\text{constant}}{v}\frac{1}{T-\theta} \tag{14.57}$$

where θ is a constant. Here v is the molar volume, which depends on T and P by the relation

$$v = v_0(1 + \alpha(T - T_0) + \kappa_T P) \tag{14.58}$$

However the temperature and pressure dependence of v is so small in comparison with the explicit temperature dependence in equation 14.58 that it is usually sufficient to ignore the variation of v and to write the so-called *Curie-Weiss law*.

$$\chi_{T,P} = \frac{C}{T-\theta} \tag{14.59}$$

The Curie constants C and θ are given for a number of paramagnetics in Table 14.1.

Table 14.1

PROPERTIES OF PARAMAGNETIC MATERIALS

Constants in Curie–Weiss Law,
$\chi_{T,P}$ (cgs magnetic moment/
mole oersted) $= C/(T - \theta)$

Substance	C	θ, °K	Néel or Curie Temperature, °K	Type below Néel or Curie Temperature
$CoCl_2$	3.19	−48	25	Antiferro.
C_2Cl_2	2.97	−116	40	Antiferro.
$CuCl_2$	0.457	−52	70	Antiferro.
FeF_2	3.88	−117	79	Antiferro.
$FeSO_4$	3.60	−39	23	Antiferro.
MnO	4.90	−680	116	Antiferro.
MnO_2	1.80	−480	90	Antiferro.
Fe	1.23	1093	1043	Ferro.
Ni	0.402	538	631	Ferro.
Co	1.24	1400	1400	Ferro.
$MnOFe_2O_3$	–	–	783	Ferri.
$FeOFe_2O_3$	–	–	848	Ferri.
$NiOFe_2O_3$	–	–	863	Ferri.

At low temperatures the Curie–Weiss law is used to define the "starred temperature" which was discussed in section 4.10. Thus measurement of the susceptibility of a paramagnetic salt is the standard way to measure very low temperatures. We shall see in section 14.6 that paramagnetic salts are also used to obtain very low temperatures.

The paramagnetic metals exhibit a much more complex temperature dependence than the nonmetals. Even the sign of the temperature dependence alternates from element to element in the periodic sequence of the transition metals. No simple equation has been devised to represent the temperature dependence of the susceptibility of the paramagnetic metals.

All paramagnetic materials undergo a phase transition at sufficiently low temperature. Such a phase transition is required by the Nernst theorem, for it can be shown by statistical mechanical methods that the entropy of a paramagnetic system would not vanish at zero temperature. Thus the reader can easily check that the Curie–Weiss law does not conform to the requirement that $\partial \chi_{T,P}/\partial T$ approach zero as T approaches zero.

One type of phase transition consists of an order-disorder transition of the electron spins. The temperature of such a phase transition is called the Néel or Curie temperature. Above this temperature, the electronic spins are disordered in direction, but below the Néel or Curie temperature the spin directions have some particular ordered arrangement. The material is then *ferromagnetic, antiferromagnetic,* or *ferrimagnetic,* depending on the specific pattern of spin order.

A second type of phase transition introduces order in the momentum distribution of the electrons rather than in the spin directions. This type of transition, which occurs in many metals and alloys, gives rise to the phenomenon of *superconductivity.*

We describe briefly each of the three types of spin ordering and return to a consideration of superconductivity in section 14.7.

3. Antiferromagnetic Materials

The antiferromagnetic materials have such arrangements of the electronic spins that the net magnetic moment in the ordered state is zero. Examples are $CoCl_2$, CuO, FeS, and MnO. Materials that are antiferromagnetic below their Néel temperature have negative Curie–Weiss constants above the Néel temperature (in the paramagnetic region). This can be checked in Table 14.1. Néel temperatures are also given in this table.

The susceptibility of antiferromagnetic materials below the Néel temperature is anisotropic. There exists a particular direction in the crystal along which the electron spins align. The susceptibility measured parallel to this axis is smaller than that measured perpendicular to this axis. The susceptibility of antiferromagnetic materials is typified by that of MnF_2, shown in Figure 14.3.

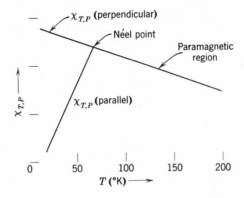

Figure 14.3   Susceptibility of MnF_2 in the antiferromagnetic and para-magnetic regions. After Griffel and Stout. From *Introduction to Solid State Physics* by C. Kittel, 2nd edition, John Wiley and Sons, New York, 1956.

4. Ferromagnetic Materials

The electronic spins in ferromagnetic materials align parallel, leading to a net magnetization in the ordered state, even in the absence of an external field. Examples are Fe, Ni, $La_{1/3}Sr_{1/3}MnO_3$.

The simplest analytic approximation to the magnetic equation of state is the *Langevin–Weiss equation*:

$$M_H(T, H) = M_0 \coth \frac{M_0 v_0 (H + \lambda M_H)}{RT} - \frac{RT}{v_0(H + \lambda M_H)} \quad (14.60)$$

in which M_0 is the magnetization at $H = T = 0$, v_0 is the molar volume at $T = 0°$, H is the internal field, R is the gas constant, and λ is a constant characteristic of the particular material. Equation 14.60 is an implicit equation for M_H and is solved most conveniently by graphical methods. The dependence of M_H on T and H is shown in Figure 14.4.

Various improved expressions, representing the magnetization more accurately than the Langevin–Weiss equation, have been given, but the Langevin–Weiss equation is sufficient for our general illustrative purposes.

The Langevin–Weiss equation is valid only within a single domain. Except under carefully controlled conditions, ferromagnetic materials break up into magnetic domains, and the net magnetization is the resultant of the inhomogeneous contributions from many domains. In such cases the sample exhibits hysteresis and consequently is excluded from the considerations of this chapter.

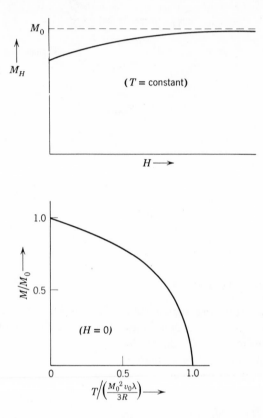

Figure 14.4   The Langevin-Weiss equation of state for ferromagnetic materials.

5. Ferrimagnetic Materials

The electronic spins in ferrimagnetic materials align in such a way that some spins are antiparallel to others but such that incomplete cancellation of their moments occurs. These materials consequently show net magnetic moments similar to, but generally smaller than, those of the ferromagnetic materials. Examples are the *ferrites* (e.g., Fe_3O_4, $MnFe_2O_4$) and the *garnets* (e.g., $Y_3Fe_5O_{12}$).

The dependence of the magnetization on T and H within a domain is qualitatively similar to that of ferromagnetics. However, an adequate representation requires a more complicated expression than the simple Langevin–Weiss equation.

Like the ferromagnetics, the ferrimagnetic materials generally exhibit hysteresis, and thermodynamic theory must be applied with caution.

Problems—Section 14.5

14.5-1. For a sphere the demagnetization coefficients are $N_x = N_y = N_z = 4\pi/3$. Find the magnetic equation of state of a spherical paramagnetic system that obeys the Curie–Weiss law (equation 14.59).

14.5-2. For a thin plate the demagnetization coefficients are $N_x = N_y = 0$, $N_z = 4\pi$. Find the magnetic equation of state of a thin plate that obeys the Curie–Weiss law if the magnetic field is perpendicular to the plate. Compare this with the case in which the magnetic field is parallel to the plate.

14.5-3. Discuss the T^* method of measuring low temperatures, particularizing to a paramagnetic salt that obeys the equation $\chi_{T,P} = C/T$ down to the temperature T_0. (See section 4.10.)

14.6 The Magnetocaloric Effect

The coupling between the thermal and magnetic properties of paramagnetic materials gives rise to the magnetocaloric effect. This effect is a decrease in temperature produced by an adiabatic decrease in the applied field. The process is known as *adiabatic demagnetization*, and it is the most convenient method of cooling in the very low temperature region (below $1°K$).

The standard technique of magnetic cooling consists of suspending a small sample of paramagnetic salt, and the sample to be cooled, in a vessel containing gaseous helium at low pressure. This vessel in turn is immersed in a bath of liquid helium, which is cooled to $1°K$ or so by other methods. The magnetic field is then turned on, and the helium gas ensures thermal equilibrium between the liquid helium and the samples. The gaseous helium is then pumped out, thermally isolating the samples from the environment. The magnetic field is decreased to a small value, and the samples are cooled to a very low temperature by the magnetocaloric effect. Any residual helium gas surrounding the samples condenses, and the samples can be maintained at the low temperature for appreciable periods if care is taken to minimize the thermal conductivity of the threads which suspend the samples.

Consider a system in the applied field H_e and at temperature T. Let the applied field be changed to $H_e + dH_e$ quasi-statically and adiabatically. Then the change in temperature dT will be

$$dT = \left(\frac{\partial T}{\partial H_e}\right)_{S,P} dH_e \qquad (14.61)$$

By the appropriate Maxwell relation, this becomes

$$dT = -\mu_o \left(\frac{\partial I_H}{\partial S}\right)_{H_e,P} dH_e \qquad (14.62)$$

$$dT = -\mu_o \left[\left(\frac{\partial I_H}{\partial T}\right)_{H_e,P} \Big/ \left(\frac{\partial S}{\partial T}\right)_{H_e,P}\right] dH_e \qquad (14.63)$$

$$dT = -\frac{\mu_o T v}{c_{P,H_e}} \left(\frac{\partial M_H}{\partial T}\right)_{H_e,P} dH_e \qquad (14.64)$$

where we have neglected the small temperature dependence of v. The derivative $(\partial M_H/\partial T)_{H_e,P}$ can be evaluated from the magnetic equation of state. For the paramagnetic and antiferromagnetic materials we have seen that $\chi_{T,P}$, hence $\kappa_{T,P}$ also, is almost independent of H_e. For these materials we can then write

$$M_H = \kappa_{T,P} H_e \qquad (14.65)$$

and equation 14.64 becomes

$$dT = -\frac{\mu_o T v H_e}{c_{P,H_e}} \frac{\partial \kappa_{T,P}}{\partial T} dH_e \qquad (14.66)$$

For ferromagnetic materials the derivative in equation 14.64 would have to be evaluated from the magnetic equation of state 14.60, and equation 14.65 would not be a valid simplification.

If the paramagnetic material satisfies the Curie–Weiss law (equation 14.59), we find

$$dT = \frac{\mu_o T v H_e}{c_{P,H_e}} \frac{\chi_{T,P}^2}{C} dH_e \qquad (14.67)$$

where we have assumed that the susceptibility is so small in comparison with the reciprocal of the demagnetization factor (which is necessarily less than 4π) that the distinction between $\chi_{T,P}$ and $\kappa_{T,P}$ can be ignored. (See equation 14.50.)

In order to evaluate equation 14.67 explicitly, we would have to know the specific heat c_{P,H_e} as a function of temperature and field. This is equivalent to an additional equation of state. The empirical temperature dependence of c_{P,H_e} at zero field is obtainable from Figure 14.5 for chromium methylamine alum, a typical salt used for magnetic cooling. The dependence of c_{P,H_e} on magnetic field can be found by noting that

$$\left(\frac{\partial c_{P,H_e}}{\partial H_e}\right)_{T,P} = \frac{T}{N} \frac{\partial^2 S}{\partial H_e \, \partial T} = \frac{T\mu_o}{N} \frac{\partial^2 I_H}{\partial T^2} = v T \mu_o H_e \frac{\partial^2 \kappa_{T,P}}{\partial T^2} \qquad (14.68)$$

where we have inverted the order of differentiation, used the appropriate

Maxwell relation, and assumed $\kappa_{T,P}$ to be independent of H_e. Again ignoring the distinction between $\kappa_{T,P}$ and $\chi_{T,P}$, and invoking the Curie–Weiss law, we find

$$\left(\frac{\partial c_{P,H_e}}{\partial H_e}\right)_{T,P} = \frac{2CTv\mu_o}{(T-\theta)^3} H_e \tag{14.69}$$

and integrating with respect to H_e gives

$$c_{P,H_e}(T, H_e) = c_{P,H_e}(T, 0) + \frac{CTv\mu_o}{(T-\theta)^3} H_e^2 \tag{14.70}$$

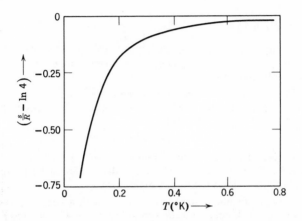

Figure 14.5 Entropy at zero field of chromium methylamine alum. The specific heat at zero field is the derivative of this curve. After DeKlerk and Steenland. From *Progress in Low Temperature Physics*, edited by C. J. Gorter, North Holland Publishing Company, 1955.

The quantity $c_{P,H_e}(T, 0)$ is obtainable from Figure 14.5. In the temperature region of interest $c_{P,H_e}(T, 0)$ is approximately given by

$$c_{P,H_e}(T, 0) = \frac{B}{T^2} \tag{14.71}$$

in which B is a constant. Also, for this salt, $\theta \simeq 0$, so that insertion of equations 14.70 and 14.71 in equation 14.67 gives

$$\frac{dT}{T} = \frac{\mu_o CvH_e}{B + \mu_o CvH_e^2} dH_e \tag{14.72}$$

Integrating,

$$\ln \frac{T_f}{T_i} = \frac{1}{2} \ln \frac{B + \mu_o CvH_{ef}^2}{B + \mu_o CvH_{ei}^2} \tag{14.73}$$

This equation is the explicit solution for the final temperature. It can be simplified further if the applied field H_e is sufficiently large that the terms in B can be neglected, whence

$$\frac{T_f}{T_i} = \frac{H_{ef}}{H_{ei}} \tag{14.74}$$

Convenient initial temperatures are of the order of $1°K$—these being obtainable by pumping on liquid helium. Conveniently obtainable initial magnetic fields are of the order of 10,000 oersteds. In this way final temperatures of the order of $10^{-3°}K$ are obtainable with salts chosen to have small values of θ.

Problems—Section 14.6

14.6–1. Using equation 14.70, show that the specific heat at constant magnetization c_{P,I_H} of a paramagnetic salt that obeys the Curie–Weiss law is a function of T only, independent of H_e.

14.6–2. For cerium magnesium nitrate the Curie constant C has a value of $0.318 \text{ cm}^3°K/\text{gram ion}$, and the Curie constant θ is zero. The specific heat c_{P,H_e}, in the temperature range $T > 0.006°K$, is

$$c_{P,H_e}(T, 0) = 7.5 \times 10^{-6} R/T^2$$

A sample of this salt is at an initial temperature of $1°K$ and an initial field of 10,000 oersteds. The sample is adiabatically demagnetized by turning off the external field entirely. Find the final temperature.

14.6–3. A paramagnetic system is in contact with a heat reservoir at temperature T. How much heat does the system exchange with the reservoir when a small applied field H_e is imposed?

In particular, if the system is 1000 cm^3 of cerium magnesium nitrate (see problem 14.6–2), $T = 1°K$, and H_e is 10,000 oersteds, what is the heat flux?

14.6–4. Discuss the electrocaloric effect, or the change in temperature of an electrically polarizable system, when an external field is applied adiabatically. Derive an expression for the electrocaloric effect, assuming that the dielectric satisfies the Langevin–Debye equation of state,

$$\chi_{T,P}^{(\text{elect.})} = \chi_{T,P}^\circ + \frac{p^2}{3kT}$$

in which p is the dipole moment per molecule (a quantity of the order of the electronic charge times the interatomic distance).

14.7 Superconductivity

Many paramagnetic metals, metallic compounds, and alloys exhibit a phase transition at low temperatures. Typical transition temperatures are shown for several metals in the first column of Table 14.2.

The superconductive phase is characterized by two spectacular properties. First, the electrical resistance of the system abruptly vanishes at the transition temperature. Currents, once started in superconducting rings, persist for hours, providing dramatic evidence that the electrical resistance does not merely become small but apparently vanishes. Second, the super-conducting transition marks a transition from paramagnetism to *perfect diamagnetism*. That is, in the superconductive phase the susceptibility

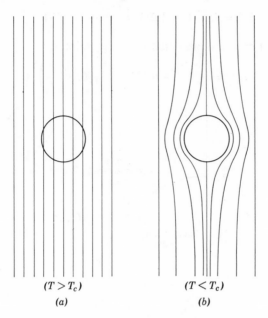

$(T > T_c)$ $(T < T_c)$

(a)   (b)

Figure 14.6   The Meissner effect in a superconductor.

$\chi_{T,P}$ is $-(1/4\pi)$. If the external field is applied along a symmetry axis of an ellipsoidal sample, the magnetic moment of the system consequently is

$$I_H = -VH_e/(4\pi - N_H) \qquad (14.75)$$

in which N_H is the demagnetization coefficient along the axis parallel to H_e. (See equation 14.49.) The external field lines therefore do not penetrate the sample. As the sample is cooled below the transition temperature, there is a change of the external field configuration from that shown in Figure 14.6a to that in Figure 14.6b. This expulsion of the external field is called the *Meissner effect*.

The temperature at which the superconductive transition takes place depends on the pressure and the external field. At a pressure of 1 atm we can draw a phase diagram in an $H_e - T$ plane, which is analogous to the $P-T$ phase diagrams of simple systems (recall Figures 9.10–9.11). A typical superconductive phase diagram is shown in Figure 14.7.

If temperatures and fields on the bounding curve are denoted as *critical temperatures* T^c and *critical fields* H_e^c, the phase curve is representable as a functional relationship among H_e^c, T^c, and the pressure.

For tin the phase boundary curve at $P = 1$ atm can be represented by the equation

$$H_e^c = H_e^\circ \left[1 - 1.2117 \left(\frac{T^c}{T_0} \right)^2 + 0.2117 \left(\frac{T^c}{T_0} \right)^3 \right] \qquad (14.76)$$

and for lead it can be represented by the equation

$$H_e^c = H_e^\circ \left[1 - 0.91 \left(\frac{T^c}{T_0} \right)^2 + 0.09 \left(\frac{T^c}{T_0} \right)^4 \right] \qquad (14.77)$$

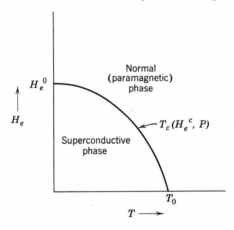

Figure 14.7 Superconductive phase diagram.

These curves, and all others which have been observed, have the properties that the slope dH_e^c/dT^c vanishes at $T^c = 0$ and is negative at $T^c = T_0$. The *critical field at zero temperature* is H_e°, and the *critical temperature at zero field* is T_0. Typical values of these quantities are given in Table 14.2.

The properties of the phase boundary curve can be understood on the basis of the analogue of the Clapeyron–Clausius equation. (Recall equation 9.26.)

As in Figure 9.12, we consider two points on the phase boundary, shown in Figure 14.8. The criterion of equilibrium is that at each point the potential $U'[T, P, H_e]$ must be equal in each phase. This potential plays the role of Gibbs function for simple systems. Then (compare equations 9.20),

$$U_B'[T, P, H_e] - U_A'[T, P, H_e] = U_{B'}'[T, P, H_e] - U_{A'}'[T, P, H_e] \qquad (14.78)$$

and because $dP = P_B - P_A = 0$, we have

$$-S \, dT^c - \mu_o I_H \, dH_e^c = -S' \, dT^c - \mu_o I_H' \, dH_e^c \qquad (14.79)$$

Table 14.2

Metal	Critical Temperature, T_0 (°K)	Critical Field $H_e{}^\circ$ (oersteds)	$-\left(\dfrac{dH_e{}^c}{dT_c}\right)_{H_e{}^c=0}$ (oersteds/°K)
Al	1.20	106	163
Cd	0.56	28.8	86
Ga	1.10	50.3	93
Hf	0.37	—	—
Hg	4.16	410	194
In	3.40	280	156
Nb	8.90	1960	453
Os	0.71	65	183
Pb	7.22	812	226
Re	1.70	188	235
Rh	0.90	—	—
Ru	0.47	46	196
Sn	3.74	307	147
Ta	4.38	860	334
Tc	11.20	—	350
Th	1.37	131	—
Ti	0.39	100	300
Tl	2.39	171	126
U	1.10	—	—
V	4.89	1340	482
Zn	0.93	52.5	121
Zr	0.55	46.6	170

By permission from *Heat and Thermodynamics*, by M. W. Zemansky, 4th edition, 1957, McGraw-Hill Book Company, Inc., New York.

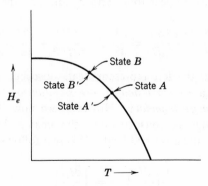

Figure 14.8

The primed quantities refer to the superconductive state, and the unprimed quantities refer to the normal state. The magnetic moment in the normal state has a .very small value, characteristic of paramagnetic materials; consequently, we neglect it, setting $I_H = 0$. The magnetic moment in the superconductive state has a value given by equation 14.75; we consider a long rod-shaped sample to avoid the complexity of the demagnetization factors, and we put

$$I'_H = \frac{-VH_e}{4\pi} \tag{14.80}$$

Inserting these values in equation 14.79, we obtain

$$S - S' = -\frac{VH_e{}^c}{4\pi} \frac{dH_e{}^c}{dT^c} \tag{14.81}$$

At zero temperature the Nernst theorem requires both S and S' to vanish, whence the slope of the phase boundary curve must also vanish. We have seen that this is, in fact, observed—it corresponds to the absence of first-order terms in T^c/T_0 in equations 14.76 and 14.77. At other temperatures we still expect the superconductive state to be more ordered than the normal state, so that $S - S'$ is positive. This requires the slope of the boundary curve to be everywhere negative, as is also observed.

The difference of entropies of the two phases leads to a latent heat L.

$$L = T^c(S - S') = -\frac{T^c V H_e{}^c}{4\pi} \frac{dH_e{}^c}{dT^c} \tag{14.82}$$

which corresponds to the Clausius–Clapeyron equation.

It should be noted that both the latent heat and the entropy difference $S - S'$ vanish at each end of the phase boundary curve.

An additional consequence can be inferred from equation 14.81. Differentiating with respect to T^c and dividing by the mole number, we obtain

$$\frac{T^c}{N}\frac{dS'}{dT^c} - \frac{T^c}{N}\frac{dS}{dT^c} = \frac{vT^c}{4\pi} H_e{}^c \frac{d^2 H_e{}^c}{(dT^c)^2} + \frac{vT^c}{4\pi}\left(\frac{dH_e{}^c}{dT^c}\right)^2 \tag{14.83}$$

The quantities on the left represent heats absorbed per mole per unit temperature increase *when T and H_e are simultaneously changed so as to move along the phase boundary.* However, we now show that only the temperature change is consequential, the change in H_e contributing almost nothing to the absorbed heat. This fact follows from the Maxwell identity

$$\frac{1}{\mu_o}\left(\frac{\partial S}{\partial H_e}\right)_{T,P} = \left(\frac{\partial I_H}{\partial T}\right)_{H_e,P} \tag{14.84}$$

But $(\partial I_H/\partial T)_{H_e,P}$ is negligibly small in each phase because $I_H = -(VH_e/4\pi)$ in the superconducting phase and because I_H is itself very small in the normal state. The entropy is virtually independent of field. Consequently, the heat absorbed if T is increased *at constant H_e* is about the same as the heat absorbed when both T and H_e are changed along

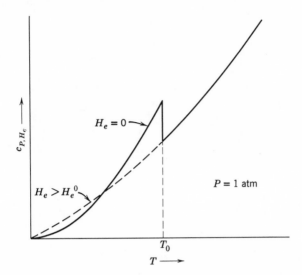

Figure 14.9 The specific heat discontinuity at the superconductive transition.

the phase curve. We can then interpret the quantities on the left of equation 14.83 as specific heats at constant field.

$$c'_{P,H_e} - c_{P,H_e} = \frac{vT^c}{4\pi} H_e^c \frac{d^2H_e^c}{(dT^c)^2} + \frac{vT^c}{4\pi} \left(\frac{dH_e^c}{dT^c}\right)^2 \qquad (14.85)$$

The first term in equation 14.85 is negative and the second, positive. The negative term predominates at low temperatures, and the specific heat in the normal state is greater than that in the superconductive state. At the upper end of the phase boundary curve, where $H_e^c = 0$ and $T^c = T_0$, the first term vanishes, and the specific heat in the superconductive state is larger than that in the normal state. The value of the slope of the phase boundary curve at $H_e^c = 0$ is given in the third column of Table 14.2. This quantity can be compared with the observed discontinuity in the specific heat.

A typical curve showing the dependence of c_{P,H_e} on temperature, and exhibiting the discontinuity through the transition, is sketched in Figure 14.9.

PART III

Chapters 15–17

Fluctuations
and Irreversible
Thermodynamics

CHAPTER 15

The Theory
of Fluctuations

15.1 The Thermodynamic Distribution Function

Thermodynamics is nominally macroscopic, whereas quantum mechanics and statistical mechanics are nominally microscopic. But as theory unfolds in a continuous sequence from quantum mechanical to gross macroscopic considerations, the transition from the microscopic to the macroscopic occurs gradually. There is no clear-cut or sharp division that establishes a rigorous boundary between statistical mechanics and thermodynamics. Some point in the continuous sequence of theoretical logic can be chosen as the point of division, more or less arbitrarily. All of the statistical mechanical theorems proved up to that point form the basis of the further development and consequently constitute the "postulates" of thermodynamics. But if the point of division is rechosen, displaced somewhat toward the logical foundations, a new set of thermodynamic postulates is obtained. The previous postulates then are provable as theorems on the basis of the new and more fundamental postulates.

The postulates of thermodynamics given in Chapter 1 correspond to the conventional point of division between thermodynamics and statistical mechanics. In this chapter the point of division is displaced one step downward toward statistical mechanics. In this way, the theory of fluctuations is removed from statistical mechanics and added to thermodynamics.

As before, a set of postulates is presented without attempt at prior justification. This set of postulates includes the previous postulates I, III, and IV although these are to be interpreted slightly differently. Postulate II (on the entropy maximum principle) is replaced by a somewhat more general statement.

Before presenting this alternate postulate we recall that a macroscopic system undergoes incessant and rapid transitions among its microstates. If a system is in contact with a heat reservoir, these transitions will lead sometimes to states of low energy and sometimes to states of high energy, as the (constant) total energy is shared in different proportions between system and reservoir. Similarly, if the system is in contact with a volume reservoir, the volume will continually fluctuate. In general, the extensive parameters of systems in contact with reservoirs undergo macroscopic fluctuations. The values of energy, volume, and other extensive parameters predicted by the entropy maximum principle are the *average* values. The alternate postulate which we shall introduce does not simply predict the average values, but it gives the probability that any specified

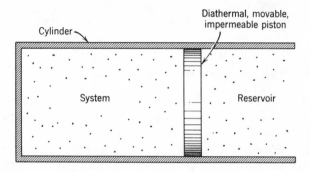

Figure 15.1   A thermodynamic system capable of energy and volume fluctuations.

value of the fluctuating extensive parameters will be realized at a given moment. It provides the *statistical distribution function* for the fluctuating variables.

As an illustration, consider the system of Figure 15.1. A gas is enclosed within a cylinder fitted with a diathermal, movable, but impermeable piston. The gas outside the cylinder constitutes a heat and volume reservoir. A gross macroscopic observation will disclose a particular value of the volume, and this is the value to which classical thermodynamics refers. But a high-speed motion picture of the piston, taken through a microscope of moderate magnification, will disclose continuous fluctuations of the piston position. Despite the fact that these observations are made at higher-than-usual resolution, they nevertheless are macroscopic. Similarly, the energy of the system fluctuates, but the mole numbers of the system are kept constant by the impermeability of the cylinder and piston walls.

Another illustration of great importance is afforded by a simple closed thermodynamic system. We consider a small portion of that system as a subsystem and the remainder of the sytem as a reservoir. Then the small system, chosen mentally as being of constant volume, undergoes fluctuations in energy and mole numbers. Such intrinsic fluctuations in energy-density and matter-density are most easily observed by the scattering of light which they produce in transparent systems. As we shall see, fluctuations of this type become particularly large in the neighborhood of the critical point and give rise to an extremely strong scattering of light, known as *critical opalescence*.

Consider a system in interaction with reservoirs appropriate to extensive variables $\hat{X}_0$, $\hat{X}_1 \cdots \hat{X}_s$ and restrictive with respect to variables $X_{s+1} \cdots X_t$. The latter variables are constant, but each of the first variables undergoes continual fluctuations. The variables $\hat{X}_k (k \leq s)$ fluctuate by virtue of transfers to and from the reservoirs, and the circumflex above X_k is inserted to stress that $\hat{X}_k$ is an instantaneous fluctuating value. The average value of $\hat{X}_k$ is X_k, the quantity with which we have dealt hitherto. The probability that $\hat{X}_0$ will be found in the range $d\hat{X}_0$, that $\hat{X}_1$ will be found in the range $d\hat{X}_1 \cdots$ and that $\hat{X}_s$ will be found in the range $d\hat{X}_s$ is defined as $W \, d\hat{X}_0 \, d\hat{X}_1 \cdots d\hat{X}_s$. W is a function of $\hat{X}_0 \cdots \hat{X}_s, X_{s+1} \cdots X_t$, and of the characteristics of the several reservoirs. The postulate to be presented specifies a particular functional form of W.

Postulate II'. *There exists a function of the instantaneous extensive parameters of any system, $\hat{S}(\hat{X}_0, \hat{X}_1 \cdots)$, called the instantaneous entropy, and having the following property. The probability $W \, d\hat{X}_0 \cdots d\hat{X}_s$ that the instantaneous extensive parameters of a system are in the range $d\hat{X}_0 \cdots d\hat{X}_s$, for a system in contact with the corresponding reservoirs, is given by*

$$W = \Omega_0 \exp \frac{1}{k} (\hat{S} - \sum_0^s F_k \hat{X}_k - S[F_0 \cdots F_s]) \qquad (15.1)$$

where

k is Boltzmann's constant

$\hat{S}$ is the "instantaneous entropy" of the system

$F_k = F_k{}^r$ is the intensive parameter of the reservoir $= \partial \hat{S}^r / \partial X_k{}^r$

$S[F_0 \cdots F_s]$ is the maximum value of $\hat{S} - \sum_0^s F_k \hat{X}_k$: we shall

see subsequently that it is, in fact, identical to the Legendre transform of the equilibrium entropy

Ω_0 is a normalizing constant such that

$$\int d\hat{X}_0 \int d\hat{X}_1 \int d\hat{X}_2 \cdots \int d\hat{X}_s W = 1 \qquad (15.2)$$

The properties imputed to the entropy in postulates III and IV of

Chapter I are now to be interpreted as applying to the instantaneous entropy.

If the extensive parameters $\hat{X}_k$ are given their average values X_k, the instantaneous entropy assumes a value referred to as the *equilibrium value of the entropy*. That is, *the equilibrium entropy S is defined by*

$$S(X_0, X_1 \cdots) = \hat{S}(X_0, X_1 \cdots) \tag{15.3}$$

This definition of S establishes contact between our new and our previous formulation.

15.2   Average or Equilibrium Values

In order to invest the distribution function W with intuitive significance, we immediately proceed to a calculation of the average values of the fluctuating parameters. These average values are the thermodynamic equilibrium values X_k, and in computing them we shall be led to our previous equilibrium criteria. We shall thus see how postulate II' implies postulate II.

Our calculation will be greatly simplified if we anticipate a fact to be justified later. Or, if we prefer, this fact may be added to our postulate. In either case the significant observation is that the distribution function for macroscopic systems is so sharply peaked that average values and most probable values are nearly identical. If W is plotted against $\hat{X}_k$, the distribution appears as in Figure 15.2a rather than as in Figure 15.2b. Although we could perfectly well compute average values directly from equation 15.1, we find it considerably more convenient to compute most probable values.

The most probable values of the $\hat{X}_k$ are the values that maximize W. But, since an exponential function is a monotonically increasing function of its argument, it follows that the most probable values of the $\hat{X}_k$ are those that maximize the quantity in parentheses in equation 15.1. The last term $S[F_0 \cdots F_s]$ is not a function of the $\hat{X}_k$, so that the most probable (or average) values of the $\hat{X}_k$ are determined by the condition

$$\hat{S}(\hat{X}_0 \cdots \hat{X}_s, X_{s+1} \cdots X_t) - \sum_0^s F_k \hat{X}_k = \text{maximum} \tag{15.4}$$

If we define *instantaneous intensive parameters* $\hat{F}_k$ by

$$\hat{F}_k = \frac{\partial \hat{S}}{\partial \hat{X}_k} \tag{15.5}$$

then the change in $\hat{S}$ associated with infinitesimal transfers $\delta \hat{X}_k$ between system and reservoir is

$$\delta \hat{S} = \sum_0^s \hat{F}_k \, \delta \hat{X}_k \tag{15.6}$$

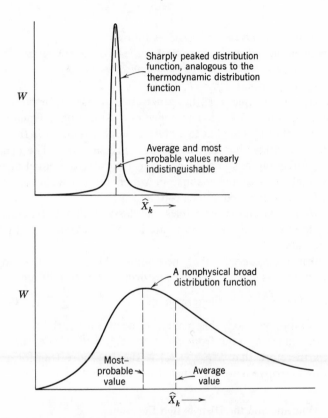

Figure 15.2 Sharply peaked and broad distribution functions. The thermodynamic distribution function is sharply peaked, and average values of the $\hat{X}_k$ are nearly indistinguishable from most probable values.

Equation 15.4 can be put in a more familiar form by setting the first differential equal to zero

$$d\left(\hat{S} - \sum_0^s F_k \hat{X}_k \right) = 0 \tag{15.7}$$

whence, by equation 15.6, the equilibrium value of $\hat{F}_k$ is

$$\text{equilibrium value } \hat{F}_k = F_k \tag{15.8}$$

The fact that the intensive parameters of system and reservoir are equal in equilibrium is, of course, by now completely familiar.

If we define the Legendre transform of the instantaneous entropy by

$$\hat{S}[\hat{F}_0 \cdots \hat{F}_s] \equiv \hat{S} - \sum_0^s \hat{F}_k \hat{X}_k \tag{15.9}$$

then equation 15.4 can be rephrased as follows:

The equilibrium values of any unconstrained extensive parameters in a system in contact with reservoirs of constant F_0, $F_1 \cdots F_s$ *maximize* $\hat{S}[\hat{F}_0 \cdots \hat{F}_s]$ *at constant* $\hat{F}_0 \cdots \hat{F}_s$ *(equal to* $F_0 \cdots F_s$*).* This is precisely the maximum principle for the generalized Massieu functions. The function in equation 15.4 is the analogue of the function in equation 6.10, although equation 15.4 applies to a more general case and is in the entropy representation rather than in the energy representation. The manner in which the foregoing equilibrium criterion follows from equation 15.4 is similarly analogous to the manner in which the particular equilibrium criterion followed from equations 6.10 and 6.11.

The various extremum principles of classical thermodynamics consequently follow directly from postulate II', which therefore can properly replace postulate II.

We return to corroborate that the quantity $S[F_0 \cdots F_s]$ that appeared in equation 15.1 is the Legendre transform of the equilibrium entropy. We defined $S[F_0 \cdots F_s]$ as the maximum value of $\hat{S} - \sum_0^s F_k \hat{X}_k$. But, from the equilibrium condition, this maximum occurs when the $\hat{X}_k$ have their equilibrium values X_k, and, from equation 15.3, $\hat{S}$ then takes the value S. It follows therefore that $S[F_0 \cdots F_s]$ is the Legendre transform of the equilibrium entropy, as we anticipated in equation 15.1.

15.3 Moments and the Distribution Function

Consider for a moment that X_0 is the only fluctuating variable, all other variables being constrained by restrictive walls. We review briefly some elementary statistical theorems for such a fluctuating variable.

The deviation $(\hat{X}_0 - X_0)$ of $\hat{X}_0$ from its average value X_0 is itself a fluctuating variable. The average value of the deviation clearly is zero. Denoting averages by $\langle \ \rangle$ brackets, so that by definition

$$\langle \hat{X}_0 \rangle = X_0 \tag{15.10}$$

the average value of the deviation is

$$\langle \hat{X}_0 - X_0 \rangle = \langle \hat{X}_0 \rangle - \langle X_0 \rangle = \langle \hat{X}_0 \rangle - X_0 = 0 \tag{15.11}$$

The average square of the deviation is not zero, since it is the average of an intrinsically positive quantity. The *mean square deviation* is a widely used and convenient measure of the magnitude of the fluctuations, although it is, of course, only a partial specification of the distribution. The mean square deviation is also called the *second moment* of the distribution.

The second moment is

$$\langle (\hat{X}_0 - X_0)^2 \rangle = \langle \hat{X}_0^2 - 2\hat{X}_0 X_0 + X_0^2 \rangle =$$

$$= \langle \hat{X}_0^2 \rangle - 2X_0^2 + X_0^2 = \langle \hat{X}_0^2 \rangle - X_0^2 \quad (15.12)$$

That is, the mean square deviation is equal to the average of the square minus the square of the average. This is a well-known and useful elementary theorem of statistics.

The third moment of the distribution is $\langle (\hat{X}_0 - X_0)^3 \rangle$ and the nth moment is $\langle (\hat{X}_0 - X_0)^n \rangle$.

If the distribution function is given, all the moments can be computed by straightforward integration. For the nth moment we have simply

$$\langle (\hat{X}_0 - X_0)^n \rangle = \int (\hat{X}_0 - X_0)^n W(\hat{X}_0) \, d\hat{X}_0 \quad (15.13)$$

Inversely, if all the moments are known, the distribution function can be computed. Although we shall not require such a calculation in our discussion, we indicate briefly the method for the interested reader. A function useful for this purpose is the so-called *characteristic function*, defined by

$$\mathcal{W}(\omega) = \int e^{-i\omega \hat{X}_0} W(\hat{X}_0) \, d\hat{X}_0 \quad (15.14)$$

The characteristic function is the Fourier transform of $W(\hat{X}_0)$. By a well-known theorem, equation 15.14 can be inverted to solve for $W(\hat{X}_0)$ in terms of $\mathcal{W}(\omega)$.

$$W(\hat{X}_0) = \frac{1}{2\pi} \int_{-\infty}^{\infty} e^{-i\omega \hat{X}_0} \mathcal{W}(\omega) \, d\omega \quad (15.15)$$

Returning now to equation 15.14, we expand the exponential in a power series by writing

$$e^{i\omega \hat{X}_0} = e^{i\omega X_0} e^{i\omega(\hat{X}_0 - X_0)} = e^{i\omega X_0} \sum_0^{\infty} \frac{1}{n!} (i\omega)^n (\hat{X}_0 - X_0)^n \quad (15.16)$$

and, inserting this series into equation 15.14, we find

$$\mathcal{W}(\omega) = e^{i\omega X_0} \sum_0^{\infty} \frac{(i\omega)^n}{n!} \int (\hat{X}_0 - X_0)^n W(\hat{X}_0) \, d\hat{X}_0 \quad (15.17)$$

or

$$\mathscr{W}(\omega) = e^{i\omega X_0} \sum_0^\infty \frac{(i\omega)^n}{n!} \langle (\hat{X}_0 - X_0)^n \rangle \qquad (15.18)$$

Therefore, if all the moments are known, $\mathscr{W}(\omega)$ can be computed by carrying out the summation in equation 15.18, and then $W(\hat{X}_0)$ can be computed in turn by equation 15.15.

The foregoing discussion stresses that the full set of moments, plus the average value X_0, is completely equivalent to the distribution function. For many purposes the moments are of great physical interest, particularly the second moments and to a lesser extent the third moments.

If more than one variable is free to fluctuate simultaneously, the number of moments increases rapidly. If the fluctuating variables are $\hat{X}_0, \hat{X}_1 \cdots \hat{X}_s$, the second moments of the distribution are

$$\langle (\hat{X}_j - X_j)(\hat{X}_k - X_k) \rangle = \int d\hat{X}_0 \int d\hat{X}_1 \cdots \int d\hat{X}_s \langle (\hat{X}_j - X_j)(\hat{X}_k - X_k) \rangle$$
$$\times \ W(\hat{X}_0 \cdots \hat{X}_s) \quad (15.19)$$

There are $(s+1)^2$ ways of choosing the indices j and k, and consequently there are $(s+1)^2$ second moments. Correspondingly, there are $(s+1)^n$ different nth moments, defined by an obvious analogue of equation 15.19. Again the full set of moments is completely equivalent to the distribution function by multidimensional analogues of equations 15.15 and 15.18, which we shall not present explicitly.

Of the second moments, those of the special form $\langle (\hat{X}_k - X_k)^2 \rangle$ measure the magnitude of the fluctuations of the variable $\hat{X}_k$. The second moments of the form $\langle (\hat{X}_j - X_j)(\hat{X}_k - X_k) \rangle$, in which $j \neq k$, measure the *correlation* between the fluctuations of $\hat{X}_j$ and $\hat{X}_k$. Even though both $\langle (\hat{X}_j - X_j)^2 \rangle$ and $\langle (\hat{X}_k - X_k)^2 \rangle$ may be large, the quantity $\langle (\hat{X}_j - X_j)(\hat{X}_k - X_k) \rangle$ may be small. In fact, the latter quantity will vanish if a positive fluctuation $(\hat{X}_j - X_j)$ is equally likely to be accompanied by a positive or a negative value of $(\hat{X}_k - X_k)$, that is, if $(\hat{X}_j - X_j)$ and $(\hat{X}_k - X_k)$ are uncorrelated.

15.4 Thermodynamic Fluctuation Moments

We now proceed to a direct calculation of the various moments of the fluctuating thermodynamic extensive parameters. Adopting the notation $\delta \hat{X}_k$ for the deviation of $\hat{X}_k$ from its average value X_k,

$$\delta \hat{X}_k \equiv (\hat{X}_k - X_k) \qquad (15.20)$$

a typical second moment is

$$\langle \delta \hat{X}_j \, \delta \hat{X}_k \rangle = \int (\delta \hat{X}_j \, \delta \hat{X}_k) W \, d\hat{X}_0 \, d\hat{X}_1 \cdots d\hat{X}_s \qquad (15.21)$$

To carry out the integration, we first observe that because of the form of W, as given in equation 15.1,

$$\frac{\partial W}{\partial F_k} = \frac{1}{k}\left(-\hat{X}_k - \frac{\partial S[F_0 \cdots F_s]}{\partial F_k}\right)W = -\frac{1}{k}(\hat{X}_k - X_k)W \qquad (15.22)$$

or

$$\frac{\partial W}{\partial F_k} = \frac{-1}{k}\,\delta\hat{X}_k W \qquad (15.23)$$

The second moment in equation 15.21 can now be written as

$$\langle \delta\hat{X}_j \, \delta\hat{X}_k \rangle = -k\int \delta\hat{X}_j \frac{\partial W}{\partial F_k}\, d\hat{X}_0 \, d\hat{X}_1 \cdots d\hat{X}_s \qquad (15.24)$$

or, by an evident identity,

$$\langle \delta\hat{X}_j \, \delta\hat{X}_k \rangle = -k\frac{\partial}{\partial F_k}\int \delta\hat{X}_j W \, d\hat{X}_0 \cdots d\hat{X}_s + k\int W\frac{\partial(\delta\hat{X}_j)}{\partial F_k}\, d\hat{X}_0 \cdots d\hat{X}_s \qquad (15.25)$$

But

$$\frac{\partial(\delta\hat{X}_j)}{\partial F_k} = \frac{\partial}{\partial F_k}(\hat{X}_j - X_j) = -\frac{\partial X_j}{\partial F_k} \qquad (15.26)$$

Equation 15.25 thereby becomes

$$\langle \delta\hat{X}_j \, \delta\hat{X}_k \rangle = -k\frac{\partial\langle\delta\hat{X}_j\rangle}{\partial F_k} - k\frac{\partial X_j}{\partial F_k} \qquad (15.27)$$

The first term vanishes because $\langle\delta\hat{X}_j\rangle$ vanishes independently of the value of F_k, whence

$$\langle \delta\hat{X}_j \, \delta\hat{X}_k \rangle = -k\left(\frac{\partial X_j}{\partial F_k}\right)_{F_0 \cdots F_{k-1}, F_{k+1} \cdots F_s, X_{s+1} \cdots X_t} \qquad (15.28)$$

or, by symmetry,

$$\langle \delta\hat{X}_j \, \delta\hat{X}_k \rangle = -k\left(\frac{\partial X_k}{\partial F_j}\right)_{F_0 \cdots F_{j-1}, F_{j+1} \cdots F_s, X_{s+1} \cdots X_t} \qquad (15.29)$$

The foregoing equation for the second moments is the most significant general result of the theory of thermodynamic fluctuations. We consider some special cases and applications of this result subsequently, but we return first to calculate the third and higher moments of the distribution.

Consider a typical third moment such as

$$\langle \delta\hat{X}_i \, \delta\hat{X}_j \, \delta\hat{X}_k \rangle = \int (\delta\hat{X}_i \, \delta\hat{X}_j \, \delta\hat{X}_k)W \, d\hat{X}_0 \, d\hat{X}_1 \cdots d\hat{X}_s \qquad (15.30)$$

Equations 15.21–15.25 can be transcribed by merely writing the product $\delta \hat{X}_i \, \delta \hat{X}_j$ in place of $\delta \hat{X}_j$ throughout. Equation 15.25 then becomes

$$\langle \delta \hat{X}_i \, \delta \hat{X}_j \, \delta \hat{X}_k \rangle = -k \frac{\partial}{\partial F_k} \int \delta \hat{X}_i \, \delta \hat{X}_j W \, d\hat{X}_0 \cdots d\hat{X}_s$$

$$+ k \int W \frac{\partial}{\partial F_k} (\delta \hat{X}_i \, \delta \hat{X}_j) \, d\hat{X}_0 \cdots d\hat{X}_s \quad (15.31)$$

The derivative of the product in the last integrand can be written as the sum of two terms, and, by equation 15.26, we find

$$\langle \delta \hat{X}_i \, \delta \hat{X}_j \, \delta \hat{X}_k \rangle = -k \frac{\partial \langle \delta \hat{X}_i \, \delta \hat{X}_j \rangle}{\partial F_k} - k \langle \delta \hat{X}_i \rangle \frac{\partial X_j}{\partial F_k} - k \langle \delta \hat{X}_j \rangle \frac{\partial X_i}{\partial F_k} \quad (15.32)$$

However

$$\langle \delta \hat{X}_i \rangle = \langle \delta \hat{X}_j \rangle = 0 \quad (15.33)$$

whence

$$\langle \delta \hat{X}_i \, \delta \hat{X}_j \, \delta \hat{X}_k \rangle = -k \frac{\partial}{\partial F_k} \langle \delta \hat{X}_i \, \delta \hat{X}_j \rangle \quad (15.34)$$

From equation 15.28 we find

$$\langle \delta \hat{X}_i \, \delta \hat{X}_j \, \delta \hat{X}_k \rangle = k^2 \frac{\partial^2 X_i}{\partial F_j \, \partial F_k} \quad (15.35)$$

The form of the iterative equation 15.32, which relates a moment to the various lower-order moments, is clearly maintained for fourth and higher moments. Analogous to equations 15.30–15.32, we have

$$\langle \delta \hat{X}_i \, \delta \hat{X}_j \, \delta \hat{X}_k \, \delta \hat{X}_l \rangle = -k \frac{\partial}{\partial F_l} \langle \delta \hat{X}_i \, \delta \hat{X}_j \, \delta \hat{X}_k \rangle - k \frac{\partial X_i}{\partial F_l} \langle \delta \hat{X}_j \, \delta \hat{X}_k \rangle$$

$$- k \frac{\partial X_j}{\partial F_l} \langle \delta \hat{X}_i \, \delta \hat{X}_k \rangle - k \frac{\partial X_k}{\partial F_l} \langle \delta \hat{X}_i \, \delta \hat{X}_j \rangle \quad (15.36)$$

and, by equation 15.35,

$$\langle \delta \hat{X}_i \, \delta \hat{X}_j \, \delta \hat{X}_k \, \delta X_l \rangle = -k^3 \frac{\partial^3 X_i}{\partial F_j \, \partial F_k \, \partial F_l}$$

$$+ k^2 \frac{\partial X_i}{\partial F_l} \frac{\partial X_j}{\partial F_k} + k^2 \frac{\partial X_j}{\partial F_l} \frac{\partial X_i}{\partial F_k} + k^2 \frac{\partial X_k}{\partial F_l} \frac{\partial X_i}{\partial F_j} \quad (15.37)$$

As special cases, which illustrate the general result above, consider the fluctuations in energy of a simple system in diathermal contact with a heat reservoir but enclosed in rigid impermeable walls. Then the only second moment is, by equation 15.28,

$$\langle (\delta \hat{U})^2 \rangle = -k \left(\frac{\partial U}{\partial (1/T)} \right)_{V, N_1, N_2 \cdots} \quad (15.38)$$

or

$$\langle(\delta\hat{U})^2\rangle = kT^2\left(\frac{\partial U}{\partial T}\right)_{V,N_1,N_2\cdots} = kT^2Nc_v \qquad (15.39)$$

The mean square deviation of energy is governed by the specific heat at constant volume in this case.

Consider now that the same system is in contact simultaneously with heat and volume reservoirs, so that both U and V may fluctuate. Then

$$\langle(\delta\hat{U})^2\rangle = -k\left(\frac{\partial U}{\partial(1/T)}\right)_{P/T,N_1,N_2\cdots} = kT^2Nc_P - kT^2PV\alpha + kTP^2V\kappa_T \qquad (15.40)$$

$$\langle\delta\hat{U}\,\delta\hat{V}\rangle = -k\left(\frac{\partial V}{\partial(1/T)}\right)_{P/T,N_1\cdots} = kT^2V\alpha - kTPV\kappa_T \qquad (15.41)$$

and

$$\langle(\delta\hat{V})^2\rangle = -k\left(\frac{\partial V}{\partial(P/T)}\right)_{1/T,N_1\cdots} = -kT\left(\frac{\partial V}{\partial P}\right)_{T,N_1\cdots} = kTV\kappa_T \qquad (15.42)$$

Comparing equations 15.40 and 15.39, we see that the fluctuation of each parameter depends upon *all* the reservoirs with which the system is in contact. The fluctuation moments in each case are related to standard thermodynamic quantities.

As mentioned earlier, one of the easily observed consequences of thermodynamic fluctuations is the scattering of light by the fluctuations in density in a fluid system. In problems 15.4–4–15.4–7 it is shown that the fraction of light intensity scattered by a fluid system of total volume V_{total} is

$$\frac{I\text{ scattered}}{I_0} = \frac{8\pi^3}{27\lambda_0^4}kT\kappa_T(\epsilon - 1)^2(\epsilon + 2)^2 \qquad (15.43)$$

where λ_0 is the vacuum wavelength of the light and ϵ is the dielectric constant. Because of the λ_0^{-4} dependence, blue light is much more strongly scattered than red. The sun appears red when it is low on the horizon because the blue light is selectively scattered, leaving the direct rays from the sun deficient in blue. On the other hand, the diffuse light of the day-time sky, composed of the indirectly scattered sunlight, is predominantly blue. The color of the sky accordingly is everyday evidence of the existence of thermodynamic fluctuations.

Having obtained an expression for the mean square deviation, we return to the question of the "sharpness" of the distribution function. We have assumed the distribution to be so sharply peaked that most probable values can be substituted for average values. A convenient measure of the sharpness of the distribution is the ratio of the width of the distribution to the average value. The width can be measured by the *root mean square deviation* $\langle (\hat{X}_j - X_j)^2 \rangle^{1/2}$. Then the sharpness is measured by the smallness of the ratio $\langle (\hat{X}_j^2 - X_j)^2 \rangle^{1/2}/X_j$. From equation 15.28 we see that this ratio is of inverse $\frac{1}{2}$-power in the extensive parameters. Therefore, the distribution becomes increasingly sharp as the size of the system increases. For a macroscopic system the distribution is very sharp indeed, as can be corroborated by inserting any of equations 15.39–15.42 into the foregoing ratio and choosing reasonable values for the parameters involved.

Problems—Section 15.4

15.4–1. A conceptual subsystem of N moles in a large single-component ideal gas system undergoes energy and volume fluctuations. The total system is at a temperature of $0°C$ and a pressure of 1 atm. What must be the size of N for the root mean square deviation in energy to be 1 per cent of the average energy of the subsystem?

15.4–2. What is the order of magnitude of the mean square deviation of the volume of a typical metal sample of average volume equal to 1 cm^3? The sample is at room temperature and pressure.

15.4–3. Consider a small volume V within a two-component simple system. Let $x_1 = N_1/(N_1 + N_2)$, in which N_1 and N_2 are the mole numbers within V. Show that

$$N^2(\delta \hat{x}_1)^2 = (\delta \hat{N}_1)^2 - 2x_1(\delta \hat{N}_1 \, \delta \hat{N}) + x_1^2 (\delta \hat{N})^2$$

and compute the mean square deviation of concentration $\langle (\delta \hat{x}_1)^2 \rangle$.

15.4–4. Consider a small quantity of matter, consisting of a fixed number N moles, in a large fluid system. Let ρ_N be the average density of these N moles: the mass divided by the volume. Show that equation 15.42 implies that the density fluctuations are

$$\frac{\langle (\delta \hat{\rho}_N)^2 \rangle}{\rho_N{}^2} = + \frac{kT\kappa_T}{V}.$$

in which V is the average volume of the N moles.

15.4–5. Recalling that $k = R/N_A$, in which N_A is Avogadro's number, show that the density fluctuations of an ideal gas are given by

$$\frac{\langle (\delta \hat{\rho}_N)^2 \rangle}{\rho_N{}^2} = \frac{1}{NN_A}$$

That is, the relative mean square density deviation is the reciprocal of the number of molecules in the subsystem.

15.4–6. Show that the relative mean square deviation in density of 10^{-3} gram of air at room temperature and pressure is negligible. Consider air as an ideal gas.

Show that the relative mean square deviation in density of 2×10^{-16} gram of air at room temperature and pressure is approximately 0.1 per cent.

Show that the average volume of the samples considered above is approximately $\frac{2}{3}$ cm^3 in the first case and equal to the cube of the wavelength of visible light in the second case.

15.4–7. The dielectric constant ϵ of a fluid varies with the density by the relation

$$\frac{\epsilon - 1}{\epsilon + 2} = A\rho$$

in which A is a constant. Show that the fluctuations in dielectric constant of a small quantity of N moles of matter in a large system are

$$\langle (\delta\hat{\epsilon})^2 \rangle = \frac{kT\kappa_T}{9V} (\epsilon - 1)^2(\epsilon + 2)^2$$

in which V is the average volume of N moles.

15.4–8. If light of intensity I_0 is incident on a region of volume V, which has a difference $\delta\hat{\epsilon}$ of dielectric constant from its average surroundings, the intensity of light I_0 scattered at an angle θ and at a distance r is

$$I_\theta = \frac{\pi^2 V^2 (\delta\hat{\epsilon})^2}{2\lambda_0^4} I_0 \frac{1 + \cos^2\theta}{r^2}$$

in which λ_0 is the vacuum wavelength of the incident light. This is called Rayleigh scattering.

In a fluid each small volume V scatters incoherently, and the total scattered intensity is the same as the scattered intensities from each region.

From the problem 15.4–7 we have

$$V^2 \langle (\delta\hat{\epsilon})^2 \rangle = \tfrac{1}{2} kT\kappa_T (\epsilon - 1)^2(\epsilon + 2)^2 V$$

and, summing this quantity over the total fluid, we find

$$\Sigma V^2 \langle (\delta\hat{\epsilon})^2 \rangle = \tfrac{1}{2} kT\kappa_T (\epsilon - 1)^2(\epsilon + 2)^2 V_{\text{total}}$$

where V_{total} is the total volume of the fluid. Consequently, the total scattered intensity at an angle θ and at a distance r from the scattering system is

$$I_\theta = \frac{\pi^2}{18} \frac{kT\kappa_T}{\lambda_0^4} (\epsilon - 1)^2(\epsilon + 2)^2 I_0 V_{\text{total}} \frac{1 + \cos^2\theta}{r^2}.$$

By integrating over the surface of a sphere, show that the total scattered intensity is

$$I_{\text{scattered}} = \frac{8\pi^3}{27\lambda_0^4} kT\kappa_T (\epsilon - 1)^2(\epsilon + 2)^2 I_0 V_{\text{total}}$$

15.5 An Alternate Form for the Second Moments

The derivatives to which the second moments are related by equation 15.28 are very similar to the derivatives met in the theory of stability. The derivative in equation 15.28 is, in fact, just the entropy-representation analogue of the derivative in equation 9.54. To state this analogy more explicitly, we adopt the notation S^s for the Legendre transform $S[F_0 \cdots F_s]$.

$$S^s \equiv S[F_0 \cdots F_s] \tag{15.44}$$

Then, if neither j nor k is greater than s,

$$S_{jk}^s \equiv \frac{\partial^2 S^s}{\partial F_j \, \partial F_k} = -\frac{\partial X_k}{\partial F_j} = -\frac{\partial X_j}{\partial F_k} \qquad (15.45)$$

and, by comparison with equation 15.28, we have

$$\langle \delta \hat{X}_j \, \delta \hat{X}_k \rangle = -k S_{jk}^s \qquad (15.46)$$

Equation 15.45 is the conventional form in which the second moments are most frequently expressed.

We may also note in passing that the quantity S_{jk}^s can be described in the language of matrices by the methods of Appendix G. If S_{jk} is the j,kth element of an $(s + 1)$ by $(s + 1)$ matrix, then S_{jk}^s is the j, kth element of the inverse matrix.

Referring again to the first of equations 9.54, we recall that $|\psi_{jk}^s| \to \infty$ at a critical point. It is evident that the analysis of critical points could be repeated in the entropy representation and that we would then obtain

$$|S_{jk}^s| \to \infty \qquad (15.47)$$

at critical points. Therefore, although thermodynamic fluctuations are generally small, *the fluctuations become enormous near critical points*.

A fluctuation in a stable system leads to a large restoring force for a small fluctuation. But at a critical point small fluctuations do not induce restoring forces, and the fluctuations grow quite large before they are limited by restoring forces. Fluctuations in stable and critical systems are analogous to the Brownian motions of a particle on a stiff spring and of a free particle, respectively.

A classical problem which played an important role in the historical development of thermodynamic fluctuation theory is *critical opalescence*. At a critical point the volume fluctuations of any small portion of a fluid become enormous. That is, the fluid has large fluctuations in density from point to point. A light beam traversing such a fluid is strongly scattered, and the scattered light gives the fluid an opalescent appearance. The theory of critical opalescence follows from equation 15.43, coupled with the observation that κ_T formally diverges (and actually becomes very large) at the critical point.

15.6 The Associated Gaussian Distribution

The moments of the fluctuating extensive parameters were first computed by Einstein in 1910. Einstein's method was an approximate one, which happens to give precisely the correct results for the second moments but which gives inexact results for the higher moments. However, the method is intrinsically interesting, analytically simple, and intuitively revealing.

The Einstein method proceeds by making a series expansion of the argument of the exponential in W (equation 15.1), neglecting higher-order terms than the second, and thereby obtaining an approximate and simple analytic form for W. The distribution becomes an $(s + 1)$-*dimensional Gaussian distribution*, a form much studied in elementary statistics. The calculation of the moments of such a distribution is not trivial, but at least it is standard.

We expand $\hat{S}$ around the equilibrium value S, in powers of the deviations $\delta \hat{X}_k = \hat{X}_k - X_k$.

$$\hat{S} = S + \sum_0^s F_k \, \delta \hat{X}_k + \frac{1}{2} \sum_0^s \sum_0^s S_{jk} \, \delta \hat{X}_j \, \delta \hat{X}_k + \cdots \qquad (15.48)$$

Inserting equation 15.48 into equation 15.1 and recalling that $S[F_0 \cdots F_s] = S - \sum_0^s F_k X_k$, we find

$$W = \Omega_0 \exp \left(\frac{1}{2k} \sum_0^s \sum_0^s S_{jk} \, \delta \hat{X}_j \, \delta \hat{X}_k + \cdots \right) \qquad (15.49)$$

If we neglect the higher-order terms, we change the normalization constant Ω_0, so that we have *approximately*

$$W = \Omega_1 \exp \left(\frac{1}{2k} \sum_0^s \sum_0^s S_{jk} \, \delta \hat{X}_j \, \delta \hat{X}_k \right) \qquad (15.50)$$

We shall leave it to a problem to show that this approximate Gaussian distribution function predicts the second moments correctly, as given in equation 15.46, but does not predict third and higher moments accurately. Because it does give second moments correctly and because these are the moments of chief physical interest, the Gaussian distribution is widely used in thermodynamic fluctuation theory.

Problems—Section 15.6

15.6–1. To compute the fluctuation moments of the approximate Gaussian distribution (equation 15.50), define a quantity $\delta \hat{F}_k$ by

$$\delta \hat{F}_k = \sum_0^s S_{jk} \, \delta \hat{X}_j \qquad (a)$$

for which the inverse equation is

$$\delta \hat{X}_j = \sum_0^r S_{kj}^s \, \delta \hat{F}_k \qquad (b)$$

First, show that

$$\delta \hat{F}_k = k \frac{\partial \ln W}{\partial \delta \hat{X}_k} \qquad (c)$$

Now let ϕ be a function of the form

$$\phi \equiv (\delta \hat{X}_0)^{n_0} (\delta \hat{X}_1)^{n_1} \cdots (\delta \hat{X}_s)^{n_s} \tag{d}$$

in which the n_j are nonnegative integers. Using the result proved above, show that

$$\langle \phi \, \delta \hat{F}_k \rangle = -k \left\langle \frac{\partial \phi}{\partial \delta \hat{X}_k} \right\rangle = -k n_k \langle \phi / \delta \hat{X}_k \rangle \tag{e}$$

Consider now the quantity $\langle \phi \, \delta \hat{X}_k \rangle$ and, using equations (b) and (e), show that

$$\langle \phi \, \delta \hat{X}_k \rangle = -k \sum_0^s S_{jk}^s n_j \langle \phi / \delta \hat{X}_j \rangle \tag{f}$$

Finally, show that if $\phi = 1$ we obtain $\langle \delta \hat{X}_k \rangle = 0$, that if $\phi = \delta \hat{X}_j$ we obtain equation 15.47, and that other choices of ϕ permit calculation of higher moments.

CHAPTER 16

Irreversible
Thermodynamics

16.1 General Remarks

As useful as the characterization of equilibrium states by thermostatic theory has proved to be, it must be conceded that our primary interest is frequently in processes rather than in states. In biology, particularly, it is the life process that captures our imagination rather than the eventual equiilbrium state to which each organism inevitably proceeds. Thermostatics does provide two methods that permit us to infer some limited information about processes, but each of these methods is indirect and each yields only the most meager return. First, by studying the initial and terminal equilibrium states, it is sometimes possible to bracket a process and thence to determine the effect of the process in its totality. Second, if some process occurs *extremely* slowly, we may compare it with an idealized, nonphysical, quasi-static process. But neither of these methods confronts the central problem of *rates* of real physical processes. The extension of thermodynamics which has reference to the rates of physical processes is the theory of *irreversible thermodynamics*.

Two basic postulates underlie equilibrium statistical mechanics. The first postulate concerns the existence of an enormous number of atomistic states among which continual spontaneous transitions occur in the course of a macroscopic observation. The second is the assumption of equal a priori probability of each of the atomistic states. From these extremely general hypotheses follows the entire general theory of statistical mechanics, culminating in the theorems that, in turn, constitute the postulates of thermostatics. Because of the general nature of the postulates, the predictions of thermostatics are similarly general. The numerical values of specific heats, compressibilities, and the like are not predicted, but certain general relationships among these quantities are predicted.

The theory of nonequilibrium statistical mechanics is based on the two postulates of the equilibrium theory, plus the additional postulate of *time symmetry of physical laws*. This additional postulate states that *all the laws of physics remain unchanged if the time t is everywhere replaced by its negative −t and if simultaneously the magnetic field* $\mathbf{H}_e$ *is replaced by its negative* $−\mathbf{H}_e$.

From the general postulates of nonequilibrium statistical mechanics there follows an extensive theory, culminating in several theorems that, in turn, constitute the postulates of irreversible thermodynamics. From these we derive thermodynamic theorems of a general nature, expressing relationships among various dynamical quantities.

The first such result was the Onsager reciprocity theorem, which expresses a certain symmetry in the response of two simultaneously occurring processes. Another theorem is the fluctuation-dissipation theorem of H. Callen and T. Welton, which expresses a relation between irreversible response and equilibrium fluctuations. Other theorems relating to the fluctuations during an irreversible process, and involving extensions to nonlinear processes, have been developed by W. Bernard and H. Callen and by M. Lax.

Despite the considerable number of results of nonequilibrium thermodynamics, by far the most practically significant result is the Onsager reciprocity theorem. Consequently, we restrict our attention to this theorem alone. We indicate in section 16.5 how this theorem is related to the underlying postulate of time symmetry.

16.2 Affinities and Fluxes

Preparatory to our discussion of the Onsager theorem, we define certain quantities that appropriately describe irreversible processes. Basically we require two types of parameters: one to describe the "force" that drives a process and one to describe the response to this force.

The processes of most general interest occur in continuous systems, such as the flow of energy in a bar with a continuous temperature gradient. However, to suggest the proper way to choose parameters in such continuous systems, we first consider the relatively simple case of a discrete system. A typical process in a discrete system would be the flow of energy from one homogeneous subsystem to another through an infinitely thin diathermal partition.

Consider a composite system composed of two subsystems. An extensive parameter has values X_k and $X_k{'}$ in the two subsystems, and the closure condition requires that

$$X_k + X_k' = X_k^\circ, \quad \text{a constant} \tag{16.1}$$

If X_k and X_k' are unconstrained, their equilibrium values are determined by the vanishing of the quantity

$$\mathscr{F}_k \equiv \left(\frac{\partial S^\circ}{\partial X_k}\right)_{X_k^\circ} = \left(\frac{\partial (S + S')}{\partial X_k}\right)_{X_k^\circ} = \frac{\partial S}{\partial X_k} - \frac{\partial S'}{\partial X_k'} = F_k - F_k' \tag{16.2}$$

Thus, if $\mathscr{F}_k$ is zero, the system is in equilibrium, but if $\mathscr{F}_k$ is nonzero an irreversible process occurs, taking the system toward the equilibrium state. The quantity $\mathscr{F}_k$, which is the difference in the entropy-representation intensive parameters, acts as a "generalized force" which "drives" the process. Such generalized forces are called *affinities*.

For definiteness, consider two systems separated by a diathermal wall, and let X_k be the energy U. Then the affinity is

$$\mathscr{F}_k = \frac{1}{T} - \frac{1}{T'} \tag{16.3}$$

No heat flows across the diathermal wall if the difference in inverse temperatures vanishes. But a nonzero difference in inverse temperature, acting as a generalized force, drives a flow of heat between the subsystems.

Similarly, if X_k is the volume, the affinity $\mathscr{F}_k$ is $[P/T - (P'/T')]$, and if X_k is a mole number the associated affinity is $[\mu_k'/T' - (\mu_k/T)]$.

We characterize the response to the applied force by the rate of change of the extensive parameter X_k. The *flux J_k* is then defined by

$$J_k \equiv \frac{dX_k}{dt} \tag{16.4}$$

Therefore, the flux vanishes if the affinity vanishes, and a nonzero affinity leads to a nonzero flux. It is the relationship between fluxes and affinities that characterizes the rates of irreversible processes.

The identification of the affinities in a particular type of system is frequently rendered more convenient by considering the rate of production of entropy. Differentiating the entropy $S(X_0, X_1 \cdots)$ with respect to the time, we have

$$\frac{dS}{dt} = \sum_k \frac{\partial S}{\partial X_k} \frac{dX_k}{dt} \tag{16.5}$$

or

$$\dot{S} = \sum_k \mathscr{F}_k J_k \tag{16.6}$$

Thus, *the rate of production of entropy is the sum of products of each flux with its associated affinity.*

The entropy production equation is particularly useful in extending the definition of affinities to continuous systems rather than to discrete systems. If heat flows from one homogeneous subsystem to another, through an infinitely thin diathermal partition, the generalized force is the difference $[1/T - (1/T')]$; but if heat flows along a metal rod, in which the temperature varies in a continuous fashion, it is difficult to apply our previous definition of the affinity. Nevertheless, we can compute the rate of production of entropy, and thereby we can identify the affinity.

With the foregoing considerations to guide us, we now turn our attention to continuous systems. We consider a three dimensional system in which energy and matter flow, driven by appropriate forces. As fluxes, we choose the components of the vector current densities of energy and matter. Thus, associated with the energy U, we have the three energy fluxes J_{ox}, J_{oy}, J_{oz}. These quantities are the x, y, and z components of the vector current density $\mathbf{J}_o$. By definition the magnitude of $\mathbf{J}_o$ is the amount of energy which flows across the unit area in unit time, and the direction of $\mathbf{J}_o$ is the direction of this energy flow. Similarly, the current density $\mathbf{J}_k$ may describe the flow of a particular chemical component per unit area and per unit time; the components J_{kx}, J_{ky}, and J_{kz} are fluxes.

In order to identify the affinities, we now seek to write the rate of production of entropy in a form analogous to equation 16.6.

One problem that immediately arises is that of defining entropy in a nonequilibrium system. This problem is solved in a formal manner as follows.

To any infinitesimal region we associate a local entropy $S(X_0, X_1 \cdots)$, where, *by definition, the functional dependence of S on the local extensive parameters $X_0, X_1 \cdots$ is taken to be identical to the dependence in equilibrium.* That is, we merely adopt the equilibrium fundamental equation to associate a local entropy with the local parameters $X_0, X_1 \cdots$. Then

$$dS = \sum_k F_k \, dX_k \tag{16.7}$$

or, taking all quantities per unit volume,*

$$ds = \sum_k F_k \, dx_k \tag{16.8}$$

The summation in this equation omits the term for volume and consequently has one less term than that in equation 16.7.

Again, the local intensive parameter F_k is taken to be the same function of the local extensive parameters as it would be in equilibrium. It is because

---

* It should be noted that in the remainder of this chapter we use lower case letters to indicate extensive parameters *per unit volume* rather than *per mole*.

of this convention, incidentally, that we can speak of the temperature varying continuously in a bar, despite the fact that thermostatics implies the existence of temperature only in equilibrium systems.

Equation 16.7 immediately suggests a reasonable definition of the _entropy current density_ $\mathbf{J}_S$.

$$\mathbf{J}_S = \Sigma F_k \mathbf{J}_k \qquad (16.9)$$

in which $\mathbf{J}_k$ is the current density of the extensive parameter X_k. The magnitude of the entropy flux $\mathbf{J}_S$ is the entropy transported through unit area per unit time.

The rate of local production of entropy is equal to the entropy leaving the region, plus the rate of increase of entropy within the region. If $\dot{s}$ denotes the rate of production of entropy per unit volume and $\partial s / \partial t$ denotes the increase in entropy per unit volume, then

$$\dot{s} = \frac{\partial s}{\partial t} + \nabla \cdot \mathbf{J}_S \qquad (16.10)$$

The various extensive parameters can be neither produced nor destroyed, so that the equations of continuity for these parameters become

$$0 = \frac{\partial x_k}{\partial t} + \nabla \cdot \mathbf{J}_k \qquad (16.11)$$

We are now prepared to compute $\dot{s}$ explicitly and thence to identify the affinities in continuous systems.

The first term in equation 16.10 is easily computed from equation 16.8.

$$\frac{\partial s}{\partial t} = \sum_k F_k \frac{\partial x_k}{\partial t} \qquad (16.12)$$

The second term in equation 16.10 is computed by taking the divergence of equation 16.9.

$$\nabla \cdot \mathbf{J}_S = \nabla \cdot \left(\sum_k F_k \mathbf{J}_k \right) = \sum_k \nabla F_k \cdot \mathbf{J}_k + \sum_k F_k \nabla \cdot \mathbf{J}_k \qquad (16.13)$$

Thus equation 16.10 becomes

$$\dot{s} = \sum_k F_k \frac{\partial x_k}{\partial t} + \sum_k \nabla F \cdot \mathbf{J}_k + \sum_k F_k \nabla \cdot \mathbf{J}_k \qquad (16.14)$$

Finally, by equation 16.11, we observe that the first and third terms cancel, giving

$$\dot{s} = \sum_k \nabla F_k \cdot \mathbf{J}_k \qquad (16.15)$$

Although the affinity is defined as the difference in the entropy-representation *intensive parameters for discrete systems, it is the gradient of the entropy-representation intensive parameters in continuous systems.*

If $\mathbf{J}_{oz}$ denotes the z component of the energy current density, the associated affinity $\mathscr{F}_{oz}$ is $\nabla_z(1/T)$, the z component of the gradient of the inverse temperature. And if $\mathbf{J}_k$ denotes the kth mole number current density (the number of moles of the kth component flowing through unit area per second), the affinity associated with J_{kz} is $\mathscr{F}_{kz} = -\nabla_z\left(\dfrac{\mu_k}{T}\right)$.

16.3   Markoffian Systems

For certain systems the fluxes at a given instant depend only on the values of the affinities at that instant. We call such systems *Markoffian*, borrowing the terminology from the theory of random processes, and we restrict our attention to this type of system.

For a non-Markoffian system the fluxes may depend upon the values of the affinities at previous times as well as upon the values at the present time. In the electrical case a pure resistor is a Markoffian system, whereas a circuit with capacitance or inductance is non-Markoffian. A non-Markoffian system has a "memory."

Although it might appear that the restriction to Markoffian systems is a very severe restriction indeed, it is found in practice that almost all systems of interest, other than electrical systems, are Markoffian. The extension of the theory to non-Markoffian systems, which we shall not present here, has been more important for its elucidation of principles than for its application to real systems.

For a Markoffian system, by definition, each local flux depends only upon the instantaneous local affinities and upon the local intensive parameters. That is, dropping the indices denoting vector components,

$$J_k = J_k(\mathscr{F}_0, \mathscr{F}_1 \cdots \mathscr{F}_j \cdots; F_0, F_1 \cdots F_j \cdots) \tag{16.16}$$

Thus, the local mole number current density of the kth component depends on the gradient of the inverse temperature, on the gradients of μ_j/T for each component, and upon the local temperature, pressure, etc. It should be noted that we do not assume that each flux depends only on its own affinity but rather that each flux depends on *all* affinities. It is true that each flux tends to depend most strongly on its own associated affinity, but the dependence of a flux on other affinities as well is the source of some of the most interesting phenomena in the field of irreversibility.

Each flux J_k is known to vanish as the affinities vanish, so we can expand J_k in powers of the affinities with no constant term.

$$J_k = \sum_j L_{jk} \mathscr{F}_j + \frac{1}{2!} \sum_i \sum_j L_{ijk} \mathscr{F}_i \mathscr{F}_j + \cdots \qquad (16.17)$$

where

$$L_{jk} = \left(\frac{\partial J_k}{\partial \mathscr{F}_j}\right)_0 \qquad (16.18)$$

and

$$L_{ijk} = \left(\frac{\partial^2 J_k}{\partial \mathscr{F}_i \, \partial \mathscr{F}_j}\right)_0 \qquad (16.19)$$

The functions L_{jk} are called *kinetic coefficients. They are functions of the local intensive parameters.*

$$L_{jk} = L_{jk}(F_0, F_1 \cdots) \qquad (16.20)$$

The functions L_{ijk} are called *second-order kinetic coefficients*, and they are also functions of the local intensive parameters. Third-order and higher-order kinetic coefficients are similarly defined.

For the purposes of the Onsager theorem, which we are about to enunciate, it is convenient to adopt a notation that exhibits the functional dependence of the kinetic coefficients on an externally applied magnetic field $\mathbf{H}_e$, suppressing the dependence on the other intensive parameters.

$$L_{jk} = L_{jk}(\mathbf{H}_e) \qquad (16.21)$$

The Onsager theorem states that

$$L_{jk}(\mathbf{H}_e) = L_{kj}(-\mathbf{H}_e) \qquad (16.22)$$

That is, the value of the kinetic coefficient L_{jk} measured in an external magnetic field $\mathbf{H}_e$ is identical to the value of L_{kj} measured in the reversed magnetic field $-\mathbf{H}_e$.

The Onsager theorem states a symmetry between the linear effect of the jth affinity on the kth flux and the linear effect of the kth affinity on the jth flux when these effects are measured in opposite magnetic fields.

16.4 Linear Processes

A situation of great practical interest arises if the affinities are so small that all quadratic and higher-order terms in equation 16.17 can be neglected. A process that can be adequately described by the truncated approximate equations

$$J_k = \sum_j L_{jk} \mathscr{F}_j \qquad (16.23)$$

is called a *linear* Markoff process. For the analysis of such processes the Onsager theorem is a particularly powerful tool.

It is perhaps surprising that so many physical processes of interest are linear. But the affinities that we commonly encounter in the laboratory are quite small in the sense of equation 16.17, and we therefore recognize that we generally deal with systems that deviate only slightly from equilibrium.

Phenomenologically, it is found that the flow of energy in a thermally conducting body is proportional to the gradient of the temperature. Denoting the energy current density by J_o, experiment yields the linear law

$$J_o = -\kappa \nabla T \tag{16.24}$$

in which κ is the thermal conductivity of the body. We can rewrite this in the more appropriate form

$$J_{oz} = \kappa T^2 \nabla_z \left(\frac{1}{T}\right) \tag{16.25}$$

and similarly for x and y components, and we see that (κT^2) is the kinetic coefficient. The absence of higher-order terms, such as $[\nabla(1/T)]^2$ and $[\nabla(1/T)]^3$, in the phenomenological law shows that commonly employed temperature gradients are small in the sense of equation 16.17.

Ohm's law of electrical conduction and Fick's law of diffusion are other linear phenomenological laws which demonstrate that for the common values of the affinities in these processes higher-order terms are negligible. On the other hand, both the linear region and the nonlinear region can be realized easily in chemical systems, depending upon the deviations of the molar concentrations from their equilibrium values. Although the class of linear processes is sufficiently common to merit special attention, it is by no means all-inclusive, and contrary to the usual statement the Onsager theorem is *not* restricted to this special class of systems.

16.5 The Statistical Basis of the Onsager Reciprocity

The Onsager reciprocity has been stated without proof in the preceding sections. Applications are made in Chapter 17. In this section we indicate the relationship of the Onsager reciprocity to the underlying principle of time symmetry of physical laws.

We consider a system in equilibrium, and we address our attention to the spontaneous fluctuations, as in Chapter 15. Consider, in particular, a correlation moment such as

$$\langle \delta \hat{X}_j \, \delta \hat{X}_k(\tau) \rangle \tag{16.26}$$

which is the average product of the deviation $\delta \hat{X}_j$ and of the deviation $\delta \hat{X}_k$, *the latter being observed a time τ after the former.* Assuming, for simplicity, that no magnetic field is present, the principle of time symmetry requires that the correlation moment (16.26) be unchanged if we replace τ by $-\tau$.

$$\langle \delta \hat{X}_j \, \delta X_k(\tau) \rangle = \langle \delta \hat{X}_j \, \delta \hat{X}_k(-\tau) \rangle \tag{16.27}$$

or, since only the relative times in the two factors are significant,

$$\langle \delta \hat{X}_j \, \delta \hat{X}_k(\tau) \rangle = \langle \delta \hat{X}_j(\tau) \, \delta \hat{X}_k \rangle \tag{16.28}$$

If we now subtract $\langle \delta \hat{X}_j \, \delta \hat{X}_k \rangle$ from each side of the equation and divide by τ, we find

$$\left\langle \delta \hat{X}_j \, \frac{\delta \hat{X}_k(\tau) - \delta \hat{X}_k}{\tau} \right\rangle = \left\langle \frac{\delta \hat{X}_j(\tau) - \delta \hat{X}_j}{\tau} \, \delta \hat{X}_k \right\rangle \tag{16.29}$$

In the limit as $\tau \to 0$ we can write the foregoing equation in terms of time derivatives.

$$\langle \delta \hat{X}_j \, \delta \dot{\hat{X}}_k \rangle = \langle \delta \dot{\hat{X}}_j \, \delta \hat{X}_k \rangle \tag{16.30}$$

Now, we *assume* that the decay of a fluctuation $\delta \hat{X}_k$ is governed by the *same* linear dynamical laws as are macroscopic processes.

$$\delta \dot{\hat{X}}_k = \sum_i L_{ik} \, \delta \hat{\mathscr{F}}_i \tag{16.31}$$

Inserting these equations in equation 16.30 gives

$$\sum_i L_{ik} \langle \delta \hat{X}_j \, \delta \hat{\mathscr{F}}_i \rangle = \sum_i L_{ij} \langle \delta \hat{\mathscr{F}}_i \, \delta \hat{X}_k \rangle \tag{16.32}$$

However, we shall show below, by the methods of Chapter 15, that

$$\langle \delta \hat{X}_j \, \delta \hat{\mathscr{F}}_i \rangle = \begin{cases} -k & \text{if} & i = j \\ 0 & \text{if} & i \neq j \end{cases} \tag{16.33}$$

in which k is Boltzmann's constant. Thus equation 16.32 becomes

$$L_{ij} = L_{ji} \tag{16.34}$$

which is the Onsager theorem in the absence of a magnetic field.

To complete the proof we now demonstrate equation 16.33. From equation 15.1 we can write the distribution function for the spontaneous fluctuations in the form

$$W = \Omega \exp \frac{1}{k} (\delta \hat{S} - \sum_0^s F_k \, \delta \hat{X}_k) \tag{16.35}$$

Combining this with equation 15.4 indicates that

$$W \, \delta \hat{\mathscr{F}}_i = k \, \frac{\partial W}{\partial \delta \hat{X}_i} \tag{16.36}$$

Consider now the average value in equation 16.33.

$$\langle \delta \hat{X}_j \, \delta \hat{\mathscr{F}}_i \rangle = \int \delta \hat{X}_j \, \delta \hat{\mathscr{F}}_i W \, d\delta \hat{X}_1 \, d\delta \hat{X}_2 \cdots \tag{16.37}$$

$$= k \int \delta \hat{X}_j \, \frac{\partial W}{\partial \delta \hat{X}_i} \, d\delta \hat{X}_1 \, d\delta \hat{X}_2 \cdots \tag{16.38}$$

If $i \neq j$, the integral over $d\delta \hat{X}_i$ vanishes at both limits. If $i = j$, we integrate by parts, immediately obtaining the result 16.33. An alternative, and easier, derivation of equation 16.33 is readily obtained on the basis of the approximate Gaussian distribution of section 15.6 rather than by the rigorous distribution used above. Such an alternative derivation is essentially given in problem 15.6–1.

Our derivation of the Onsager reciprocity is that given by Onsager. Extension to the case in which a magnetic field is present is quite simple. However, justification of the assumption that the macroscopic dynamical laws can be applied to the decay of a spontaneous fluctuation is not simple. Justification of this assumption requires rather powerful statistical mechanical analysis, so that this section should be viewed as a demonstration of plausibility rather than as a statistical mechanical derivation.

CHAPTER 17

Thermoelectric
and Thermomagnetic
Effects

17.1 The Dynamical Equations

As applications of the Onsager theorem we shall consider the thermo-electric and thermomagnetic effects, which are phenomena associated with the simultaneous flow of electric current and heat in a system. These phenomena, and certain relations among them, were proposed in 1854 by Lord Kelvin on the basis of empirical observations. Kelvin also presented a suggestive argument leading to the relations, carefully pointing out, however, that the argument was not only unjustifiable but that it could be made to yield incorrect relations as well as correct ones. It is a curious fact that many modern thermodynamics texts still present Kelvin's argument as a rigorous proof, completely ignoring Kelvin's own admonition to the contrary and ignoring the methods of modern irreversibility theory.

As remarked above, the thermoelectric and thermomagnetic effects are phenomena associated with the simultaneous flow of heat and electric current in a system. For definiteness of expression we shall think of a solid in which the charge carriers are electrons. Then, if s is the local entropy density, we have

$$ds = \frac{1}{T} du - \frac{\mu}{T} du - \sum_k \left(\frac{\mu_k}{T}\right) dn_k \tag{17.1}$$

in which u is the local energy density, μ is the electrochemical potential (per particle) of the electrons, n is the number of electrons per unit

293

volume, and in which the sum refers to other "components." These other components refer to the various types of atomic nuclei that together with the electrons constitute the solid. It will be noted that we have taken n as the number of electrons rather than the number of moles of electrons, and μ is accordingly the electrochemical potential per particle rather than per mole. In this regard we deviate from the more usual parameters merely by multiplication and division by Avogadro's number, respectively.

Just as equation 16.7 led to equation 16.9, equation 17.1 now leads to

$$\mathbf{J}_S = \frac{1}{T}\mathbf{J}_U - \frac{\mu}{T}\mathbf{J}_N \tag{17.2}$$

in which $\mathbf{J}_S$, $\mathbf{J}_U$, and $\mathbf{J}_N$ are current densities of entropy, energy, and number of electrons, respectively. The other components in equation 17.1 are assumed immobile and consequently do not contribute flux terms to equation 17.2.

Repeating the logic leading to equation 16.15, we find

$$\dot{s} = \nabla \frac{1}{T} \cdot \mathbf{J}_U - \nabla \frac{\mu}{T} \cdot \mathbf{J}_N \tag{17.3}$$

Thus, if the components of $\mathbf{J}_U$ and $-\mathbf{J}_N$ are taken as fluxes, the associated affinities are the components of $\nabla \frac{1}{T}$ and $\nabla \frac{\mu}{T}$. Assuming for simplicity that all flows and forces are parallel to the x-direction, and omitting the subscript x, the linear dynamical laws become

$$-J_N = L'_{11} \nabla \frac{\mu}{T} + L'_{12} \nabla \frac{1}{T} \tag{17.4}$$

$$J_U = L'_{21} \nabla \frac{\mu}{T} + L'_{22} \nabla \frac{1}{T} \tag{17.5}$$

and the Onsager theorem gives the relation

$$L'_{12}(\mathbf{H}_e) = L'_{21}(-\mathbf{H}_e) \tag{17.6}$$

In writing the foregoing dynamical equations we have assumed one-dimensional flow, such as occurs in wires or bars. This is the case of interest to us in the analysis of the thermoelectric effects. When we consider the thermomagnetic effects in section 17.6, however, we shall have to take explicit cognizance of the fact that the kinetic coefficients for the x-directed currents may differ from the kinetic coefficients for the y-directed currents.

Before drawing physical conclusions from equation 17.6, we recast the dynamical equations into an equivalent but instructive form. Although

J_U is a current density of total internal energy, we generally prefer to discuss the current density of heat. In analogy with the relation $dQ = T\,dS$ we therefore define a heat current density J_Q by the relation

$$J_Q = T J_S \tag{17.7}$$

or, by equation 17.2,

$$J_Q = J_U - \mu J_N \tag{17.8}$$

In a very rough intuitive way we can look on μ as the potential energy per particle and on μJ_N as a current density of potential energy; subtraction of the potential energy current density from the total energy current density yields the heat current density as a sort of kinetic energy current density. At any rate, eliminating J_U in favor of J_Q from equation 17.3 gives

$$\dot{s} = \nabla \frac{1}{T} \cdot J_Q - \frac{1}{T} \nabla \mu \cdot J_N \tag{17.9}$$

It follows from this equation that if the components of J_Q and of $-J_N$ are chosen as fluxes the associated affinities are the corresponding components of $\nabla(1/T)$ and of $(1/T)\nabla\mu$, respectively. The dynamical equations can then be written, in the one-dimensional case, as

J_Q = kinetic energy current density

$$-J_N = L_{11} \frac{1}{T} \nabla \mu + L_{12} \nabla \frac{1}{T} \tag{17.10}$$

, $L_{22}, L_{12} \to$ kinetic coefficients

$$J_Q = L_{21} \frac{1}{T} \nabla \mu + L_{22} \nabla \frac{1}{T} \tag{17.11}$$

and the Onsager relation is

$$\boxed{L_{12}(H_e) = L_{21}(-H_e)} \tag{17.12}$$

The reader should verify that the dynamical equations 17.10 and 17.11 can also be obtained by direct substitution of equation 17.8 into the previous pair of dynamical equations 17.4 and 17.5 without recourse to the entropy production equation 17.9.

The significance of the heat current can be exhibited in another manner. We consider, for a moment, a steady-state flow. Then both J_U and J_N are divergenceless and taking the divergence of equation 17.8 gives

$$\nabla \cdot J_Q = -\nabla \mu \cdot J_N \quad \text{(in the steady state)} \tag{17.13}$$

which states that in the steady state the rate of increase in heat current is equal to the rate of decrease in the potential energy current. Furthermore, the insertion of this equation into equation 17.9 gives

$$\dot{s} = \nabla \frac{1}{T} \cdot J_Q + \frac{1}{T} \nabla \cdot J_Q \tag{17.14}$$

which can be interpreted as stating that the production of entropy is due to two causes; the first term is the production of entropy due to the flow of heat from high to low temperature, and the second term is the increase in entropy due to the appearance of heat current.

We now accept the dynamical equations 17.10 and 17.11 and the symmetry condition (equation 17.12) as the basic equations with which to study the flow of heat and electric current in a system.

17.2   The Conductivities

We consider a system in which an electric current and a heat current flow parallel to the x-axis in a steady state, with no applied magnetic field. Then, omitting the subscript x,

$$-J_N = L_{11} \frac{1}{T} \nabla \mu + L_{12} \nabla \frac{1}{T} \tag{17.15}$$

$$J_Q = L_{12} \frac{1}{T} \nabla \mu + L_{22} \nabla \frac{1}{T} \tag{17.16}$$

where the Onsager theorem has reduced to the simple symmetry

$$L_{12} = L_{21} \tag{17.17}$$

The three kinetic coefficients appearing in the dynamical equations can be related to more familiar quantities, such as conductivities. In developing this connection we first comment briefly on the nature of the electrochemical potential μ of the electrons. We can consider μ as composed of two parts, a chemical portion μ_c and an electrical portion μ_e

$$\mu = \mu_c + \mu_e \tag{17.18}$$

If the charge on an electron is e, then μ_e is simply $e\phi$, where ϕ is the ordinary electrostatic potential. The chemical potential μ_c is a function of the temperature and of the electron concentration. Restating these facts in terms of gradients, the electrochemical potential *per unit charge* is $(1/e)\mu$; its gradient $(1/e)\nabla \mu$ is the sum of the *electric field* $(1/e)\nabla \mu_e$, plus an effective driving force $(1/e)\nabla \mu_c$ arising from a concentration gradient.

The *electric conductivity* σ is defined as the electric current density (eJ_N) per unit potential gradient $(1/e)\nabla \mu$ in an isothermal system. It is easily seen that $(1/e)\nabla \mu$ is actually the emf, for in a homogeneous isothermal system $\nabla\mu_c = 0$ and $\nabla\mu = \nabla\mu_e$. Thus, by definition,

$$\sigma \equiv -eJ_N \Big/ \frac{1}{e}\nabla\mu \qquad \text{for} \qquad \nabla T = 0 \tag{17.19}$$

whence equation 17.15 gives

$$\sigma = e^2 L_{11}/T \tag{17.20}$$

Similarly the _heat conductivity_ κ is defined as the heat current density per unit temperature gradient for zero electric current.

$$\kappa \equiv -J_Q/\nabla T \qquad \text{for} \qquad J_N = 0 \tag{17.21}$$

Solving the two kinetic equations simultaneously, we find

$$\kappa = \frac{D}{T^2 L_{11}} \tag{17.22}$$

where D denotes the determinant of the kinetic coefficients

$$D \equiv L_{11}L_{22} - L_{12}^2 \tag{17.23}$$

17.3 The Seebeck Effect and the Thermoelectric Power

The Seebeck effect refers to the production of an electromotive force in a thermocouple under conditions of zero electric current.

Consider a thermocouple with junctions at temperatures T_1 and $T_2(T_2 > T_1)$, as indicated in Figure 17.1. A voltmeter is inserted in one arm of the thermocouple at a point at which the temperature is T'. This voltmeter is such that it allows no passage of electric current but offers no resistance to the flow of heat. We designate the two materials composing the thermocouple by A and B. With $J_N = 0$, we obtain from the kinetic equations, for either conductor,

$$R_e = \infty$$
$$R_{th} = 0$$

$$\nabla\left(T\cdot\frac{1}{T}\right) = (\nabla T)\frac{1}{T} + T\nabla\frac{1}{T} = 0$$

$$-T\nabla\frac{1}{T} = \frac{1}{T}\nabla T$$

$$\nabla\mu = \frac{L_{12}}{TL_{11}}\nabla T = \frac{-L_{12}}{L_{11}}T\nabla\frac{1}{T} \tag{17.24}$$

Thus

$$\mu_2 - \mu_1 = \int_1^2 \frac{L_{12}^A}{TL_{11}^A}\,dT \tag{17.25}$$

$$\mu_2 - \mu_r' = \int_r^2 \frac{L_{12}^B}{TL_{11}^B}\,dT \tag{17.26}$$

$$\mu_l' - \mu_1 = \int_1^l \frac{L_{12}^B}{TL_{11}^B}\,dT \tag{17.27}$$

Eliminating μ_1 and μ_2 from these equations,

$$\mu'_r - \mu'_l = \int_1^2 \left(\frac{L_{12}^A}{TL_{11}^A} - \frac{L_{12}^B}{TL_{11}^B} \right) dT \tag{17.28}$$

But, because there is no temperature difference across the voltmeter, the voltage is simply

$$V = \frac{1}{e}(\mu'_r - \mu'_l) = \int_1^2 \left(\frac{L_{12}^A}{eTL_{11}^A} - \frac{L_{12}^B}{eTL_{11}^B} \right) dT \tag{17.29}$$

The *thermoelectric power* of the thermocouple, ϵ_{AB}, is defined as the change in voltage per unit change in temperature difference. The sign of

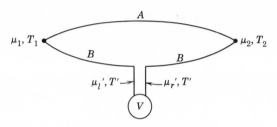

$$\mu_1, T_1 \qquad\qquad A \qquad\qquad \mu_2, T_2$$
$$B \qquad\qquad B$$
$$\mu_l', T' \rightarrow \quad \leftarrow \mu_r', T'$$
$$V$$

Figure 17.1

ϵ_{AB} is chosen as positive if the voltage increment is such as to drive the current from A to B at the hot junction. Then

$$\epsilon_{AB} = \frac{\partial V}{\partial T_2} = \left(\frac{-L_{12}^B}{eTL_{11}^B} \right) - \left(\frac{-L_{12}^A}{eTL_{11}^A} \right) \tag{17.30}$$

Defining the *absolute thermoelectric power* of a single medium by the relation

$$\epsilon_A \equiv \frac{-L_{12}^A}{eTL_{11}^A} \tag{17.31}$$

the thermoelectric power of the thermocouple is

$$\epsilon_{AB} = \epsilon_B - \epsilon_A \tag{17.32}$$

If we accept the electric conductivity σ, the heat conductivity κ, and the absolute thermoelectric power ϵ as the three physically significant dynamical properties of a medium, we can eliminate the three kinetic coefficients in favor of these quantities and rewrite the kinetic equations in the following form:

$$-J_N = \left(\frac{T\sigma}{e^2} \right) \frac{1}{T} \nabla \mu - \left(\frac{T^2 \sigma \epsilon}{e} \right) \nabla \frac{1}{T} \tag{17.33}$$

$$J_Q = -\left(\frac{T^2 \sigma \epsilon}{e} \right) \frac{1}{T} \nabla \mu + (T^3 \sigma \epsilon^2 + T^2 \kappa) \nabla \frac{1}{T} \tag{17.34}$$

An interesting insight to the' physical meaning of the absolute thermo-electric power can be obtained by eliminating $(1/T) \nabla \mu$ between the two foregoing dynamical equations and writing J_Q in terms of J_N and $\nabla(1/T)$:

$$J_Q = T \epsilon e J_N + T^2 \kappa \nabla \frac{1}{T} \tag{17.35}$$

or, recalling that $J_S = J_Q/T$,

$$J_S = \epsilon e J_N + T \kappa \nabla \frac{1}{T} \tag{17.36}$$

According to this equation, each electron involved in the electric current carries with it an entropy of ϵe. This flow of entropy is in addition to the entropy current $T\kappa \nabla(1/T)$, which is independent of the electronic current. The thermoelectric power can be looked on as the entropy transported per coulomb by the electron flow.

17.4 The Peltier Effect

The Peltier effect refers to the evolution of heat accompanying the flow of an electric current across an isothermal junction of two materials. Consider an isothermal junction of two conductors A and B and an electric current eJ_N to flow as indicated in Figure 17.2. Then the total energy

$$A \qquad\qquad B$$
$$J_N, J_U{}^A \qquad\qquad J_N, J_U{}^B$$

Figure 17.2

current will be discontinuous across the junction, and the energy difference appears as *Peltier heat* at the junction. We have $J_U = J_Q + \mu J_N$, and since both μ and J_N are continuous across the junction it follows that the discontinuity in J_U is equal to the discontinuity in J_Q.

$$J_U{}^A - J_U{}^B = J_Q{}^A - J_Q{}^B \tag{17.37}$$

Because of the isothermal condition the dynamical equations 17.33 and 17.34 give, in either conductor,

$$J_Q = T\epsilon(eJ_N) \tag{17.38}$$

whence

$$J_Q{}^B - J_Q{}^A = T(\epsilon_B - \epsilon_A)(eJ_N) \tag{17.39}$$

The *Peltier coefficient* π_{AB} is defined as the heat that must be supplied to the junction when unit electric current passes from conductor A to conductor B. Thus

$$\pi_{AB} \equiv (J_Q{}^B - J_Q{}^A)/eJ_N = T(\epsilon_B - \epsilon_A) \tag{17.40}$$

Equation 17.40, which relates the Peltier coefficient to the absolute thermoelectric powers, is one of the relations presented on empirical evidence by Kelvin in 1854. It is called the *second Kelvin relation.*

The method by which we have derived equation 17.40 is typical of all applications of the Onsager relations, so that it may be appropriate to review the procedure. We first write the linear dynamical equations, reducing the number of kinetic coefficients appearing therein by invoking the Onsager relations. We then proceed to analyze various effects, expressing each in terms of the kinetic coefficients. When we have analyzed as many effects as there are kinetic coefficients, we rewrite the dynamical equations in terms of those effects rather than in terms of the kinetic coefficients (as in equations 17.33 and 17.34). Thereafter every additional effect analyzed on the basis of the dynamical equations results in a relation analogous to equation 17.40 and expresses this new effect in terms of the coefficients in the dynamical equation.

17.5   The Thomson Effect

The Thomson effect refers to the evolution of heat as an electric current traverses a temperature gradient in a material.

Consider a conductor carrying a heat current but no electric current. A temperature distribution governed by the temperature dependence of the kinetic coefficients will be set up. Let the conductor now be placed in contact at each point with a heat reservoir of the same temperature as that point, so that there is no heat interchange between conductor and reservoirs. Now let an electric current pass through the conductor. An interchange of heat will take place between conductor and reservoirs. This heat exchange consists of two parts—the *Joule heat* and the *Thomson heat.*

As the electric current passes along the conductor, any change in total energy flow must be supplied by an energy interchange with the reservoirs. Thus we must compute $\nabla \cdot \mathbf{J}_U$.

$$\nabla \cdot \mathbf{J}_U = \nabla \cdot (\mathbf{J}_Q + \mu \mathbf{J}_N) = \nabla \cdot \mathbf{J}_Q + \nabla \mu \cdot \mathbf{J}_N \qquad (17.41)$$

which can be expressed in terms of $\mathbf{J}_N$ and $\nabla(1/T)$ by using equations 17.35 and 17.33.

$$\nabla \cdot \mathbf{J}_U = \nabla \cdot \left(T\epsilon e \mathbf{J}_N + T^2 \kappa \, \nabla \frac{1}{T} \right) + \left(-\frac{e^2}{\sigma} \mathbf{J}_N + T^2 e\epsilon \, \nabla \frac{1}{T} \right) \cdot \mathbf{J}_N \qquad (17.42)$$

or

$$\nabla \cdot \mathbf{J}_U = T \, \nabla \epsilon \cdot (e \mathbf{J}_N) + \nabla \cdot \left(T^2 \kappa \, \nabla \frac{1}{T} \right) - \frac{e^2}{\sigma} \mathbf{J}_N \cdot \mathbf{J}_N \qquad (17.43)$$

However the temperature distribution is that which is determined by the steady state with no electric current, and we know that $\nabla \cdot \mathbf{J}_U$ vanishes in that state. By putting $\mathbf{J}_N = 0$ and $\nabla \cdot \mathbf{J}_U = 0$ in equation 17.43, we conclude that the temperature distribution is such as to make the second term vanish, and consequently

$$\nabla \cdot \mathbf{J}_U = T \nabla \epsilon \cdot (e\mathbf{J}_N) - \frac{1}{\sigma}(e\mathbf{J}_N)^2 \qquad (17.44)$$

Furthermore, noting that the thermoelectric power is a function of the local temperature, we write

$$\nabla \epsilon = \frac{d\epsilon}{dT} \nabla T \qquad (17.45)$$

and

$$\nabla \cdot \mathbf{J}_U = T\frac{d\epsilon}{dT} \nabla T \cdot (e\mathbf{J}_N) - \frac{1}{\sigma}(e\mathbf{J}_N)^2 \qquad (17.46)$$

The second term is the Joule heat, produced by the flow of electric current, even in the absence of a temperature gradient. The first term represents the Thomson heat, absorbed from the heat reservoirs when the current $e\mathbf{J}_N$ traverses the temperature gradient ∇T. The Thomson coefficient τ is defined as the Thomson heat absorbed per unit electric current and per unit temperature gradient.

$$\tau \equiv \frac{\text{Thomson heat}}{\nabla T \cdot (e\mathbf{J}_N)} = T\frac{d\epsilon}{dT} \qquad (17.47)$$

Although we have obtained the foregoing relation between τ and ϵ by our standard procedure, it is of interest that this relation can be derived by an alternate procedure, combining the *second Kelvin relation* (equation 17.40) with considerations of energy conservation.

To carry out this alternate derivation, we consider a thermocouple subjected to a very small temperature difference dT. Into one arm of this thermocouple is inserted a battery of just such a voltage as to negate the Seebeck voltage, causing no electric current to flow in the thermocouple circuit.

In accordance with equations 17.30 and 17.32, the required emf of the battery is $\epsilon_B - \epsilon_A$. The thermocouple circuit is indicated in Figure 17.3.

We now consider the virtual transfer of a unit of charge around the circuit, and we list the various energy transfers that take place in the process. As the charge crosses the cold junction, from B to A, a Peltier heat of $+\pi_{BA}$ is absorbed from the reservoir. As the charge traverses the leg A of the thermocouple, the Thomson heat $\tau_A\, dT$ is absorbed from the reservoirs. However, we ignore the Joule heat because we assume the charge to be transported so slowly that the Joule heat, which is quadratic in the currents, is negligible compared to the Thomson heat, which is linear in the currents. In traversing the hot junction from A to B the Peltier heat $\pi_{AB}(T + dT)$ is absorbed. In traversing the leg B the Thomson heat $-\tau_B \, dT$ is absorbed. And in traversing the battery an amount of

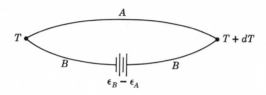

Figure 17.3

work equal to the emf of the battery, or $\epsilon_B - \epsilon_A$, is performed. Equating the total energy absorbed to the work done on the battery gives

$$\pi_{BA}(T) + \tau_A \, dT + \pi_{AB}(T + dT) - \tau_B \, dT = \epsilon_B - \epsilon_A \quad (17.48)$$

But

$$\pi_{AB}(T + dT) = \pi_{AB}(T) + \frac{d\pi_{AB}}{dT} \, dT \quad (17.49)$$

whence

$$\frac{d\pi_{AB}}{dT} + \tau_A - \tau_B = \epsilon_A - \epsilon_B \quad (17.50)$$

Finally, inserting equation 17.40 for the Peltier coefficient gives the equivalent of equation 17.47.

Zemansky   Equation 17.50, which depends on energy conservation alone and which does not require the Onsager theorem for its demonstration, was given by Kelvin and is called the *first Kelvin relation.*

17.6 The Thermomagnetic Dynamical Equations

Having demonstrated the technique of application of the Onsager theorem in some detail, we can now treat the thermomagnetic effects relatively concisely. These effects occur when electric and heat currents are permitted to flow in a plane perpendicular to an applied magnetic field, as shown in Figure 17.4.

The dynamical equations 17.10 and 17.11 apply specifically to one-dimensional flow. To obtain their analogues for two-dimensional flow, we return to equation 17.9, which we rewrite explicitly in its Cartesian components. To simplify the notation we write N_x for J_{Nx}, Q_x for J_{Qx}, and similarly for the y-components.

$$\dot{s} = \left(\nabla_x \frac{1}{T}\right)Q_x + \left(\nabla_y \frac{1}{T}\right)Q_y - \left(\frac{1}{T}\nabla_x\mu\right)N_x - \left(\frac{1}{T}\nabla_y\mu\right)N_y \quad (17.51)$$

where ∇_x denotes the partial derivative $\partial/\partial x$. We conclude that if $-N_x$, $-N_y$, Q_x, and Q_y are fluxes the associated affinities are $(1/T)\nabla_x\mu$,

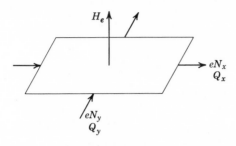

Figure 17.4

$(1/T)\nabla_y\mu$, $\nabla_x(1/T)$, and $\nabla_y(1/T)$, respectively. The dynamical equations then become

$$-N_x = L'_{11}\frac{1}{T}\nabla_x\mu + L'_{12}\frac{1}{T}\nabla_y\mu + L'_{13}\nabla_x\frac{1}{T} + L'_{14}\nabla_y\frac{1}{T}$$

$$-N_y = L'_{21}\frac{1}{T}\nabla_x\mu + L'_{22}\frac{1}{T}\nabla_y\mu + L'_{23}\nabla_x\frac{1}{T} + L'_{24}\nabla_y\frac{1}{T}$$

$$Q_x = L'_{31}\frac{1}{T}\nabla_x\mu + L'_{32}\frac{1}{T}\nabla_y\mu + L'_{33}\nabla_x\frac{1}{T} + L'_{34}\nabla_y\frac{1}{T} \quad (17.52)$$

$$Q_y = L'_{41}\frac{1}{T}\nabla_x\mu + L'_{42}\frac{1}{T}\nabla_y\mu + L'_{43}\nabla_x\frac{1}{T} + L'_{44}\nabla_y\frac{1}{T}$$

The Onsager theorem states that

$$L'_{ij}(H_e) = L'_{ji}(-H_e) \quad (17.53)$$

If we assume isotropy in the xy-plane, the symmetry of the x- and y-axes requires that $L'_{11} = L'_{22}$, etc., reducing the dynamical equations to

$$-N_x = L'_{11}\frac{1}{T}\nabla_x\mu + L'_{12}\frac{1}{T}\nabla_y\mu + L'_{13}\nabla_x\frac{1}{T} + L'_{14}\nabla_y\frac{1}{T}$$

$$-N_y = L'_{12}\frac{1}{T}\nabla_x\mu + L'_{11}\frac{1}{T}\nabla_y\mu + L'_{14}\nabla_x\frac{1}{T} + L'_{13}\nabla_y\frac{1}{T}$$

$$Q_x = L'_{31}\frac{1}{T}\nabla_x\mu + L'_{32}\frac{1}{T}\nabla_y\mu + L'_{33}\nabla_x\frac{1}{T} + L'_{34}\nabla_y\frac{1}{T} \quad (17.54)$$

$$Q_y = -L'_{32}\frac{1}{T}\nabla_x\mu + L'_{31}\frac{1}{T}\nabla_y\mu - L'_{34}\nabla_x\frac{1}{T} + L'_{33}\nabla_y\frac{1}{T}$$

in which, furthermore, L'_{11}, L'_{13}, L'_{31}, and L'_{33} are identified as even functions of the magnetic field, whereas L'_{12}, L'_{14}, L'_{32}, and L'_{34} are identified as odd functions of the magnetic field.

From the Onsager relation (equation 17.53) we now have

$$L'_{13}(H_e) = L'_{31}(-H_e) \tag{17.55}$$

However L'_{31} is an even function of the field, so that

$$L'_{31}(-H_e) = L'_{31}(H_e) \tag{17.56}$$

These two equations imply that

$$L'_{31}(H_e) = L'_{13}(H_e) \tag{17.57}$$

Similarly, from the Onsager relation,

$$L'_{14}(H_e) = L'_{41}(-H_e) \tag{17.58}$$

But examination of equations 17.54 shows that we have already identified L'_{41} as equal to $-L'_{32}$ by symmetry considerations, so that

$$L'_{14}(H_e) = -L'_{32}(-H_e) \tag{17.59}$$

Again, L'_{32} is an odd function of the magnetic field, implying finally that

$$L'_{14}(H_e) = L'_{32}(H_e) \tag{17.60}$$

The Onsager relation therefore enables us to eliminate two kinetic coefficients from the dynamical equations, which thereby become

$$-N_x = L'_{11}\frac{1}{T}\nabla_x\mu + L'_{12}\frac{1}{T}\nabla_y\mu + L'_{13}\nabla_x\frac{1}{T} + L'_{14}\nabla_y\frac{1}{T}$$

$$-N_y = -L'_{12}\frac{1}{T}\nabla_x\mu + L'_{11}\frac{1}{T}\nabla_y\mu - L'_{14}\nabla_x\frac{1}{T} + L'_{13}\nabla_y\frac{1}{T}$$

$$\tag{17.61}$$

$$Q_x = L'_{13}\frac{1}{T}\nabla_x\mu + L'_{14}\frac{1}{T}\nabla_y\mu + L'_{33}\nabla_x\frac{1}{T} + L'_{34}\nabla_y\frac{1}{T}$$

$$Q_y = -L'_{14}\frac{1}{T}\nabla_x\mu + L'_{13}\frac{1}{T}\nabla_y\mu - L'_{34}\nabla_x\frac{1}{T} + L'_{33}\nabla_y\frac{1}{T}$$

We are now prepared to undertake our analysis of the various thermomagnetic effects in principle. There are six kinetic coefficients in the dynamical equations. By introducing six effects and defining six descriptive coefficients for those effects, we can eliminate the kinetic coefficients in favor of these six descriptive coefficients. Any further effects analyzed will result in relations analogous to the Kelvin relations. However, Mazur and Prigogine have shown that the algebra is greatly simplified if we first invert the dynamical equations in such a way that the electrical current and temperature gradients, which are the experimentally controlled variables, appear on the right.

In carrying out the inversion of the dynamical equations it is convenient also to introduce explicitly the electric current eN_x and the electrochemical potential per unit charge $(1/e)\nabla_x\mu$ and to write the equations in terms of $\nabla_x T$ instead of $\nabla_x(1/T)$. The various resulting factors of $1/e$, e, and $-1/T^2$ are absorbed into the new kinetic coefficients. We thus obtain

$$-\frac{1}{e}\nabla_x\mu = L_{11}eN_x + L_{12}eN_y - L_{13}\nabla_x T - L_{14}\nabla_y T$$

$$-\frac{1}{e}\nabla_y\mu = -L_{12}eN_x + L_{11}eN_y + L_{14}\nabla_x T - L_{13}\nabla_y T$$

$$(17.62)$$

$$Q_x = -TL_{13}eN_x - TL_{14}eN_y - L_{33}\nabla_x T - L_{34}\nabla_y T$$

$$Q_y = TL_{14}eN_x - TL_{13}eN_y + L_{34}\nabla_x T - L_{33}\nabla_y T$$

The new kinetic coefficients L_{ij} are, of course, fairly complicated functions of the old kinetic coefficients L'_{ij}. But the precise form of these relationships is of no consequence to us. The only significant fact is that the symmetry of the coefficients in equation 17.62 is implied by the symmetry of the coefficients in equation 17.61, as the reader may convince himself without recourse to detailed algebraic inversion of the equations.

17.7 The Thermomagnetic Effects

We now proceed with the definition of a number of effects and of their associated descriptive coefficients.

1. The Absolute Thermoelectric Power

In the presence of a magnetic field the definition of the absolute thermoelectric power is conveniently taken as

$$\epsilon \equiv \frac{1}{e}\nabla_x\mu/\nabla_x T \quad \text{with} \quad N_x = N_y = \nabla_y T = 0 \quad (17.63)$$

whence

$$\epsilon = L_{13} \quad (17.64)$$

2. The Isothermal Electric Conductivity

$$\sigma_i \equiv -eN_x\bigg/\frac{1}{e}\nabla_x\mu \quad \text{with} \quad \nabla_x T = \nabla_y T = N_y = 0 \quad (17.65)$$

whence

$$\sigma_i = 1/L_{11} \tag{17.66}$$

3. The Adiabatic Electric Conductivity

$$\sigma_a \equiv -eN_x \Big/ \frac{1}{e}\,\nabla_x\mu \quad \text{with} \quad \nabla_x T = Q_y = N_y = 0 \tag{17.67}$$

whence

$$\sigma_a = (L_{11} - TL_{13}^3/L_{33})^{-1} \tag{17.68}$$

4. The Isothermal Heat Conductivity

$$\kappa_i \equiv -Q_x/\nabla_x T \quad \text{with} \quad N_x = N_y = \nabla_y T = 0 \tag{17.69}$$

whence

$$\kappa_i = L_{33} \tag{17.70}$$

5. The Adiabatic Heat Conductivity

$$\kappa_a \equiv -Q_x/\nabla_x T \quad \text{with} \quad N_x = N_y = Q_y = 0 \tag{17.71}$$

whence

$$\kappa_a = (L_{33}^2 + L_{34}^2)/L_{33} \tag{17.72}$$

6. The Isothermal Hall Effect

$$R_i \equiv \frac{1}{e}\,\nabla_y\mu/H_e e N_x \quad \text{with} \quad \nabla_x T = \nabla_y T = N_y = 0 \tag{17.73}$$

whence

$$R_i = L_{12}/H_e \tag{17.74}$$

7. The Adiabatic Hall Effect

$$R_a \equiv \frac{1}{e}\,\nabla_y\mu/H_e e N_x \quad \text{with} \quad \nabla_x T = Q_y = N_y = 0 \tag{17.75}$$

whence

$$R_a = (L_{12} + TL_{13}L_{14}/L_{33})/H_e \tag{17.76}$$

8. The Isothermal Nernst Effect

$$\eta_i \equiv -\frac{1}{e}\,\nabla_y\mu/H_e\nabla_x T \quad \text{with} \quad N_x = N_y = \nabla_y T = 0 \tag{17.77}$$

whence

$$\eta_i = L_{14}/H_e \tag{17.78}$$

9. The Adiabatic Nernst Effect

$$\eta_a \equiv -\frac{1}{e} \nabla_y \mu / H_e \nabla_x T \quad \text{with} \quad N_x = N_y = Q_y = 0 \quad (17.79)$$

whence

$$\eta_a = (L_{14} - L_{13}L_{34}/L_{33})/H_e \quad (17.80)$$

10. The Ettingshausen Effect

$$E = \nabla_y T / H_e e N_x \quad \text{with} \quad N_y = Q_y = \nabla_x T = 0 \quad (17.81)$$

whence

$$E = TL_{14}/H_e L_{33} \quad (17.82)$$

11. The Leduc-Righi Effect

$$\mathscr{L} \equiv \nabla_y T / H_e \, \nabla_x T \quad \text{with} \quad N_x = N_y = Q_y = 0 \quad (17.83)$$

whence

$$\mathscr{L} = L_{34}/H_e L_{33} \quad (17.84)$$

The fundamental set of dynamical equations can now be written in the matrix form

$$
\begin{bmatrix}
-\frac{1}{e}\nabla_x \mu \\[2mm]
-\frac{1}{e}\nabla_y \mu \\[2mm]
Q_x \\[2mm]
Q_y
\end{bmatrix}
=
\begin{bmatrix}
\sigma_i^{-1} & H_e R_i & -\epsilon & -H_e \eta_i \\[2mm]
-H_e R_i & \sigma_i^{-1} & H_e \eta_i & -\epsilon \\[2mm]
-T\epsilon & -TH_e \eta_i & -\kappa_i & -H_e \kappa_i \mathscr{L} \\[2mm]
TH_e \eta_i & -T\epsilon & H_e \kappa_i \mathscr{L} & -\kappa_i
\end{bmatrix}
\begin{bmatrix}
eN_x \\[2mm]
eN_y \\[2mm]
\nabla_x T \\[2mm]
\nabla_y T
\end{bmatrix}
$$

$$(17.85)$$

We further find the relations

$$\kappa_i E = T\eta_i \quad (17.86)$$

$$\kappa_a - \kappa_i = H_e \kappa_i^2 \mathscr{L}^2 \quad (17.87)$$

$$\sigma_i^{-1} - \sigma_i^{-1} = H_e^2 \eta_i E \quad (17.88)$$

$$R_a - R_i = \epsilon E \quad (17.89)$$

$$\eta_i - \eta_a = \epsilon \mathscr{L} \quad (17.90)$$

Each of the coefficients is an even function of the magnetic field. Thus the isothermal conductivity can be expanded in powers of H_e to give

$$\sigma_i = \sigma_i^\circ + \sigma_i^{(2)} H_e^2 + \sigma_i^{(4)} H_e^4 + \cdots \quad (17.91)$$

and the coefficient of the quadratic term is called a *magneto-conductivity coefficient*.

Any experimental situation can be directly analyzed by equation 17.85, relating it to the thermomagnetic coefficients appearing therein. The resultant equations, analogous to the thermomagnetic relations 17.86–17.90, represent the fruits of the theory of irreversible processes applied to conductivity phenomena.

Some Relations Involving Partial Derivatives

A.1 Partial Derivatives

In thermodynamics we are interested in continuous functions of three (or more) variables.

$$\psi = \psi(x, y, z) \tag{A.1}$$

If two independent variables, say y and z, are held constant, ψ becomes a function of only one independent variable x, and the derivative of ψ with respect to x may be defined and computed in the standard fashion. The derivative so obtained is called the *partial derivative* of ψ with respect to x and is denoted by the symbol $(\partial\psi/\partial x)_{y,z}$ or simply by $\partial\psi/\partial x$. The derivative depends upon x and also upon the values at which y and z are held during the differentiation; that is $\partial\psi/\partial x$ is a function of x, y, and z. The derivatives $\partial\psi/\partial y$ and $\partial\psi/\partial z$ are defined in an identical manner.

The function $\partial\psi/\partial x$, if continuous, may itself be differentiated to yield three derivatives which are called the *second partial derivatives* of ψ:

$$\frac{\partial}{\partial x}\left(\frac{\partial\psi}{\partial x}\right) \equiv \frac{\partial^2\psi}{\partial x^2}$$

$$\frac{\partial}{\partial y}\left(\frac{\partial\psi}{\partial x}\right) \equiv \frac{\partial^2\psi}{\partial y\,\partial x} \tag{A.2}$$

$$\frac{\partial}{\partial z}\left(\frac{\partial\psi}{\partial x}\right) \equiv \frac{\partial^2\psi}{\partial z\,\partial x}$$

By partial differentiation of the functions $\partial\psi/\partial y$ and $\partial\psi/\partial z$, we obtain other second partial derivatives of ψ:

$$\frac{\partial^2\psi}{\partial x\,\partial y}, \quad \frac{\partial^2\psi}{\partial y^2}, \quad \frac{\partial^2\psi}{\partial z\,\partial y}, \quad \frac{\partial^2\psi}{\partial x\,\partial z}, \quad \frac{\partial^2\psi}{\partial y\,\partial z}, \quad \text{and} \quad \frac{\partial^2\psi}{\partial z^2}$$

It may be shown that under the continuity conditions which we have assumed for ψ and its partial derivatives the order of differentiation is immaterial, so that

$$\frac{\partial^2\psi}{\partial x\,\partial y} = \frac{\partial^2\psi}{\partial y\,\partial x}, \quad \frac{\partial^2\psi}{\partial x\,\partial z} = \frac{\partial^2\psi}{\partial z\,\partial x}, \quad \frac{\partial^2\psi}{\partial y\,\partial z} = \frac{\partial^2\psi}{\partial z\,\partial y} \qquad \text{(A.3)}$$

There are therefore just six nonequivalent second partial derivatives of a function of three independent variables (three for a function of two variables, and $\frac{1}{2}n(n+1)$ for a function of n variables).

A.2 Taylor's Expansion

The relationship between $\psi(x, y, z)$ and $\psi(x + dx, y + dy, z + dz)$, where dx, dy, and dz denote arbitrary increments in x, y, and z, is given by Taylor's expansion:

$$\psi(x + dx, y + dy, z + dz) = \psi(x, y, z) + \left(\frac{\partial\psi}{\partial x}\,dx + \frac{\partial\psi}{\partial y}\,dy + \frac{\partial\psi}{\partial z}\,dz\right)$$

$$+ \frac{1}{2}\left[\frac{\partial^2\psi}{\partial x^2}(dx)^2 + \frac{\partial^2\psi}{\partial y^2}(dy)^2 + \frac{\partial^2\psi}{\partial z^2}(dz)^2 + 2\frac{\partial^2\psi}{\partial x\,\partial y}\,dx\,dy\right.$$

$$\left. + 2\frac{\partial^2\psi}{\partial x\,\partial z}\,dx\,dz + 2\frac{\partial^2\psi}{\partial y\,\partial z}\,dy\,dz\right] + \cdots \qquad \text{(A.4)}$$

This expansion can be written in a convenient symbolic form:

$$\psi(x + dx, y + dy, z + dz) = e^{\left(dx\frac{\partial}{\partial x} + dy\frac{\partial}{\partial y} + dz\frac{\partial}{\partial z}\right)}\psi(x, y, z) \qquad \text{(A.5)}$$

Expansion of the symbolic exponential according to the usual series

$$e^x = 1 + x + \frac{1}{2!}x^2 + \cdots + \frac{1}{n!}x^n + \cdots \qquad \text{(A.6)}$$

then reproduces the Taylor expansion (equation A.4)

A.3 Differentials of ψ

The Taylor expansion (equation A.4) can also be written in the form

$$\psi(x + dx, y + dy, z + dz) - \psi(x, y, z)$$

$$= d\psi + \frac{1}{2!}d^2\psi + \cdots + \frac{1}{n!}d^n\psi \cdots \qquad \text{(A.7)}$$

where

$$d\psi \equiv \frac{\partial \psi}{\partial x}\,dx + \frac{\partial \psi}{\partial y}\,dy + \frac{\partial \psi}{\partial z}\,dz \tag{A.8}$$

$$d^2\psi = \frac{\partial^2 \psi}{\partial x^2}\,(dx)^2 + \frac{\partial^2 \psi}{\partial y^2}\,(dy)^2 + \frac{\partial^2 \psi}{\partial z^2}\,(dz)^2 + 2\,\frac{\partial^2 \psi}{\partial x\,\partial y}\,dx\,dy$$

$$+ 2\,\frac{\partial^2 \psi}{\partial x\,\partial z}\,dx\,dz + 2\,\frac{\partial^2 \psi}{\partial y\,\partial z}\,dy\,dz \tag{A.9}$$

and generally

$$d^n\psi = \left(dx\,\frac{\partial}{\partial x} + dy\,\frac{\partial}{\partial y} + dz\,\frac{\partial}{\partial z}\right)^n \psi(x, y, z) \tag{A.10}$$

These quantities $d\psi, d^2\psi \cdots, d^n\psi \cdots$ are called the *first, second, and nth order differentials* of ψ.

A.4 Composite Functions

Returning to the first-order differential,

$$d\psi = \left(\frac{\partial \psi}{\partial x}\right)_{y,z} dx + \left(\frac{\partial \psi}{\partial y}\right)_{x,z} dy + \left(\frac{\partial \psi}{\partial z}\right)_{x,y} dz \tag{A.11}$$

an interesting case arises when x, y, and z are not varied independently but are themselves considered to be functions of some variable u. Then

$$dx = \frac{dx}{du}\,du, \qquad dy = \frac{dy}{du}\,du \qquad \text{and} \qquad dz = \frac{dz}{du}\,du$$

whence

$$d\psi = \left[\left(\frac{\partial \psi}{\partial x}\right)_{y,z} \frac{dx}{du} + \left(\frac{\partial \psi}{\partial y}\right)_{x,z} \frac{dy}{du} + \left(\frac{\partial \psi}{\partial z}\right)_{x,y} \frac{dz}{du}\right] du \tag{A.12}$$

or

$$\frac{d\psi}{du} = \left(\frac{\partial \psi}{\partial x}\right)_{y,z} \frac{dx}{du} + \left(\frac{\partial \psi}{\partial y}\right)_{x,z} \frac{dy}{du} + \left(\frac{\partial \psi}{\partial z}\right)_{x,y} \frac{dz}{du} \tag{A.13}$$

If x and y are function of two (or more) variables, say u and v, then

$$dx = \left(\frac{\partial x}{\partial u}\right)_v du + \left(\frac{\partial x}{\partial v}\right)_u dv, \qquad \text{etc.}$$

and

$$d\psi = \left[\left(\frac{\partial \psi}{\partial x}\right)_{y,z}\left(\frac{\partial x}{\partial u}\right)_v + \left(\frac{\partial \psi}{\partial y}\right)_{x,z}\left(\frac{\partial y}{\partial u}\right)_v + \left(\frac{\partial \psi}{\partial z}\right)_{x,y}\left(\frac{\partial z}{\partial u}\right)_v\right] du$$

$$+ \left[\left(\frac{\partial \psi}{\partial x}\right)_{y,z}\left(\frac{\partial x}{\partial v}\right)_u + \left(\frac{\partial \psi}{\partial y}\right)_{x,z}\left(\frac{\partial y}{\partial v}\right)_u + \left(\frac{\partial \psi}{\partial z}\right)_{x,y}\left(\frac{\partial z}{\partial v}\right)_u\right] dv \tag{A.14}$$

or

$$dψ = \left(\frac{∂ψ}{∂u}\right)_v du + \left(\frac{∂ψ}{∂v}\right)_u dv \tag{A.15}$$

where

$$\left(\frac{∂ψ}{∂u}\right)_v = \left(\frac{∂ψ}{∂x}\right)_{y,z}\left(\frac{∂x}{∂u}\right)_v + \left(\frac{∂ψ}{∂y}\right)_{x,z}\left(\frac{∂y}{∂u}\right)_v + \left(\frac{∂ψ}{∂z}\right)_{x,y}\left(\frac{∂z}{∂u}\right)_v \tag{A.16}$$

and similarly for $(∂ψ/∂v)_u$.

It may happen that u is identical to x itself. Then

$$\left(\frac{∂ψ}{∂x}\right)_v = \left(\frac{∂ψ}{∂x}\right)_{y,z} + \left(\frac{∂ψ}{∂y}\right)_{x,z}\left(\frac{∂y}{∂x}\right)_v + \left(\frac{∂ψ}{∂z}\right)_{x,y}\left(\frac{∂z}{∂x}\right)_v \tag{A.17}$$

Other special cases can be treated similarly.

A.5 Implicit Functions

If $ψ$ is held constant, the variations of x, y, and z are not independent, and the relation

$$ψ(x, y, z) = \text{constant} \tag{A.18}$$

gives an implicit functional relation among x, y, and z. This relation may be solved for one variable, say z, in terms of the other two.

$$z = z(x, y) \tag{A.19}$$

This function can then be treated by the techniques described above to derive certain relations among the partial derivatives. However, a more direct method of obtaining the appropriate relations among the partial derivatives is merely to put $dψ = 0$ in equation A.8.

$$0 = \left(\frac{∂ψ}{∂x}\right)_{y,z} dx + \left(\frac{∂ψ}{∂y}\right)_{x,z} dy + \left(\frac{∂ψ}{∂z}\right)_{x,y} dz \tag{A.20}$$

If we now put $dz = 0$ and divide through by dx, we find

$$0 = \left(\frac{∂ψ}{∂x}\right)_{y,z} + \left(\frac{∂ψ}{∂y}\right)_{x,z}\left(\frac{∂y}{∂x}\right)_{ψ,z} \tag{A.21}$$

in which the symbol $(∂y/∂x)_{ψ,z}$ appropriately indicates that the implied functional relation between y and x is that determined by the constancy of $ψ$ and z. Equation A.21 can be written in the convenient form

$$\left(\frac{∂y}{∂x}\right)_{ψ,z} = \frac{-(∂ψ/∂x)_{y,z}}{(∂ψ/∂y)_{x,z}} \tag{A.22}$$

This equation plays a very prominent role in thermodynamic calculations.

By successively putting $dy = 0$ and $dx = 0$ in equation A.20, we find the two similar relations

$$\left(\frac{\partial z}{\partial x}\right)_{\psi,y} = \frac{-(\partial\psi/\partial x)_{y,z}}{(\partial\psi/\partial z)_{x,y}} \tag{A.23}$$

and

$$\left(\frac{\partial z}{\partial y}\right)_{\psi,x} = \frac{-(\partial\psi/\partial y)_{x,z}}{(\partial\psi/\partial z)_{x,y}} \tag{A.24}$$

Returning to equation A.20 we again put $dz = 0$, but we now divide through by dy rather than by dx.

$$0 = \left(\frac{\partial\psi}{\partial x}\right)_{y,z}\left(\frac{\partial x}{\partial y}\right)_{\psi,z} + \left(\frac{\partial\psi}{\partial y}\right)_{x,z} \tag{A.25}$$

whence

$$\left(\frac{\partial x}{\partial y}\right)_{\psi,z} = \frac{-(\partial\psi/\partial y)_{x,z}}{(\partial\psi/\partial x)_{y,z}} \tag{A.26}$$

and, on comparison with equation A.21, we find the very reasonable result that

$$\left(\frac{\partial x}{\partial y}\right)_{\psi,z} = \frac{1}{(\partial y/\partial x)_{\psi,z}} \tag{A.27}$$

From equations A.22–A.24 we then find

$$\left(\frac{\partial x}{\partial y}\right)_{\psi,z}\left(\frac{\partial y}{\partial z}\right)_{\psi,x}\left(\frac{\partial z}{\partial x}\right)_{\psi,y} = -1 \tag{A.28}$$

Finally we return to our basic equation, which defines the differential $d\psi$, and consider the case in which x, y, and z are themselves functions of a variable u (as in equation A.12)

$$d\psi = \left[\left(\frac{\partial\psi}{\partial x}\right)_{y,z}\frac{dx}{du} + \left(\frac{\partial\psi}{\partial y}\right)_{x,z}\frac{dy}{du} + \left(\frac{\partial\psi}{\partial z}\right)_{x,y}\frac{dz}{du}\right]du \tag{A.29}$$

If ψ is to be constant, there must be a relation among x, y, and z, hence also among dx/du, dy/du, and dz/du. We find

$$0 = \left(\frac{\partial\psi}{\partial x}\right)_{y,z}\left(\frac{dx}{du}\right)_{\psi} + \left(\frac{\partial\psi}{\partial y}\right)_{x,z}\left(\frac{dy}{du}\right)_{\psi} + \left(\frac{\partial\psi}{\partial z}\right)_{x,y}\left(\frac{dz}{du}\right)_{\psi} \tag{A.30}$$

If we further require that z shall be a constant independent of u we find

$$0 = \left(\frac{\partial\psi}{\partial x}\right)_{y,z}\left(\frac{\partial x}{\partial u}\right)_{\psi,z} + \left(\frac{\partial\psi}{\partial y}\right)_{x,z}\left(\frac{\partial y}{\partial u}\right)_{\psi,z} \tag{A.31}$$

or

$$\frac{(\partial y/\partial u)_{\psi,z}}{(\partial x/\partial u)_{\psi,z}} = -\frac{(\partial\psi/\partial x)_{y,z}}{(\partial\psi/\partial y)_{x,z}} \tag{A.32}$$

Comparison with equation A.22 shows that

$$\left(\frac{\partial y}{\partial x}\right)_{\psi,z} = \frac{(\partial y/\partial u)_{\psi,z}}{(\partial x/\partial u)_{\psi,z}} \qquad (A.33)$$

Equations A.22, A.27, and A.33 are among the most useful formal manipulations in thermodynamic calculations.

APPENDIX B

Statistical
Significance
of the Entropy

The purpose of this appendix is to provide the reader with a descriptive, intuitive insight to the statistical significance of the entropy. An appreciation of the qualitative meaning of the entropy at the atomic level gives valuable perspective to macroscopic thermodynamic theory.

In Chapter 1 it is pointed out that each macroscopic system possesses an enormous number of atomic coordinates. Transitions among different atomic states occur extremely rapidly, whereas macroscopic observations are relatively slow. Macroscopic observations consequently correspond to statistical averages over the atomic coordinates.

Among the myriads of atomic coordinates there exist a very few with such symmetry and coherence properties that, unlike the vast majority, they are not "averaged out" in a macroscopic measurement. These coordinates are the energy, volume, mole numbers, and other macroscopic thermodynamic extensive parameters. The observed values of these parameters characterize a thermodynamic state or a *macrostate* of a system. Each such macrostate is, then, consistent with a very large number of *microstates*, or underlying atomic states.

As an example, consider two simple systems contained within a closed cylinder and separated by an internal piston. The macrostate of such a system is completely characterized by the extensive parameters of each of the simple systems; $U^{(1)}$, $V^{(1)}$, $N_1^{(1)} \cdots N_r^{(1)}$ and $U^{(2)}$, $V^{(2)}$, $N_1^{(2)} \cdots N_r^{(2)}$. However, for any given set of values of these variables there is an enormous number of ways in which the molecules of the system can be distributed at any instant. These different positions correspond to different microstates, and continual transitions among the microstates occur as the molecules move about in the system.

It is a fundamental law of quantum statistics that *every microstate consistent with a given macrostate is equally probable in a closed system.*

Thus *any* two sets of positions of the molecules, each consistent with the known values of energy, volume, and mole numbers, will occur with equal likelihood as the molecules dance about in their random trajectories.

The far-reaching significance of the law of equal probability of microstates can be appreciated by consideration of a simple analogy.

Consider a shallow box containing a steel ball bearing, free to roll about. The bottom of the box is ruled off into a very large number of equal square areas, or *cells*. Each cell carries an electrical contact, which is normally open but which is closed by the steel ball if it happens to roll into the cell (Figure B.1).

One cell is connected to a red light, so that the red light flashes if the ball rolls through that particular cell.

One hundred cells are connected to a yellow light, so that the yellow light flashes if the ball rolls through any of the cells in this *yellow field*.

Ten thousand cells are connected to a green light.

One million cells are connected to a blue light. This exhausts the total number of cells in the box.

The box is now shaken by a mechanical vibrator, so that the ball rolls around rapidly and at random. The ball, in fact, moves so very rapidly that we cannot visually follow its position at all. We can, however, observe the blending of the rapidly flashing lights, as they merge in the eye into a single apparent color.

Since every microstate (cell) is equally likely, there will be 10^6 blue flashes, 10^4 green flashes, and 10^2 yellow flashes for every red flash. Because the number of blue flashes is so much greater than those of any other color, we will see a blue light only, the slight admixture of other colors being undiscernible.

We now insert a barrier in the box, so that the ball is excluded from the blue field. Again it rolls rapidly and at random, producing 10^4 green flashes and 10^2 yellow flashes for every red flash. The apparent color seen is now green.

The macrostate (color) observed is that corresponding to the maximum number of microstates (cells) consistent with the imposed constraints.

The fact that in each case one field completely dominates all others results from the rapid increase in number of cells in going from red, to yellow, to green, to blue fields. If X is a parameter that describes the macrostate (as, for instance, the frequency of the light) and if $N(X)$ is the number of cells in the corresponding field, then $N(X)$ is a very rapidly increasing function of X. The value of X observed is that which maximizes $N(X)$, subject to the imposed constraints.

It is convenient to consider not $N(X)$ but the logarithm of $N(X)$. The numbers so obtained are more moderate, and there are other formal

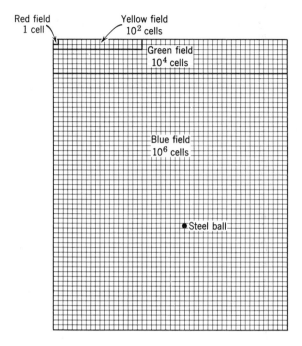

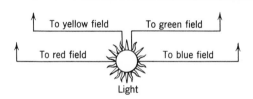

Figure B.1

advantages which are discussed subsequently. As $\ln N$ is a monotonically increasing function of N, maximizing N is equivalent to maximizing $\ln N$. *The entropy of the system is defined as*

$$S(X) = k \ln N(X) \qquad \text{(B.1)}$$

in which k is Boltzman's constant. Consequently, the macrostate (X)

observed is that corresponding to the maximum value of the entropy, consistent with the imposed constraints. The entropy of any macrostate is proportional to the logarithm of the number of microstates associated with that macrostate.

The foregoing statements, although made in reference to a highly artificial model of a system, are actually general. They are valid for any closed thermodynamic system.

A second example, again highly artificial, although considerably more realistic than the first example, will give further insight.

We consider a cylinder containing an internal movable and diathermal piston. There are $N^{(1)}$ molecules to the left of the piston and $N^{(2)}$ molecules to the right of the piston (note that $N^{(1)}$ and $N^{(2)}$ here are numbers of molecules rather than numbers of moles; this is purely a matter of temporary convenience). We wish to find the position of the piston in equilibrium.

We set out to compute the entropy as a function of the position of the piston. To do so we must count the number of microstates consistent with a given position of the piston.

The actual number of microstates is fairly complicated to compute, since we would have to understand precisely how the motion of the molecules as well as their positions enter into an atomistic description. However, we can get a good qualitative understanding of the situation by counting the number of microstates in a naive manner, suggested by our first example.

Again we consider the interior of the cylinder to be subdivided into some very large number, M, of cells. We shall assume that an adequate description of the atomic state of each molecule is furnished merely by specifying the cell it happens to occupy momentarily. It then becomes quite simple to count the number of atomic states associated with any given position of the piston.

Let the total volume of the cylinder be V_0; let the volume to the left of the piston be $V^{(1)}$ and that to the right of the piston be $V^{(2)} = V_0 - V^{(1)}$, as shown in Figure B.2. The number of cells to the left of the piston is then $(V^{(1)}/V_0)M$, and the number of cells to the right of the piston is $(V^{(2)}/V_0)M$. The number of ways in which the $N^{(1)}$ molecules to the left can be distributed among the $(V^{(1)}/V_0)M$ cells to the left is simply $[(V^{(1)}/V_0)M]^{N^{(1)}}$, provided we ignore such complicating features as the interference of the molecules (when more than one attempts to enter the same cell simultaneously) and the quantum mechanical "indistinguishability" of the molecules. Similarly, the number of ways in which the $N^{(2)}$ molecules to the right can be distributed among the $(V^{(2)}/V_0)M$ cells to the right is simply $[(V^{(2)}/V_0)M]^{N^{(2)}}$. The total number of microstates of the whole system is the product of these numbers, or

$$\left(\frac{V^{(1)}}{V_0}M\right)^{N^{(1)}}\left(\frac{V^{(2)}}{V_0}M\right)^{N^{(2)}}$$

and the entropy is

$$S(V^{(1)}, N^{(1)}, V^{(2)}, N^{(2)}) = k \ln\left[\left(\frac{V^{(1)}}{V_0}M\right)^{N^{(1)}}\left(\frac{V^{(2)}}{V_0}M\right)^{N^{(2)}}\right] \qquad (\text{B.2})$$

$$S(V^{(1)}, N^{(1)}, V^{(2)}, N^{(2)}) = N^{(1)} k \ln\left(\frac{V^{(1)}}{V_0}M\right) + N^{(2)} k \ln\left(\frac{V^{(2)}}{V_0}M\right) \qquad (\text{B.3})$$

This is the fundamental equation of our system. It should be noted that the energy does not appear—this is a result of our simplification of the

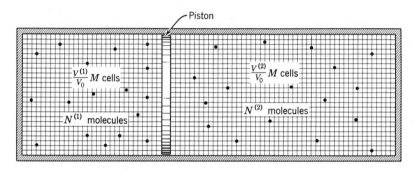

Figure B.2

model, in which we focused only on the positions of the molecules and ignored their motions, thereby disregarding their kinetic energy. Despite the naiveté of this treatment, we shall see that the fundamental equation (B.3) does contain the essential features to be expected.

We now compute the equilibrium position of the piston by seeking the values of $V^{(1)}$ and $V^{(2)}$ which maximize the entropy, subject to the condition that

$$V^{(1)} + V^{(2)} = V_0 \qquad (\text{B.4})$$

Consequently, we write the entropy in terms of $V^{(1)}$ alone, eliminating $V^{(2)}$ by the foregoing condition.

$$S = N^{(1)}k \ln\left(\frac{V^{(1)}}{V_0}M\right) + N^{(2)}k \ln\left(\frac{V_0 - V^{(1)}}{V_0}M\right) \qquad (\text{B.5})$$

Differentiating with respect to $V^{(1)}$ gives

$$\frac{\partial S}{\partial V^{(1)}} = \frac{N^{(1)}k}{V^{(1)}} - \frac{N^{(2)}k}{V_0 - V^{(1)}} \qquad (\text{B.6})$$

Setting this derivative equal to zero and solving for $V^{(1)}$ gives

$$\frac{V^{(1)}}{V_0} = \frac{N_1}{N_1 + N_2} \tag{B.7}$$

This solution is clearly correct; the piston will divide the total volume in direct proportion to the numbers of molecules to the left and to the right. Thus we see that the fundamental equation (B.3) is a reasonable one. In this case, as in every case, the entropy is simply proportional to the logarithm of the number of microstates consistent with a given macrostate in a closed system.

In systems that are not closed the entropy is given by more complicated expressions, but the intuitive significance is not altered.

The fundamental equation (B.3) is *not* homogeneous first-order. This shortcoming traces back to the naiveté of our method of counting states. The correct equation for the system considered would, in fact, be that given in section 3.4. The terms appearing in equation B.3 are simply the volume dependent terms of equation 3.34.

A final observation should be made concerning the choice of the logarithm of the number of microstates rather than the number of microstates itself, as the entropy. If we have two systems forming a composite system, the number of microstates is multiplicative. That is, the number of microstates of the composite system is the *product* of the numbers of microstates of each subsystem. Consequently, the logarithm of the number of microstates is additive (equation B.5). By choosing the entropy as the logarithm of the number of microstates, we obtain an *extensive* parameter, which then fits naturally into the thermodynamic formalism, along with energy, volume, and mole numbers.

APPENDIX C

Equilibrium
with Internal
Adiabatic Constraints

The problem of prediction of the equilibrium state in a composite system with an adiabatic internal wall is a uniquely delicate problem. We first consider the problem from the physical point of view, and we show that the solution is not entirely determinate. We shall then formulate the problem carefully in the entropy representation, and we shall find that the mathematical solution again in only partially determinate—in just such a way as to correspond to the expected physical solution.

The physical problem can be appreciated best in terms of a particular example. We accordingly consider a cylinder containing two subsystems separated by a movable adiabatic piston. The piston is impermeable to matter, so that the mole numbers of each of the subsystems are fixed. We inquire as to the conditions of equilibrium.

Suppose that the pressures of the two subsystems are initially unequal, and that the piston is then set free and allowed to move spontaneously. It will move, of course, in the direction of the subsystem of lower pressure. If there were no viscous damping within the systems, the piston would overshoot and would oscillate forever without coming to equilibrium. But in any real case the motion of the piston will cause viscous damping within the systems and the kinetic energy of the piston will eventually be dissipated. The piston will come to rest with the pressures of each of the subsystems equal. But it is obviously impossible to predict the final temperatures of the individual subsystems, since these depend upon the relative viscosity of the two subsystems and upon various other kinetic parameters lying outside of the domain of thermodynamic description.

321

Therefore, the equilibrium state of the system cannot be predicted completely, although we are able to specify the necessary but not sufficient condition that $P^{(1)} = P^{(2)}$ in equilibrium.

The physical situation described can be reconsidered from another point of view. Suppose we attempt to bring about equilibrium not by simply freeing the piston but by coupling it to a reversible work source and permitting it to move slowly, doing work quasi-statically on the reversible work source. It is clear that the piston will come to equilibrium when the pressures of the two subsystems are equal. As we have described the process, the entropy of each subsystem is unaltered, and the final equilibrium state seems to be uniquely determined. But we now realize that we can alter the individual entropies at will, keeping only the sum constant. Suppose we withdraw a small amount of energy in the form of heat from one subsystem, decreasing its entropy by $dS^{(1)} = dQ^{(1)}/T^{(1)}$. We then insert an amount of heat $dQ^{(2)}$ into the second subsystem, increasing its entropy so that $dS^{(2)} = -dS^{(1)}$. Each of these transfers is between a subsystem and an external agent and is not across the internal adiabatic wall. The system can again be brought to equilibrium as described, but the entropies of the subsystems will now be altered. The final equilibrium state consequently is defined only incompletely, and only the condition $P^{(1)} = P^{(2)}$ can be predicted.

We now attempt to set up the problem formally in the entropy representation. The fundamental equation is

$$S = S^{(1)}(U^{(1)}, V^{(1)}) + S^{(2)}(U^{(2)}, V^{(2)}) \qquad (C.1)$$

in which we have suppressed the (constant) mole numbers in the notation. The closure condition on the volume is

$$V^{(1)} + V^{(2)} = V, \qquad \text{a constant} \qquad (C.2)$$

and we must now formalize the meaning of the adiabatic constraint. Since no heat flux is permitted by the wall, the change in energy of each subsystem is due entirely to the work term, and the adiabatic constraint is expressed by the condition that

$$dU^{(1)} = -P^{(1)} \, dV^{(1)}; \qquad dU^{(2)} = -P^{(2)} \, dV^{(2)} \qquad (C.3)$$

The change in total entropy in a virtual process is now, from equation 2.47,

$$dS = \frac{1}{T^{(1)}} dU^{(1)} + \frac{P^{(1)}}{T^{(1)}} dV^{(1)} + \frac{1}{T^{(2)}} dU^{(2)} + \frac{P^{(2)}}{T^{(2)}} dV^{(2)} \qquad (C.4)$$

By inserting the adiabatic condition (C.3), the quantity dS vanishes identically. We would ordinarily expect to insert the closure condition

(C.2) and then set $dS = 0$ to obtain the condition of equilibrium, but the sudden disappearance of the quantity dS halfway through our calculation certainly prevents the continuation of the analysis. As expected on physical grounds, a mathematical solution of the problem does not exist. However, a partial solution can be obtained, for we have not yet written down the second closure condition, which is to be applied to every problem in the entropy representation. This is the closure condition on the energy

$$U^{(1)} + U^{(2)} = U, \quad \text{a constant} \tag{C.5}$$

We then have

$$dU^{(1)} = -dU^{(2)} \tag{C.6}$$

and, by inserting the adiabatic conditions (C.3),

$$-P^{(1)} \, dV^{(1)} = P^{(2)} \, dV^{(2)} \tag{C.7}$$

Finally, from equation C.2 we find $dV^{(1)} = -dV^{(2)}$, whence

$$P^{(1)} = P^{(2)} \tag{C.8}$$

Again this necessary but not sufficient characterization of the equilibrium state is in agreement with our expectation on physical grounds.

Properties of Gases

Thermodynamic theory, as an abstract subject, is not dependent on the form of the fundamental equation of any particular system. Nevertheless it is of considerable interest to examine the explicit fundamental equations of some particular systems as representative illustrations of the general formalism. A convenient system is the *general ideal gas*, of which the monatomic ideal gas, described in section 3.4, is a special case. We shall also discuss various specific real gases.

D.1 The Single-Component General Ideal Gas

If a gas composed of noninteracting molecules is treated by classical (i.e., nonquantum-mechanical) statistical mechanics, it is found to obey the following fundamental equation:

$$S = \frac{N}{N_0} S_0 + N f\left(\frac{U}{N}\right) + NR \ln \left(\frac{V}{V_0} \frac{N_0}{N}\right) \tag{D.1}$$

The function $f(U/N)$ is determined by the internal structure of the molecules and consequently has a different form for different ideal gases. We shall return subsequently to a discussion of the function $f(U/N)$, but we now proceed to discuss those properties of an ideal gas which are independent of the particular form of $f(U/N)$. We assume, however, that

$$f\left(\frac{U_0}{N_0}\right) = 0 \tag{D.2}$$

so that the entropy has the value S_0 when the gas is in the fiducial state U_0, V_0, N_0. Furthermore the derivative of f is intrinsically positive, as required by postulate III.

At low temperatures, quantum-mechanical effects always come into play, vitiating the calculation leading to equation D.1. On the other hand, the fundamental equation of every real gas approaches equation D.1 at sufficiently high temperatures, so that this fundamental equation is of great practical importance.

Because the fundamental equation D.1 is valid only at high temperature, it need not and does not satisfy the Nernst postulate.

We compute the equations of state by differentiation of the fundamental equation.

$$\frac{1}{T} \equiv \frac{\partial S}{\partial U} = N \frac{df}{du}\frac{du}{dU} = \frac{df}{du} \tag{D.3}$$

As f is a function of u only, the temperature is also a function of u only, independent of v. The function f therefore can be written as

$$f = \int_{U_0/N_0}^{U/N} \frac{df}{du}\,du = \int_{U_0/N_0}^{U/N} \frac{du}{T(u)} \tag{D.4}$$

and the fundamental equation becomes

$$S\,(U,V,N) = S = \frac{N}{N_0} S_0 + N \int_{U_0/N_0}^{U/N} \frac{du}{T(u)} + NR \ln \left(\frac{V}{V_0}\frac{N_0}{N}\right) \tag{D.5}$$

The unspecified functional form of the relationship $T(u)$ in this equation corresponds to the unspecified functional relationship $f(u)$ in equation D.1. That is, the function $T(u)$ depends on the internal structure of the molecules and varies from ideal gas to ideal gas.

The second equation of state is

$$\frac{P}{T} = \frac{\partial S}{\partial V} = \frac{NR}{V} \tag{D.6}$$

or

$$PV = NRT \tag{D.7}$$

Thus this familiar equation does not depend on a particular form of $f(u)$ or $T(u)$; it holds for all ideal gases, independent of the internal structure of the molecules.

Finally, the third equation of state is

$$\frac{\mu}{T} = -\frac{\partial S}{\partial N} = -\frac{S_0}{N_0} - \int_{U_0/N_0}^{U/N} \frac{du}{T(u)} + \frac{U}{NT} - R \ln \left(\frac{V}{V_0}\frac{N_0}{N}\right) + R \tag{D.8}$$

in which, in carrying out the differentiation, we use the mathematical fact that

$$\frac{d}{dx}\int_c^{g(x)} f(y)\,dy = f(g)\frac{dg}{dx} \tag{D.9}$$

D.2 Compressibility and Expansion Coefficient of General Ideal Gases

We first compute the quantities κ_T and α. From the equation of state (D.7) we find

$$\kappa_T = -\frac{1}{V}\left(\frac{\partial V}{\partial P}\right)_T = \frac{1}{P} \tag{D.10}$$

and

$$\alpha = \frac{1}{V}\left(\frac{\partial V}{\partial T}\right)_P = \frac{1}{T} \tag{D.11}$$

Also, from the identity (equation 3.47),

$$c_P - c_v = \frac{TV\alpha^2}{N\kappa_T} \tag{D.12}$$

we find

$$c_P - c_v = R \tag{D.13}$$

Thus, κ_T, α, and the difference $c_P - c_v$ are independent of the internal structure of the molecules. Equation D.11 provides the basis of a practical method of measuring the temperature by "gas thermometry."

The specific heats c_v and c_P individually depend on the internal structure of the molecules of the ideal gas.

However, since T is a function of u only, independent of v, it follows that u is a function of T only, independent of v. Then, in turn, c_v is a function of T only, independent of v.

$$c_v = c_v(T) \tag{D.14}$$

The fact that c_v is a function only of the temperature suggests a convenient way to rewrite the fundamental equation (D.5). We introduce into that equation the fact that

$$du = c_v(T)\,dT \tag{D.15}$$

and we denote $T(U_0/N_0)$ by T_0, the temperature in the fiducial state. Then

$$S = \frac{N}{N_0}S_0 + N\int_{T_0}^T \frac{c_v(T')}{T'}\,dT' + NR\ln\frac{V}{V_0}\frac{N_0}{N} \tag{D.16}$$

Also, integrating equation D.15.

$$U = U_0 + N\int_{T_0}^T c_v(T')\,dT' \tag{D.17}$$

Equations D.16 and D.17 taken together can be considered as a pair of parametric equations. Elimination of the parameter T between these two equations gives the fundamental relation $S(U, V, N)$. The internal structure of the molecules is characterized by the dependence of c_v on T.

Problems—Section D.2

D.2–1. Assume that O_2 is an ideal gas with a specific heat as given in Table D.2. Using equations D.13, D.16, and D.17, find the explicit fundamental equation of oxygen.

D.2–2. Find the equations of the adiabatic curves in a T-V plane for oxygen, using the results of the preceding problem. Find the equations of the adiabatic curves in a P-V plane.

One mole of oxygen at standard temperature and pressure (0°C; 1 atm) is compressed adiabatically until its temperature rises to 1000°K. What is its final volume?

D.2–3. The velocity of sound in a gas is given by

$$\text{velocity} = \sqrt{B_s/\rho}$$

in which ρ is the density and B_s is the adiabatic bulk modulus.

$$B_s = -V\left(\frac{\partial P}{\partial V}\right)_S$$

Find the velocity of sound in nitrogen at $P = 1$ atm and at $T = 350°C$, 1000°C, and 1500°C. Use the specific heat given in Table D.2 and assume that nitrogen is a perfect gas.

D.3 Gibbs–Duhem Relation for General Ideal Gas

The integrated form of the Gibbs–Duhem relation is a relationship among T, P, and μ. It is of interest to examine this relationship for a general ideal gas. Equation D.8 may be written as

$$\mu = RT\left[\phi(T) + \ln\frac{NRT}{V}\right] = RT[\phi(T) + \ln P] \qquad (D.18)$$

where

$$\phi(T) = 1 - \frac{S_0}{N_0 R} - \frac{1}{R}\int_{U_0/N_0}^{U/N}\frac{du}{T(u)} + \frac{U}{NRT} - \ln\frac{N_0 RT}{V_0} \qquad (D.19)$$

or, by equation D.15,

$$\phi(T) = 1 - \frac{S_0}{N_0 R} - \frac{1}{R}\int_{T_0}^{T}\frac{c_v(T)}{T}dT + \frac{1}{RT}\int_{T_0}^{T}c_v\,dT + \frac{U_0}{N_0 RT} - \ln\frac{N_0 RT}{V_0}$$

$$(D.20)$$

Integrating the first integral by parts gives

$$\phi(T) = 1 + \frac{U_0 - TS_0}{N_0 RT} - \frac{1}{R} \int_{T_0}^{T} \frac{dT'}{T'^2} \left(\int_{T_0}^{T'} c_v \, dT'' \right) - \ln \frac{N_0 RT}{V_0} \quad (D.21)$$

This equation takes a simpler form if we replace c_V by c_P, in accordance with equation D.13.

$$\phi(T) = \frac{U_0 + N_0 RT_0}{N_0 RT} - \frac{S_0}{N_0 R} - \frac{1}{R} \int_{T_0}^{T} \frac{dT'}{T'^2} \left(\int_{T_0'}^{T'} c_P \, dT'' \right) - \ln \frac{N_0 RT_0}{V_0}$$

$$(D.22)$$

or, introducing the notation

$$h_0 = \frac{1}{N_0} (U_0 + N_0 RT_0) = \frac{1}{N_0} (U_0 + P_0 V_0) \quad (D.23)$$

we have

$$\phi(T) = \frac{h_0}{RT} - \frac{S_0}{N_0 R} - \frac{1}{R} \int_{T_0}^{T} \frac{dT'}{T'^2} \left(\int_{T_0'}^{T'} c_P \, dT'' \right) - \ln P_0 \quad (D.24)$$

Equations D.24 and D.18 together provide the most convenient form of the Gibbs–Duhem relation among the intensive parameters of a general ideal gas. Reference is made to these equations particularly in our discussion of chemical thermodynamics.

D.4   The Monatomic Ideal Gas

The monatomic ideal gas, discussed in section 3.4, is a special case of the general ideal gas, for which

$$c_v = \tfrac{3}{2} R \quad (D.25)$$

The conditions leading to this form of specific heat are discussed further in the following section, where we consider more general forms of the specific heat.

Equation D.17 leads to

$$U = \tfrac{3}{2} NRT \quad (D.26)$$

and equation D.16 becomes

$$S = \frac{N}{N_0} S_0 + \frac{3}{2} NR \ln \frac{T}{T_0} + NR \ln \left(\frac{V}{V_0} \frac{N_0}{N} \right) \quad (D.27)$$

Eliminating T between these two equations gives the fundamental equation

$$S = \frac{N}{N_0} S_0 + NR \ln \left[\left(\frac{U}{U_0} \right)^{3/2} \frac{V}{V_0} \left(\frac{N_0}{N} \right)^{5/2} \right] \quad (D.28)$$

in agreement with the results of section 3.4.

D.5   Specific Heats of Ideal Gases

The specific heat $c_v(T)$ of a general ideal gas has been left unspecified in the preceding discussion. The specific heat depends upon the temperature in a fashion determined by the internal structure of the molecules. No completely general formula can be given for this dependence, but several approximate formulas have been developed. Each of these formulas is predicated upon a particular simplified model of the molecular structure.

An individual molecule of a gas can be imagined to possess various *modes of excitation.* Each such mode is a possible repository of energy. Thus energy can be put into the vibrational mode of a diatomic molecule, the two atoms then vibrating as if they were connected by a spring.* Also, energy can be put into the rotational modes of a diatomic molecule; the molecule then spins like a dumbbell around an axis perpendicular to the line joining the atoms. There are two such rotational modes for a diatomic molecule corresponding to the two axes perpendicular to the line joining the atoms. Rotation around the line joining the atoms is not a meaningful concept because the atomic nuclei are essentially point-masses, and the classical moment of inertia about the molecular axis vanishes. The final modes of excitation of a diatomic molecule are the electronic modes which consist of the various ways of exciting the electrons to higher-energy states. The one vibrational, two rotational, and various electronic modes are the only modes of excitation of a diatomic molecule.

A monatomic molecule, such as that of a rare gas (argon, neon, or xenon), has neither vibrational nor rotational modes of excitation. It has only electronic modes.

A polyatomic molecule consisting of n atoms has $3n - 6$ vibrational modes and three rotational modes, unless the atoms lie in a single line. For such a linear molecule there are $3n - 5$ vibrational and only two rotational modes (compare with the diatomic case $n = 2$). In addition, there are the electronic modes in each case.

In the simplest approximation *each mode of excitation is found to contribute additively and independently to the specific heat.* That is, the specific heat can be approximately represented as a sum of terms, each associated with a single mode of excitation. To a higher order of precision, it is found that each mode of excitation slightly alters the contribution of each other mode, but we shall not concern ourselves with these refinements.

In addition to the contribution to the specific heat from the modes of

---

* The vibrational modes of excitation correspond to the normal modes discussed in section 1.1.

excitation, the specific heat at constant volume always contains a term $\frac{3}{2}R$. This term can be considered as arising from the translational kinetic energy of the molecules. The specific heat at constant volume c_v is equal to $\frac{3}{2}R$, plus terms for each mode of excitation. And, by equation D.13, the specific heat at constant pressure is equal to $\frac{5}{2}R$, plus terms for each mode of excitation.

The contribution to the specific heats from electronic modes of excitation is generally negligible, except at very high temperatures. The characteristic temperature above which the electronic modes begin to contribute appreciably to the specific heat is of the order of 10,000°K.

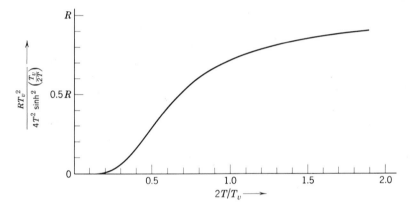

Figure D.1 Contribution to the specific heat of a vibrational mode of characteristic temperature T_v.

However, in a certain few unique gases this temperature may be appreciably lower; the electronic contribution becomes significant above about 1000°K in a gas of free halogen atoms.

The contribution to the specific heat of each rotational mode of excitation is simply $\frac{1}{2}R$ at common temperatures. This contribution remains constant down to a characteristic temperature for each gas and then falls to zero at zero temperature. This characteristic temperature, below which the rotational contribution decreases, is of the order of 5°K or less for molecules that do not contain hydrogen atoms; it may be as high as 30°K for diatomic hydrides and is of the order of room temperature for hydrogen (H_2) and deuterium (D_2) gases. Consequently, the total contribution of the rotational modes to the specific heat at normal temperatures and for all gases except H_2 and D_2, is R for linear molecules and $\frac{3}{2}R$ for nonlinear molecules.

The final contribution to the specific heat comes from the vibrational modes of excitation. To each vibrational mode there is associated a characteristic vibrational temperature T_v. The contribution of each mode to the specific heat is

$$c_v = R \frac{(T_v/2T)^2}{\sinh^2 (T_v/2T)} \tag{D.29}$$

The behavior of this contribution as a function of T is shown in Figure D.1. It becomes equal to R at temperatures appreciably higher than T_v and falls to zero at zero temperature.

There is one term of the form D.29 for each vibrational mode; $3n - 5$ for linear molecules and $3n - 6$ for each nonlinear molecule.

The characteristic temperature T_v of a vibrational mode is proportional to the natural frequency with which the molecule vibrates. It is therefore highest for molecules with strong interatomic forces and light atoms. Representative values of T_v are given for several gases in Table D.1.

Table D.1

CHARACTERISTIC VIBRATIONAL TEMPERATURES (°K) FOR VARIOUS GASES

Diatomic Molecules

N_2; 3350°	O_2; 2240°	CO; 3080°
NO; 2700°	HCl; 4150°	HBr; 3680°
Cl_2; 796°	Br_2; 462°	I_2; 307°

Nonlinear Triatomic Molecules

H_2O	2290°	5250°	5400°
H_2S	1855°	3760°	3860°
CH_2	2080°	4270°	4310°
SO_2	753°	1660°	1960°
NO_2	931°	1900°	2330°

Linear Triatomic Molecules

CO_2	960°	960°	2000°	3380°
N_2O	847°	847°	1850°	3200°

Linear Polyatomic Molecules

C_2H_2	880°	880°	1050°	1050°	2840°	4730°	4850°

Nonlinear Polyatomic Molecules

NH_3	1368°	2340°	2340°	4800°	4910°	4910°		
CH_4	1880°	1880°	1880°	2190°	2190°	4190°	4350°	4350°	4350°
CCl_4	314°	314°	452°	452°	452°	659°	1120°	1120°	1120°

From G. Hertzberg, Molecular Spectra and Molecular Structure; Vol. I, *Diatomic Molecules*, 2nd Edition, Copyright 1950, and Vol. II, *Infrared and Raman Spectra of Polyatomic Molecules*, 2nd Edition, Copyright 1945, D. Van Nostrand Company, Inc., Princeton, New Jersey.

By adding the translational, rotational, and vibrational contributions to the specific heat, we find

$$c_v = \tfrac{3}{2}R \qquad \text{(monatomic molecules)} \qquad \text{(D.30)}$$

$$c_v = 3R + \sum_{T_v} R\left(\frac{T_v}{2T}\right)^2 \sinh^{-2}\left(\frac{T_v}{2T}\right) \qquad \text{(nonlinear molecules)} \quad \text{(D.31)}$$

$$c_v = \frac{5}{2}R + \sum_{T_v} R\left(\frac{T_v}{2T}\right)^2 \sinh^{-2}\left(\frac{T_v}{2T}\right) \qquad \text{(linear molecules)} \qquad \text{(D.32)}$$

The sums in these equations are over the various values of T_v for each vibrational mode; the sum in equation D.31 contains $(3n - 6)$ terms and that in equation D.32 contains $(3n - 5)$ terms, in which n is the number of atoms per molecule. Equation D.30 should be compared with equation D.25.

Table D.2
SPECIFIC HEATS OF VARIOUS GASES

$$c_P = A + BT + CT^2$$

	A	B	C
	$\dfrac{\text{cal}}{\text{mole °K}}$	$\dfrac{10^{-3}\,\text{cal}}{\text{mole (°K)}^2}$	$\dfrac{10^{-6}\,\text{cal}}{\text{mole (°K)}^3}$
H_2	6.88	0.066	+0.279
N_2, HBr	6.30	1.819	−0.345
O_2	6.26	2.746	−0.770
CO, HI	6.25	2.091	−0.459
NO	6.21	2.436	−0.612
HCl	6.64	0.959	−0.057
H_2S	6.48	5.558	−1.204
H_2O	6.89	3.283	−0.343
SO_2	8.12	6.825	−2.103
HCN	7.01	6.600	−1.642
CO_2	6.85	8.533	−2.475
COS	8.32	7.224	−2.146
CS_2	9.76	6.102	−1.894
NH_3	5.92	8.963	−1.764
C_2H_2	8.28	10.501	−2.644
CH_4	3.38	17.905	−4.188

Compiled by W. M. C. Bryant. By permission, from *Heat and Thermodynamics*, by M. W. Zemansky, 4th Edition, 1957, McGraw-Hill Book Company, Inc., New York.

In the foregoing equations it is implicitly assumed that the temperature is above the characteristic temperature for rotation and below the characteristic temperature for electronic excitations.

For practical purposes it is convenient to represent equations such as D.31 and D.32 by simple algebraic approximate expressions. In one such procedure the specific heat is represented by a power series in T, with empirically determined coefficients. Three terms in the expansion are found to be sufficient to represent the specific heat to an accuracy of about 2 per cent in the temperature range from 300 to 2000°K.

$$c_P = A + BT + CT^2 \tag{D.33}$$

Coefficients A, B, and C for various gases are given in Table D.2.

Problems—Section D.5

D.5–1. Choose a specific gas that is listed in both Tables D.1 and D.2. Plot its specific heat as a function of temperature, using equations D.31 or D.32. Also plot its specific heat, using equation D.33. Does equation D.33 approximate equation D.31 or D.32 reasonably well?

D.5–2. Using the data given in Table D.1, and assuming that Cl_2 is an ideal gas, plot the coefficient of adiabatic expansion $1/V(\partial V/\partial T)_S$ as a function of the temperature from 100 to 5000°K.

D.5–3. A triatomic molecule is composed of three identical atoms. It is not known whether the linear arrangements or the equilateral triangular arrangement is the proper structure, and it is desired to distinguish between those models by specific heat measurements.

If a linear model is chosen, as shown,

the vibrational modes and their natural frequencies are

$$\nu_1 = 2\pi\sqrt{3K/M}$$
$$\nu_2 = 2\pi\sqrt{K/M}$$
$$\nu_3 \simeq 0$$
$$\nu_4 \simeq 0$$

The fourth of these modes is identical to the third, rotated 90° around the axis of the molecule.

Let $T_v = (h/k)\nu_v$, where ν_v is the natural frequency of a given mode of vibration, h is Planck's constant, k is Boltzmann's constant, and T_v is the characteristic temperature for the mode. Then plot c_v against $T/[(h/k)\sqrt{K/M}]$ for the linear model of the molecule.

If an equilateral triangular model is chosen, as shown,

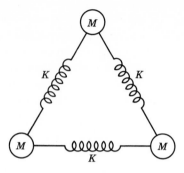

the vibrational modes and their natural frequencies are

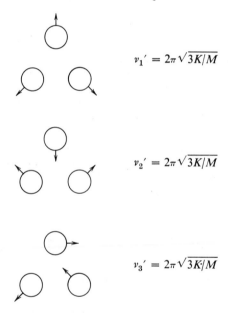

$$\nu_1' = 2\pi\sqrt{3K/M}$$

$$\nu_2' = 2\pi\sqrt{3K/M}$$

$$\nu_3' = 2\pi\sqrt{3K/M}$$

again plot c_v against $T/[(h/k)\sqrt{K/M}]$.

Discuss how one could determine the structure by specific heat measurements. Could one determine the binding force constant K as well?

D.5-4. One half mole of oxygen is taken through the following process. From the initial state ($V_0 = 2$ liters, $P_0 = 1$ atm) the gas is expanded at constant pressure to a volume of 30 liters. It is then heated at constant volume, until its final pressure is 100 atm. Find the total input of heat in this process. Assume that oxygen is an ideal gas with specific heat as given in Table D.2.

D.5-5. Two moles of CO_2 at an initial temperature of 500°C and a pressure of 20 atm are expanded adiabatically until the final temperature is 100°C. Plot the adiabatic curve on a $P-V$ diagram. Find the final pressure. Assume that CO_2 is an ideal gas with specific heat as given in Table D.2.

D.5-6. From the data of Table D.2 find the fundamental equation of N_2.

D.5-7. Assume that H_2S is an ideal gas with specific heat as given in Table D.2. Find the change in entropy accompanying a change in state from $T = 300°K$, $P = 1$ atm to $T = 1000°K$, $P = \frac{1}{10}$ atm.

D.6 The Multicomponent Ideal Gas

The same type of statistical calculation that leads to the fundamental equation of a single-component ideal gas leads to the fundamental equation of a multicomponent ideal gas.

We first suppose that we have several *separate* single-component ideal gases. The fundamental equation of the jth gas is given by the parametric equations

$$S = \frac{N}{N_0} S_{0j} + N \int_{T_0}^{T} \frac{c_{vj}(T')}{T'} dT' + NR \ln \left(\frac{V}{V_0} \frac{N_0}{N} \right) \qquad \text{(D.34)}$$

$$U = U_{0j} + N \int_{T_0}^{T} c_{vj}(T') dT' \qquad \text{(D.35)}$$

It will be noted that in specifying a fiducial state for each gas we have adopted the convention that T_0, V_0, and N_0 are the same for each gas. However, U_0 and S_0 vary from gas to gas and consequently carry the subscript j in the foregoing equations.

If the several single-component gases are mixed together to make a multicomponent ideal gas, the fundamental equation will be

$$S = \sum_j N_j \left(\frac{S_{0j}}{N_0} \right) + \sum_j N_j \int_{T_0}^{T} \frac{c_{vj}}{T'} dT' + \sum_j N_j R \ln \left(\frac{V}{V_0} \frac{N_0}{N_j} \right) \qquad \text{(D.36)}$$

$$U = \sum_j N_j \left(\frac{U_{0j}}{N_0} \right) + \sum_j N_j \int_{T_0}^{T} c_{vj}(T') dT' \qquad \text{(D.37)}$$

That is, the entropy of a mixture of ideal gases is equal to the sum of the entropies that each of the gases would have if it alone were to occupy the same volume at the same temperature. And the energy of the mixture is the sum of the energies that each of the individual gases would have at the same temperature. These statements are known as *Gibbs' theorem.*

It is of interest to corroborate that the quantity T, which enters into equations D.36 and D.37 as a parameter, retains its significance as the thermodynamic temperature. This may be done by a straightforward calculation of the derivative

$$\left(\frac{\partial U}{\partial S} \right)_{V,N_1,N_2\cdots} = \left(\frac{\partial U}{\partial T} \right)_{V,N_1,N_2\cdots} \bigg/ \left(\frac{\partial S}{\partial T} \right)_{V,N_1,N_2\cdots}$$

To find the equations of state, we first compute the pressure. The definition can be recast in a form convenient for calculation with a parametric form of the fundamental equation:

$$P = -\left(\frac{\partial U}{\partial V}\right)_{S,N_1,N_2,\cdots} = \left(\frac{\partial U}{\partial S}\right)_{V,N_1\cdots} \left(\frac{\partial S}{\partial V}\right)_{U,N_1\cdots}$$

$$= \left(\frac{\partial U}{\partial T}\right)_{V,N_1\cdots} \left(\frac{\partial T}{\partial S}\right)_{V,N_1\cdots} \left(\frac{\partial S}{\partial V}\right)_{U,N_1\cdots} \tag{D.38}$$

But constant $U, N_1, N_2 \cdots$ implies constant $T, N_1, N_2 \cdots$, since in our case U is a function of T and the mole numbers only. Thus equation D.38 becomes

$$P = \left(\frac{\partial U}{\partial T}\right)_{V,N_1\cdots} \left(\frac{\partial S}{\partial V}\right)_{T,N_1\cdots} \Big/ \left(\frac{\partial S}{\partial T}\right)_{V,N_1\cdots} \tag{D.39}$$

Each of these derivatives can be evaluated directly from equations D.36 and D.37, and we find

$$P = \frac{(\Sigma N_j)RT}{V} \tag{D.40}$$

or

$$PV = NRT \tag{D.41}$$

in which N is the sum of the mole numbers. The equation of state (D.41) is formally identical to the corresponding equation of state of a single-component ideal gas, and α, κ_T, and $(c_P - c_V)$, consequently, have the values given by equations D.10–D.13.

The chemical potential of the jth component in the mixture is most conveniently computed by recalling that

$$dU = T\,dS - P\,dV + \sum_j \mu_j\,dN_j \tag{D.42}$$

whence, putting $dN_k = 0$ for all $k \neq j$,

$$\mu_j = \left(\frac{\partial U}{\partial N_j}\right)_{V,T,N_1,N_2\cdots} - T\left(\frac{\partial S}{\partial N_j}\right)_{V,T,N_1,N_2\cdots} \tag{D.43}$$

Evaluating these derivatives from equations D.36 and D.37 and replacing c_v by c_P, as in section D.3, gives

$$\mu_j = \frac{U_{0j} + N_0 RT_0}{N_0} - T\frac{S_{0j}}{N_0} + \int_{T_0}^{T} c_{Pj}\,dT' - T\int_{T_0}^{T} \frac{c_{Pj}}{T'}\,dT'$$

$$+ RT\ln\left(\frac{N_j RT}{V}\frac{V_0}{N_0 RT_0}\right) \tag{D.44}$$

or

$$\mu_j = \frac{U_{0j} + N_0 R T_0}{N_0} - T\frac{S_{0j}}{N_0} - RT\ln\left(\frac{N_0 R T_0}{V_0}\right)$$

$$- T\int_{T_0}^{T}\frac{dT'}{T'^2}\int_{T_0'}^{T'} c_P\, dT'' + RT\ln\left(P\frac{N_j}{N}\right) \quad (D.45)$$

We thus find that

$$\mu_j = RT(\phi_j(T) + \ln P_j) \quad (D.46)$$

in which $\phi_j(T)$ is defined as in equation D.22 or D.24 and in which the *partial pressure of the jth component P_j* is defined by

$$P_j = P\frac{N_j}{N} \quad (D.47)$$

The partial pressures are purely mathematical constructs with no direct physical meaning. *The chemical potential of a single component in a mixture of perfect gases is equal to the chemical potential that component would have alone if it were at the same temperature and the reduced pressure P_j.*

Returning to equation D.36 and Gibb's theorem, we note that the additivity of the entropy when expressed in terms of T and V does *not* imply additivity when expressed in terms of other variables. As an example, consider several separate single-component gases, each at temperature T and pressure P. From equation D.34 and the equation of state we write the entropy of each gas as

$$S_j = \frac{N}{N_0}S_{0j} + N\int_{T_0}^{T}\frac{c_{vj}(T')}{T'}\, dT' + NR\ln\frac{N_0 RT}{PV_0} \quad (D.48)$$

Now replacing V by P in equation D.36, we find for the mixture

$$S = \sum_j N_j\left(\frac{S_{0j}}{N_0}\right) + \sum_j N_j\int_{T_0}^{T}\frac{c_{vj}}{T'}\, dT' + \sum_j N_j R\ln\frac{N_0 RT}{PV_0} - \sum_j N_j R\ln\frac{N_j}{N}$$

$$(D.49)$$

That is, the entropy of a mixture of ideal gases is equal to the sum of the entropies which the individual gases would have if each were at the same temperature and pressure as the mixture, *plus a correction term*. This correction term is called the *entropy of mixing* and is given by

$$\Delta S_{\text{mixing}} = -R\sum_j N_j\ln\frac{N_j}{N} \quad (D.50)$$

Problems—Section D.6

D.6–1.   Ten grams each of He, N_2, and O_2 are in separate containers, each at a pressure of 1 atm and a temperature of 150°C. Valves connecting the three containers are opened and the system is allowed to come to equilibrium. The walls of the containers are assumed to be rigid and adiabatic, and the gases are assumed to be ideal. What is the final temperature and pressure of the gas mixture? What is the change in entropy?

D.6–2.   If the initial pressure of each of the three gases in problem D.6–1 is 1 atm, but the initial temperature is 100°C, 150°C, and 200°C, respectively, what is the final temperature and pressure and what is the change in entropy?

D.6–3.   If the initial temperature of each of the three gases in problem D.6–1 is 150°C, but the initial pressure is 1.0, 1.5, and 2.0 atm, respectively, what is the final temperature and pressure and what is the change in entropy?

D.6–4.   Find the heat capacity at constant pressure of a mixture of 30 grams of O_2 and 70 grams of I_2. In particular, find the values of the heat capacity at 200°K, 500°K, and 4000°K.

D.6–5.   The velocity of sound in a mixture of xenon and HI is found to be 162.0 meters/sec at 0°C. Xenon is an inert (monatomic) gas with atomic weight 131.3. The atomic weight of I is 126.9. The specific heat of HI is given in Table D.2. What is the composition of the mixture?
Note: Recall problem D.2–3.

D.6–6.   Assume air to be four fifths N_2 and one fifth O_2. Using the specific heat data given in Table D.2, find the fundamental equation of air.

Good !

D.7   Nonideal Gases—The Virial Expansion

All gases behave like ideal gases at sufficiently high temperatures and sufficiently high molar volume. As the molar volume (V/N) is decreased, however, real gases exhibit a more complicated behavior. As a gas is compressed, its properties at first deviate only slightly from those of an ideal gas. Under sufficient compression, however, every real gas undergoes a condensation to the liquid or solid state, in which condition it deviates very far indeed from ideal gas behavior. Condensation phenomena are discussed subsequently, but in this section we describe the properties of real gases only in that region in which they deviate but slightly from ideal gas behavior.

As real gases deviate from ideal gas behavior, their fundamental equations become analytically complicated. It is more convenient to discuss their properties in terms of the equations of state rather than in terms of the fundamental equation. We recall, however, that two equations of state are equivalent, except for an additive constant, to the fundamental equation.

We consider first the ideal gas equation of state

$$\frac{P}{T} = \frac{R}{v} \tag{D.51}$$

It is found that with decreasing v the properties of every real gas can be expressed in a power series in $1/v$, of the form

$$\frac{P}{T} = \frac{R}{v}\left(1 + \frac{B(T)}{v} + \frac{C(T)}{v^2} + \cdots\right) \tag{D.52}$$

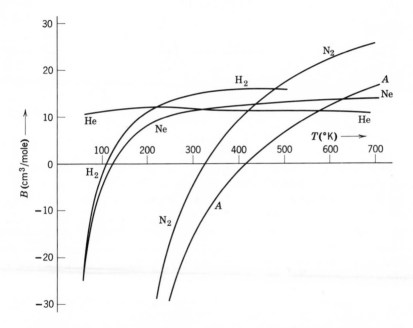

Figure D.2   Second virial coefficient as a function of temperature for several gases. Measurements by Holborn and Otto. Data from *Statistical Thermodynamics*, by R. H. Fowler and E. A. Guggenheim, Cambridge University Press, 1939.

The coefficients $B(T)$, $C(T) \cdots$ are functions of temperature. The forms of these functions depend on the types of intermolecular forces in the gas. $B(T)$ is called the *second virial coefficient*, $C(T)$ the *third virial coefficient*, etc.

The second virial coefficient is shown as a function of temperature for several gases in Figure D.2.

The specific heat c_v of a real gas also depends upon the virial coefficients. It is found by statistical mechanical calculations that

$$c_v(\text{real}) = c_v(\text{ideal}) - \frac{R}{v}\frac{d}{dT}\left(T^2\frac{dB}{dT}\right) - \frac{R}{2v^2}\frac{d}{dT}\left(T^2\frac{dC}{dT}\right) \quad \text{(D.53)}$$

in which $c_v(\text{ideal})$ is the specific heat of the ideal gas, as described in section D.5.

Equations D.52 and D.53 determine the fundamental equation as follows. We write

$$ds = \left(\frac{\partial s}{\partial T}\right)_v dT + \left(\frac{\partial s}{\partial v}\right)_T dv \quad \text{(D.54)}$$

whence

$$ds = \frac{c_v(T)}{T} dT + \left(\frac{\partial P}{\partial T}\right)_v dv \quad \text{(D.55)}$$

Integration of this equation yields

$$s = s(T, v) \quad \text{(D.56)}$$

We also have

$$u = \int c_v\, dT \quad \text{(D.57)}$$

These two equations are a parametric representation of the fundamental equation; elimination of T between them yields $s(u, v)$.

One simple theoretical model of the intermolecular interactions is of special interest. That is the so-called "hard-sphere" model. The molecules are treated as though they were minute marbles, exerting no forces except when in contact. This model yields virial coefficients, all of which are constants. Each virial coefficient can be expressed in terms of the volume of an individual molecule.

$$B = 4N_A\tau \qquad C = 10N_A^2\tau^2 \qquad D = 18.362N_A^3\tau^3 \quad \text{(D.58)}$$

Here N_A is Avogadro's number, and τ is the volume of a single hard-sphere molecule.

Examination of Figure D.2 shows that the second virial coefficients of real gases are not generally constants, so that the assumption of hard spherical molecules is not a particularly realistic model. Nevertheless, if the empirical second virial coefficient does become approximately constant over a reasonable temperature range, as in He, Ne, and H_2, a crude estimate of the molecular volume can be obtained from equation D.58.

The virial coefficients of multicomponent gases are not completely determined by the virial coefficients of each of the components. For a mixture of N_1 moles of component 1 and of N_2 moles of component 2 the equation of state of the mixture is of the virial form equation D.52, with

$$B(T) = \left(\frac{N_1}{N}\right)^2 B_1(T) + 2\frac{N_1}{N}\frac{N_2}{N} B_{12}(T) + \left(\frac{N_2}{N}\right)^2 B_2(T) \quad \text{(D.59)}$$

in which $B_1(T)$ and $B_2(T)$ are the virial coefficients of the individual components and in which $B_{12}(T)$ is a new coefficient. Similarly, the third virial coefficient is cubic in the mole fractions, and the nth virial coefficient is nth-order in the mole fractions.

Problems—Section D.7

D.7-1. From the second virial coefficient of He, as given in Figure D.2, find the volume of 1 atom of He. Show that this volume corresponds to a radius of the order of 10^{-8} cm.

D.7-2. Find the fundamental equation of a monatomic hard-sphere gas, neglecting all virial coefficients beyond the third.

D.8   The van der Waals and Berthelot Equations of State

Rather than writing the equation of state in the virial form equation D.52, a number of suggestions of closed-form expressions have been advanced. These expressions are phenomenological; that is, they are merely contrived to fit empirical behavior, with little or no theoretical basis. Nevertheless, such expressions can be extremely convenient, and myriads have been proposed. One of the simplest and most useful is the van der Waals equation of state,

$$P = \frac{NRT}{V - bN} - \frac{N^2 a}{V^2} \quad \text{(D.60)}$$

in which a and b are constants. This equation not only fits the behavior of most gases quite well in the region in which they are almost ideal, but it also describes the behavior in the liquid phase. A detailed discussion of the van der Waals equation in the region of the gas-liquid condensation is given in Chapter 9. Values of the van der Waals constants a and b, for several common gases, are given in Table D.3.

The Berthelot equation of state is

$$P = \frac{NRT}{V - b'N} - \frac{N^2 a'}{TV^2} \quad \text{(D.61)}$$

in which a' and b' are constants. It appears to represent the properties of real gases somewhat more satisfactorily than the van der Waals equation.

Table D.3
Constants of the van der Waals Equation of State

Gas	a (10^6 atm cm^6)	b (cm^3)
He	0.03415	23.71
Ne	0.2120	17.10
H_2	0.2446	26.61
A	1.301	30.22
N_2	1.346	38.52
O_2	1.361	32.58
CO	1.486	39.87
CO_2	3.959	42.69
N_2O	3.788	44.18
H_2O	5.468	30.52
Cl_2	6.501	56.26
SO_2	6.707	56.39

From Paul S. Epstein, *Textbook of Thermodynamics*, John Wiley and Sons, New York, 1937.

Problems—Section D.8

D.8-1. Show that the virial coefficients of a system obeying the van der Waals equation of state are

$$B = b - \frac{a}{RT}$$

and

$$C = b^2$$

D.8-2. Show that the virial coefficients of a system obeying the Berthelot equation of state are

$$B = b' - \frac{a'}{RT^2}$$

and

$$C = b'^2$$

Properties
of Simple Solids
and Liquids

E.1 General Properties

Thermodynamic theory, as developed in the body of the text, stresses the central role played by the fundamental equation of a thermodynamic system. Such an equation contains all thermodynamic information about a system. In Appendix D the fundamental equations of gases are described as illustrations of the general theory. Unfortunately, it is not always practical to compute or measure the fundamental equation of a thermodynamic system, and we content ourselves with lesser information. This lesser information may be simply one equation of state, or it may be in some other equivalent form. This is, in fact, the usual situation with liquid or solid systems. To illustrate the type of thermodynamic information that is generally available for real systems, we describe the general properties of liquid and solid systems in this appendix.

The reason that fundamental equations are available for gases but are not generally known for solids and liquids is fairly evident. From the quantum-statistical point of view gases are comparatively simple because the molecules are almost independent. But the molecules of solids and liquids are strongly interacting and lead to enormous difficulties in the mathematical analysis of the quantum-statistical models. Even so, the mathematics of solids is somewhat more tractable than that of liquids because the molecules in solids are located in a regular array, whereas the molecules of liquids are randomly distributed. Consequently, we shall see that the properties of solids have a more extensive theoretical basis than those of liquids.

A convenient organization of the known properties of liquids and solids is in terms of the dependence on temperature and pressure of the four quantities α, κ_T, c_P, and c_v. The first three of these quantities can be measured in fairly straightforward ways, although no measurement is truly simple at either very low or very high temperature or at high pressure. The specific heat at constant volume is very difficult to measure because of the lack of strict rigidity of any container, but c_v can be related to the other coefficients by the relation (see equation 3.47)

$$c_v = c_P - \frac{T v \alpha^2}{\kappa_T} \qquad (E.1)$$

To summarize the general characteristics, which are considered subsequently in greater detail, the following behavior is found for most liquids and solids. All four coefficients, α, κ_T, c_v, and c_P, are roughly independent of pressure. The coefficient of thermal expansion α depends on temperature, being zero at zero temperature and generally rising with increasing temperature in both the solid and the liquid phase. The coefficient of isothermal compressibility, κ_T, is very small; it is of the order of 10^{-4}/atm for both liquids and solids. It varies fairly slowly with temperature, but because it is so small it is generally sufficiently accurate merely to consider it as a constant. Finally, c_P for some liquids is almost independent of temperature, but for solids both c_v and c_P depend upon temperature. There is an extensive theory of the temperature dependence of c_v for solids, to be described below.

E.2 Liquids

Before considering the properties of liquids in greater detail, it should be noted that the distinction between gases and liquids is a fairly subtle one. In the vicinity of the *critical temperature* and *critical pressure*, which are defined and discussed in Chapter 9, the distinction vanishes. Nevertheless, at temperatures and pressures far removed from these unique values the distinction is apparent and intuitive. The description of liquids given below is valid only away from the critical temperature and pressure.

We have remarked in the preceding section that α, κ_T, c_v, and c_P are all roughly independent of pressure. The pressure dependence of these quantities is shown in Table E.1 for mercury. It is seen that the specific heat at constant pressure c_P undergoes a negligible change over a pressure range of 7000 atm. The pressure dependence of α and κ_T is somewhat larger, their changes being about 16 and 20 per cent, respectively, over 7000 atm. However in the pressure region of practical interest, say from

Table E.1

Pressure Variation of Properties of Mercury at 0°C

p	v	$10^6\alpha$	$10^{12}\kappa_T$	c_P	c_v
Kg/cm²			cm²/dyne		
(=0.968 atm)	cm³/mole	(°K)$^{-1}$	(=1.013 × 10⁶/atm)	cal/mole °K	cal/mole °K
0	14.72	181	3.88	6.69	5.88
1000	14.67	174	3.79	6.69	5.92
2000	14.62	168	3.66	6.69	5.96
3000	14.57	164	3.60	6.68	5.97
4000	14.51	160	3.48	6.68	5.98
5000	14.45	158	3.38	6.68	5.98
6000	14.42	155	3.25	6.68	5.99
7000	14.38	152	3.12	6.68	5.99

By permission, from *Heat and Thermodynamics*, by M. W. Zemansky, 4th Edition, 1957, McGraw-Hill Book Company, Inc., New York.

0 to 100 atm, the changes are only of the order of 0.4 and 0.24 per cent, respectively. Other liquids show pressure dependences of the same order, so that α, κ_T, c_v, and c_P can be considered as independent of pressure for all practical purposes.

We consider the temperature dependence of α, κ_T, and the specific heats, in turn.

The temperature dependence of α can be represented by a series expansion of the form

$$\alpha = \alpha_0 + 2\alpha_1(T - T_0) + 3\alpha_2(T - T_0)^2 + \cdots \quad (E.2)$$

in which T_0 is some conveniently chosen fiducial temperature. Values of α_0, α_1, and α_2 are given for several common liquids in Table E.2. It may be noted from that table that α is of the order of $10^{-3}/°K$ and that it varies by the order of 10 per cent between 0 and 100°C.

Equation E.2 is equivalent to an expansion of the molar volume in a power series in $T - T_0$ at constant P.

$$v(T, P) = v(T_0, P)[1 + \alpha_0(T - T_0) + \alpha_1(T - T_0)^2$$
$$+ \alpha_2(T - T_0)^3 + \cdots] \quad (E.3)$$

$$= v(T_0, P)[1 + \alpha(T - T_0)] \quad (E.4)$$

The isothermal compressibilities of several liquids are given in Table E.3. It is seen that the isothermal compressibilities are of the order of $10^{-6}/atm$.

Table E.2

TEMPERATURE DEPENDENCE OF COEFFICIENT OF THERMAL
EXPANSION OF LIQUIDS

$$v(T, P) = v_0[1 + \alpha_0 t + \alpha_1 t^2 + \alpha_2 t^3]$$
where $t = T - 273.15°K$ and $v_0 = v(273.15°K, P)$

Liquid	Temperature Range, °C	$10^3\alpha_0$	$10^6\alpha_1$	$10^8\alpha_2$
Acetic Acid	16 to 107	1.0630	0.1264	1.0876
Acetone	0 to 54	1.3240	3.8090	0.8798
Alcohol (methyl)	−38 to 70	1.1856	1.5649	0.9111
Benzene	11 to 81	1.1763	1.2775	0.8065
Carbon disulphide	−34 to 60	1.1398	1.3706	1.9122
Ether	−15 to 38	1.5132	2.3592	4.0051
Glycerine	—	0.4853	0.4895	—
Mercury	24 to 299	0.18182	0.00078	—
Olive oil	—	0.6821	1.1405	−0.539
Phenol	36 to 157	0.8340	0.1073	0.4446
Petroleum (sp. grav. 0.8467)	24 to 120	0.8994	1.396	—
Sulphuric acid	0 to 30	0.5758	0.864	—
Turpentine	−9 to 106	0.9003	1.959	—
Water	0 to 33	−0.0643	8.505	6.790

From *Handbook of Chemistry and Physics*, The Chemical Rubber Publishing Company, Cleveland, Ohio.

Table E.3

ISOTHERMAL COMPRESSIBILITY OF LIQUIDS (AT 0°C)

	Pressure Range (atm)	$10^5\kappa_T$ (atmospheres^{-1})
Acetone	1 to 500	8.2
Carbon disulphide	1 to 500	6.6
Chloroform	—	10.1
Ethyl Alcohol	1 to 50	9.6
Methyl Alcohol	1 to 500	7.94
Water	1 to 25	5.25
	25 to 50	5.16
	100 to 200	4.92

From *Handbook of Chemistry and Physics*, The Chemical Rubber Publishing Company, Cleveland, Ohio.

If the fiducial pressure is chosen as zero, we can expand $v(T, P)$ as a double power series in $(T - T_0)$ and P, around $v(T_0, 0)$.

$$v(T, P) = v(T_0, 0) + \left(\frac{\partial v}{\partial T}\right)_0 (T - T_0) + \frac{1}{2}\left(\frac{\partial^2 v}{\partial T^2}\right)_0 (T - T_0)^2$$
$$+ \cdots + \left(\frac{\partial v}{\partial P}\right)_0 P + \cdots \quad (E.5)$$

The terms involving powers of $T - T_0$ are precisely the terms in equation E.3 or E.4, so that

$$v(T, P) = v(T_0, 0)[1 + \alpha(T - T_0) - \kappa_T P] \quad (E.6)$$

The term $\kappa_T P$ represents only a 1 per cent correction even for pressures of 100 atm. Hence only the constant term in κ_T need be kept, and κ_T can be considered as a constant for most practical purposes.

We finally turn our attention to the temperature dependence of the specific heats of liquids. c_P is given for various liquids and at several temperatures in Table E.4. For many liquids c_P is almost independent of temperature, as for water and mercury. However the variation of c_P with T is not always negligible, as illustrated by benzene, ether, and glycerine. One can say only that in *some* liquids c_P is roughly constant.

The temperature dependence of c_v is related to that of c_P by equation E.1. Even for those liquids with constant c_P there consequently is a temperature dependence of c_v.

Table E.4

SPECIFIC HEATS AT CONSTANT PRESSURE OF LIQUIDS

Liquid	Temperature (°C)	c_P ("15° cal"/gram °K)
Acetic acid	0	0.468
Acetone	0	0.506
Alcohol (ethyl)	0	0.535
	25	0.581
Alcohol (methyl)	0	0.566
	20	0.600
Benzene	5	0.389
	20	0.406
	60	0.444
	90	0.473

Table E.4—*continued*

Liquid	Temperature (°C)	c_P ("15° cal"/gram °K)
Ether	−50	0.517
	0	0.529
	30	0.547
	120	0.803
	180	1.041
Glycerine	0	0.540
	50	0.600
	100	0.669
Mercury	0	0.03346
	20	0.03325
	40	0.03308
	60	0.03294
	80	0.03284
	100	0.03269
	150	0.0324
	190	0.0320
Olive oil	6.6	0.471
Phenol	14 to 26	0.561
Petroleum	21 to 58	0.511
Sulphuric acid	10	0.339
Turpentine	0	0.411
Water	0	1.00874
	15	1.00000
	20	0.99859
	40	0.99761
	60	0.99934
	80	1.00239
	100	1.00645
	150	1.0240
	200	1.0439

From *Handbook of Chemistry and Physics*, The Chemical Rubber Publishing Company, Cleveland, Ohio.

E.3   Effect of Changing Pressure

The fact that α, κ_T, c_v, and c_P are all nearly independent of pressure simplifies calculations of the effect of pressure changes. Consider, as an example, the heat absorbed by a system in a process in which the pressure is increased to maintain the temperature constant. We have

$$\Delta Q = T \int dS = T \int_{P_i}^{P_f} \left(\frac{\partial S}{\partial P} \right)_T dP \tag{E.7}$$

and, by equation 3.50, this becomes

$$\Delta Q = -TV \int_{P_i}^{P_f} \alpha \, dP \tag{E.8}$$

Now, for a liquid system α is almost independent of pressure, so that it can be taken out of the integral to give

$$\Delta Q = -TV\alpha \, \Delta P \tag{E.9}$$

Even if α varies slightly with pressure, equation E.9 is approximately valid if the value of α inserted is the average value in the pressure range ΔP.

By referring to Table E.1, we find that for mercury the heat absorbed when a pressure of 1000 atm is applied at a temperature of $0°C$ is

$$\frac{\Delta Q}{V} = -T\alpha_{\text{average}} \, \Delta P = -273.15 \times \frac{181 + 174}{2}$$

$$\times 10^{-6} \times 10^3 = -48.5 \, \text{atm} = -1.17 \, \text{cal/cm}^3 \tag{E.10}$$

The negative sign, of course, means that the heat is emitted.

Similarly, the work done *on* the mercury in the process is

$$\Delta W = -\int P \, dV = -\int P \left(\frac{\partial V}{\partial P} \right)_T dP = +\int PV\kappa_T \, dP \tag{E.11}$$

But from equation E.6 we have

$$V(T, P) = V(T, 0)(1 - \kappa_T P) \tag{E.12}$$

whence

$$\frac{\Delta W}{V} = +\kappa_T \int_{P_i}^{P_f} (1 - \kappa_T P) P \, dP \tag{E.13}$$

$$= +0.044 \, \text{cal/cm}^3 \tag{E.14}$$

It will be noted that the second term in equation E.13 is negligible, so that we could merely have taken V out of the integral in equation E.11, rather than having used equation E.12.

The fact that so small an amount of work is done on the mercury is, of course, due to the small change in volume, which makes $P \, dV$ correspondingly small. The relatively large amount of heat liberated is obviously supplied by the internal energy of the mercury.

Problems—Section E.3

E.3–1. Find the change in temperature of 1 cm³ of mercury if a pressure of
10^3 atm is applied isentropically.

Hint: To transform the integrand write

$$\left(\frac{\partial T}{\partial P}\right)_S = -\frac{(\partial S/\partial P)_T}{(\partial S/\partial T)_P}$$

and use equation 3.50 for the denominator.

E.4 Simple Solids

In order to discuss the thermodynamics of solids adequately, we should
recognize that solid bodies are capable of shear and uniaxial strain.
Extension of the thermodynamic formalism to include the elastic strain
components is made in Chapter 13. We discuss here the properties of
isotropic solids subject only to a hydrostatic pressure (as contrasted with
uniaxial or shear stresses).

As in liquids, α, κ_T, c_v, and c_P are all roughly independent of pressure.
We consider the temperature dependence of each of these quantities
in turn.

The temperature dependence of α can be represented by a series
expansion such as employed for liquids (equation E.2)

$$\alpha = \alpha_0 + 2\alpha_1(T - T_0) + 3\alpha_2(T - T_0)^2 + \cdots \qquad \text{(E.15)}$$

For many applications the quantity of direct interest is not the coefficient
of volume expansion α but rather the *coefficient of linear expansion* α^L,
defined by

$$\alpha^L = \frac{1}{V^{\frac{1}{3}}}\left(\frac{\partial V^{\frac{1}{3}}}{\partial T}\right)_P \qquad \text{(E.16)}$$

$$= \frac{1}{3}\frac{1}{V}\left(\frac{\partial V}{\partial T}\right)_P = \frac{1}{3}\alpha \qquad \text{(E.17)}$$

Whereas α specifies the fractional increase in volume per unit increase in
temperature, α^L specifies the fractional increase in length per unit increase
in temperature. The linear coefficient α^L is merely one third of the volume
coefficient α.

Equation E.15 can be rewritten (dividing through by 3) as

$$\alpha^L = \alpha_0^L + 2\alpha_1^L(T - T_0) + 3\alpha_2^L(T - T_0)^2 + \cdots \qquad \text{(E.18)}$$

in which

$$\alpha_0^L = \tfrac{1}{3}\alpha_0, \qquad \alpha_1^L = \tfrac{1}{3}\alpha_1, \qquad \alpha_2^L = \tfrac{1}{3}\alpha_2 \qquad \text{(E.19)}$$

Values of α_0^L and α_1^L are given for several common metals in Table

E.5. In Figure E.1 the coefficient of expansion is plotted over a wide temperature range for several metals; it is of interest to note that the larger the normal melting temperature of the metal, the lower its coefficient of thermal expansion. (The normal melting temperature is the temperature at which the metal melts under a pressure of 1 atm.) Finally, it should be noted that although the behavior shown in Figure E.1 is the usual case

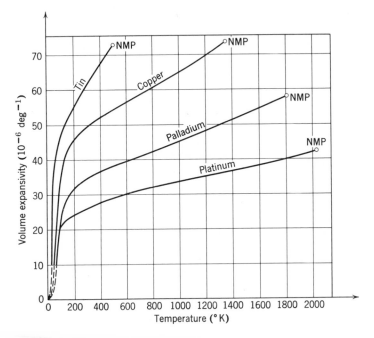

Figure E.1 Temperature dependence of the coefficient of thermal expansion of representative metals. The notation NMP designates the normal melting point. By permission, from *Heat and Thermodynamics*, by M. W. Zemansky, 4th edition, McGraw-Hill Book Company Inc., New York, 1957.

a few solids display an anomalous temperature dependence of α. The most important anomaly is that of ice, shown in Figure E.2.

The value of the isothermal compressibility of solids is generally smaller than of liquids. For most applications it is sufficient to take κ_T as independent of temperature, although it generally rises somewhat with increasing temperature. Thus in copper κ_T rises approximately linearly with temperature in the range 100 to 1300°K, increasing by about 35 per cent over that range. The compressibilities of several metals, at room temperature, are given in Table E.5.

Equation E.6 is applicable to solids as well as to liquids.
Finally, we consider the temperature dependence of the specific heats
of simple solids.

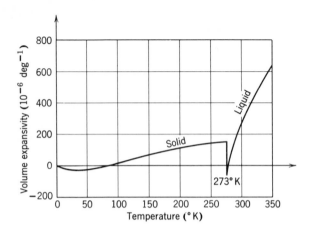

Figure E.2 Temperature dependence of coefficient of thermal expansion
of ice and water at $P = 1$ atm. By permission, from *Heat and Thermodynamics*, by M. W. Zemansky, 4th edition, McGraw-Hill Book Company
Inc., New York, 1957.

Table E.5

LINEAR COEFFICIENT OF THERMAL EXPANSION AND
COMPRESSIBILITY OF METALS

Metal $\alpha^L = \alpha_0{}^L + 2\alpha_1{}^L(T - 273.15°) + \cdots$

Metal	Temperature limits °C	$10^4\alpha_0{}^L$	$10^7\alpha_1{}^L$	$10^7\kappa_T$ (atmospheres^{-1})
Aluminum	10–90	0.2221	0.114	13.0
Brass	10–90	0.1781	0.098	
Copper	10–90	0.1596	0.102	7.0
Gold	10–90	0.1410	0.042	5.6
Iron, pure	0–38	0.1145	0.071	5.7
Lead	10–90	0.2829	0.120	23.0
Nickel	0–38	0.1255	0.057	5.1
Platinum	0–1000	0.0868	0.013	3.5
Silver	10–90	0.1862	0.074	9.6
Tin	10–90	0.2094	0.175	18.2
Zinc	10–90	0.2969	−0.0635	16.4

E.5 Specific Heats of Solids

The specific heat at constant volume of a solid is the sum of an "electronic contribution" and a "lattice contribution." The electronic contribution to c_v is very small in comparison with the lattice contribution, but it is observable at very low temperatures (in the vicinity of $1°K$) because it goes to zero as $T \to 0$ more slowly than the lattice contribution. In this low-temperature region the electronic contribution is simply linear in T.

$$c_v(\text{electronic}) = aT \qquad (\text{E.20})$$

The proportionality constant a is related to the density of conduction electrons in the solid; consequently, it is large for metals and zero for insulators. Values of a are given for several metals in Table E.6.

Table E.6

SPECIFIC HEAT CONSTANTS FOR METALS

Metal	Electronic Specific Heat Constant $a \times 10^4$ (cal/mole °K)	Debye Temperature θ_D (°K)	Gruneisen Constant γ
Al	3.48	419	2.1
Ag	1.54	229	2.2
Cu	1.78	335	1.9
Pt	16.07	233	2.7
Pb	7.15	90	2.3
Mg	42.1	410	—
Sn	4.0	185	1.8

From *Phenomena at the Temperature of Liquid Helium*, Burton, Smith and Wilhelm, Reinhold, New York, 1940.

The lattice contribution to c_v arises from the vibrational energy of the ions in the solid. A great deal of theoretical attention has been given to this contribution, but the most generally useful results are those obtained in 1912 by Debye on the basis of a very simple model. Debye treated the vibrations of a solid as if it were a continuous medium rather than a collection of discrete ions but disregarded all vibrations with wavelengths smaller than the interionic distance. This model gives a contribution to the molar entropy of the form

$$s(\text{lattice}) = 3nR\left\{\frac{4}{3}D\left(\frac{\theta_D}{T}\right) - \ln\left[1 - e^{-\theta_D/T}\right]\right\} \qquad (\text{E.21})$$

in which R is the gas constant, n is the number of ions per molecule, θ_D is a function of the volume but not of the temperature, and $D(\theta_D/T)$ is the *Debye function*, defined by

$$D(x) \equiv \frac{3}{x^2} \int_0^x \frac{y^2 \, dy}{e^y - 1} \qquad (E.22)$$

The *Debye temperature* θ_D at the normal molar volume is related to the elastic constants of the solid or to the velocity of sound in the solid. It is largest for hard solids with light ions or for solids with high melting temperatures and light ions. Lindemann has shown that for most solids θ_D is approximately given by

$$\theta_D(^\circ K) \simeq \frac{200}{v^{1/3}} \left(\frac{T_m}{M}\right)^{1/2} \qquad (E.23)$$

in which v is the molar volume (cm^3/mole), T_m the melting temperature ($^\circ$K), and M the molar mass (gram/mole). Values of θ_D are given for several metals in Table E.6.

The lattice contribution to the entropy s(lattice) implies a lattice contribution to the specific heat, which is

$$c_v(\text{lattice}) = T\left(\frac{\partial s}{\partial T}\right)_{\theta_D} = 3nR\left[4D\left(\frac{\theta_D}{T}\right) - \frac{3\theta_D/T}{e^{\theta_D/T} - 1}\right] \qquad (E.24)$$

This contribution to the specific heat is plotted in Figure E.3. At low temperatures a series expansion in T/θ_D gives

$$c_v(\text{lattice}) = 3nR\left[\frac{4}{5}\pi^4\left(\frac{T}{\theta_D}\right)^3 + \cdots\right] \qquad (E.25)$$

$$= 464.4n\left(\frac{T}{\theta_D}\right)^3 + \cdots [\text{cal}/(^\circ K)^3] \qquad (E.26)$$

At high temperature a series expansion in θ_D/T gives

$$c_v(\text{lattice}) = 3nR\left[1 - \frac{1}{20}\left(\frac{\theta_D}{T}\right)^2 + \frac{1}{560}\left(\frac{\theta_D}{T}\right)^4 + \cdots\right] \qquad (E.27)$$

At low temperatures the lattice contribution to the specific heat goes to zero as T^3. At high temperature it asymptotes to the "Dulong Petit" value of $3nR$; 6 cal/mole for monatomic solids such as the metals, 12 cal/mole for diatomic solids such as NaCl, 18 cal/mole for quartz (SiO$_2$), etc.

The Debye temperature θ_D is a function of the volume with a functional dependence that has not yet been specified. The Lindemann equation E.23 merely correlates the value of θ_D for the normal value of the molar volume v, with other properties, but it gives no indication of the manner in which θ_D varies when v changes. On the basis of empirical data, Gruneisen has suggested that

$$\theta_D = \text{constant } v^{-\gamma} \qquad (E.28)$$

where γ is the *Gruneisen constant*. The value of γ is given for several metals in Table E.6.

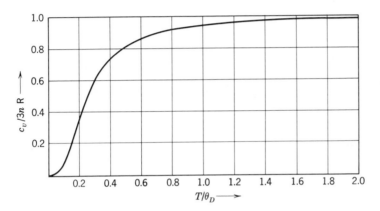

Figure E.3 The Debye specific heat.

Equation E.28 implies a relationship that is in a particularly convenient form for comparison with experiment. Consider the derivative

$$\left(\frac{\partial P}{\partial T}\right)_v = -\frac{(\partial v/\partial T)_P}{(\partial v/\partial P)_T} = \frac{\alpha}{\kappa_T} \qquad (E.29)$$

We can also write this derivative as

$$\left(\frac{\partial P}{\partial T}\right)_v = \left(\frac{\partial s}{\partial v}\right)_T \qquad (E.30)$$

as proved in Chapter 6. To differentiate s with respect to v, we note from equation E.21 that s is a function of θ_D/T only whence

$$\frac{\alpha}{\kappa_T} = \left(\frac{\partial s}{\partial v}\right)_T = \frac{\partial s}{\partial(\theta_D/T)}\frac{\partial(\theta_D/T)}{\partial v} = \left(-\frac{T^2}{\theta_D}\frac{\partial s}{\partial T}\right)\left(\frac{1}{T}\frac{\partial \theta_D}{\partial v}\right) \qquad (E.31)$$

and

$$\frac{\alpha}{\kappa_T} = \frac{\gamma c_v \theta_D}{v} \qquad (E.32)$$

In deriving this relation, we have assumed implicitly that the lattice contribution to the entropy and to the specific heat is the only contribution; in fact it is the dominant contribution, except at very low or very high temperatures.

If the Gruneisen equation were correct, we would conclude that $\alpha v/c_v \kappa_T$ would be constant as the temperature is changed. It was on the basis of the observed approximate constancy of this quantity that Gruneisen was led to postulate equation E.28.

Several Common
Cyclic Processes

Many cycles, other than the Carnot cycle, are of great practical importance. None of these cycles has the theoretical simplicity of the Carnot cycle. Nevertheless, they are of some interest as representatives of practical engines or refrigerators, and we consequently describe several of these cycles very briefly.

F.1 The Otto Cycle

The *Otto cycle* is a rough approximation to the operation of a gasoline engine. The cycle is shown in Figure F.1 in a V–S diagram. The gas is compressed adiabatically in the step $A \to B$. It is then heated isochorically (i.e., at constant volume) in $B \to C$; this step corresponds to the combustion of the gasoline in the gasoline engine. The gas is then expanded

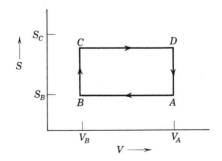

Figure F.1 The Otto cycle.

357

adiabatically; this is the power stroke. Finally, the gas is cooled isochorically to bring it from D to the initial state A.

In the gasoline engine the gas, when brought to D, is not returned to A nor taken around the cycle a second time. Instead, it is ejected from the cylinder and a fresh charge of air and gasoline vapor are taken in. The process $D \rightarrow A$ occurs outside the cylinder and a fresh sample of gas participates in the succeeding cycle. Finally, we remark that the compression stroke of the piston in a gasoline engine is very far indeed from quasi-static and isentropic, so that the Otto cycle is only a qualitative representation of the real engine.

Unlike the Carnot cycle, the heat absorption in step $B \rightarrow C$ of the Otto cycle does not occur at constant temperature. Nor does the heat ejection in step $D \rightarrow A$ occur at constant temperature. The ideal thermodynamic engine efficiency applies to each infinitesimal portion of the Otto cycle, but the over-all efficiency must be computed by integrating this ideal efficiency over the changing temperatures. The over-all efficiency therefore depends upon the specific way in which the temperature changes during the isentropic steps; hence it depends upon the particular properties of the gas used. It is left to the reader to show that for an ideal gas, with temperature-independent heat capacities, the Otto cycle efficiency is

$$\epsilon_e = 1 - \left(\frac{V_B}{V_A}\right)^{(c_P - c_v)/c_v} \tag{F.1}$$

The ratio V_A/V_B is called the compression ratio of the engine.

F.2 The Brayton or Joule Cycle

The *Brayton or Joule cycle* consists of two isentropic and two isobaric steps. It is shown on a P–S diagram in Figure F.2. In a working engine air (and fuel) is compressed adiabatically ($A \rightarrow B$), heated by fuel

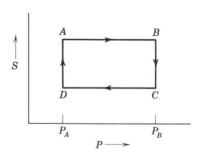

Figure F.2 The Brayton or Joule cycle.

combustion at constant pressure $(B \rightarrow C)$, expanded $(C \rightarrow D)$, and rejected to the atmosphere. The process $D \rightarrow A$ occurs outside the engine, and a fresh charge of air is taken in to repeat the cycle. If the working gas is an ideal gas, with temperature-independent heat capacities, the efficiency of a Brayton cycle is

$$\epsilon_e = 1 - \left(\frac{P_A}{P_B}\right)^{(c_P - c_v)/c_P} \tag{F.2}$$

F.3   The Air-Standard Diesel Cycle

The *air-standard diesel cycle* consists of two isentropic processes, alternating with isochoric and isobaric steps. The cycle is represented in Figure F.3. After compression of the air and fuel mixture $(A \rightarrow B)$, the

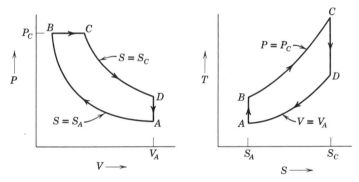

Figure F.3   The air-standard diesel cycle.

fuel combustion occurs at constant pressure $(B \rightarrow C)$. The gas is adiabatically expanded $(C \rightarrow D)$ and then cooled at constant volumes $(D \rightarrow A)$.

Many other cycles find practical applications in various engine and refrigerator designs and are described in texts of engineering thermodynamics.

Problems—Appendix F

F.1   Assuming that the working gas is a monatomic ideal gas, with a fundamental equation as given in section 3.4, plot a T–S diagram for the Otto cycle.

F.2   Assuming that the working gas is an ideal gas, with temperature-independent heat capacities, show that the engine efficiency of the Otto cycle is given by equation F.1.

F.3 Assuming that the working gas is an ideal gas, with temperature-independent heat capacities, show that the engine efficiency of the Brayton cycle is given by equation F.2.

F.4 Assuming that the working gas is a monatomic ideal gas, plot a T–S diagram of the Brayton cycle.

F.5 Assuming that the working gas is a monatomic ideal gas, plot a T–S diagram of the air-standard diesel cycle.

Matrices
and the Stability
Quadratic Form

As remarked in the last paragraph of section 8.4, the analysis of quadratic forms can be recast in terms of an algebra of associated matrices. We describe here the relationship between the matrix algebra and the theory of stability developed in section 8.4.

We return temporarily to a single-component system and to the requirement that the following homogeneous quadratic form be positive-definite.

$$d^2u = \tfrac{1}{2}[u_{ss}(ds)^2 + 2u_{sv}\,ds\,dv + u_{vv}(dv)^2] \tag{G.1}$$

The properties of this quadratic form are determined completely by the three coefficients u_{ss}, u_{sv}, u_{vv}. These coefficients are called the *stiffness moduli*, and they can be considered as elements of a *stiffness matrix:*

$$\begin{bmatrix} u_{ss} & u_{vs} \\ u_{sv} & u_{vv} \end{bmatrix} = \begin{bmatrix} \dfrac{\partial T}{\partial s} & \dfrac{\partial T}{\partial v} \\ \dfrac{d(-P)}{ds} & \dfrac{\partial(-P)}{\partial v} \end{bmatrix} = \begin{bmatrix} T/c_v & \dfrac{T\alpha}{\kappa_T c_v} \\ T\alpha & c_P \\ \dfrac{}{\kappa_T c_v} & v\kappa_T c_v \end{bmatrix} \tag{G.2}$$

The stiffness moduli relate the "forces" dT and $d(-P)$ to the "displacements" ds and dv by the linear equations

$$dT = u_{ss}\,ds + u_{vs}\,dv \tag{G.3}$$

and

$$d(-P) = u_{sv}\,ds + u_{vv}\,dv \tag{G.4}$$

If $\begin{bmatrix} ds \\ dv \end{bmatrix}$ is a column "vector," with components ds and dv, and if $[dT, d(-P)]$ is a row "vector," with components dT and $d(-P)$, then equations G.3 and G.4 can be written in conventional matrix form:

$$[dT, d(-P)] = \begin{bmatrix} u_{ss} & u_{sv} \\ u_{sv} & u_{vv} \end{bmatrix} \cdot \begin{bmatrix} ds \\ dv \end{bmatrix} \tag{G.5}$$

The term "stiffness" moduli arises from the analogy of the foregoing equations to the equations of elasticity.

Although the variables ds and dv play the role of independent variables in equation G.5 and dT and $d(-P)$ play the role of dependent variables, these roles can be interchanged. If equation G.5 (or equations G.3 and G.4) is partially inverted to solve for $-ds$ and $d(-P)$ in terms of dT and dv, we obtain

$$[-ds, d(-P)] = \begin{bmatrix} f_{TT} & f_{vT} \\ f_{Tv} & f_{vv} \end{bmatrix} \cdot \begin{bmatrix} dT \\ dv \end{bmatrix} \tag{G.6}$$

in which

$$\begin{bmatrix} f_{TT} & f_{vT} \\ f_{Tv} & f_{vv} \end{bmatrix} = \begin{bmatrix} -1/u_{ss} & \dfrac{u_{sv}}{u_{ss}} \\ \dfrac{u_{sv}}{u_{ss}} & \dfrac{u_{ss}u_{vv} - u_{sv}^2}{u_{ss}} \end{bmatrix} \tag{G.7}$$

$$= \begin{bmatrix} -\left(\dfrac{\partial s}{\partial T}\right)_v & -\left(\dfrac{\partial s}{\partial v}\right)_T \\ -\left(\dfrac{\partial P}{\partial T}\right)_v & -\left(\dfrac{\partial P}{\partial v}\right)_T \end{bmatrix} = \begin{bmatrix} -c_{v/T} & -\alpha/\kappa_T \\ -\dfrac{\alpha}{\kappa_T} & \dfrac{1}{v\kappa_T} \end{bmatrix} \tag{G.8}$$

It is evident from equation G.8 that

$$f_{TT} = \frac{\partial^2 f}{\partial T^2}, \quad f_{vT} = f_{Tv} = \frac{\partial^2 f}{\partial T\, \partial v}, \quad f_{vv} = \frac{\partial^2 f}{\partial v^2} \tag{G.9}$$

in which f is the molar Helmholtz potential, F/N.

If equation G.5 is partially inverted to solve for dT and $-dv$ in terms of ds and $d(-P)$, we obtain in a precisely similar manner

$$[dT, -dv] = \begin{bmatrix} h_{ss} & h_{Ps} \\ h_{sP} & h_{PP} \end{bmatrix} \cdot \begin{bmatrix} ds \\ d(-P) \end{bmatrix} \tag{G.10}$$

in which

$$
\begin{bmatrix} h_{ss} & h_{Ps} \\ h_{sP} & h_{PP} \end{bmatrix} = \begin{bmatrix} \dfrac{u_{ss}u_{vv} - u_{sv}^2}{u_{vv}} & -\dfrac{u_{sv}}{u_{vv}} \\[2ex] -\dfrac{u_{sv}}{u_{vv}} & -\dfrac{1}{u_{vv}} \end{bmatrix} \tag{G.11}
$$

$$
= \begin{bmatrix} \dfrac{\partial T}{\partial s} & \dfrac{\partial T}{\partial P} \\[2ex] \dfrac{\partial v}{\partial s} & \dfrac{\partial v}{\partial P} \end{bmatrix} = \begin{bmatrix} T/c_P & T\dfrac{v\alpha}{c_P} \\[2ex] T\dfrac{v\alpha}{c_P} & -\dfrac{v\kappa_T c_v}{c_P} \end{bmatrix} \tag{G.12}
$$

And it is evident from equation G.12 that

$$
h_{ss} = \frac{\partial^2 h}{\partial s^2}, \qquad h_{Ps} = h_{sP} = \frac{\partial^2 h}{\partial P\,\partial s}, \qquad h_{PP} = \frac{\partial^2 h}{\partial P^2} \tag{G.13}
$$

in which h is the molar enthalpy.

Finally, we consider the complete inversion of equation G.5, solving for $-ds$ and $-dv$ in terms of dT and $d(-P)$.

$$
[-ds, -dv] = \begin{bmatrix} g_{TT} & g_{PT} \\ g_{TP} & g_{PP} \end{bmatrix} \cdot \begin{bmatrix} dT \\ d(-P) \end{bmatrix} \tag{G.14}
$$

This inversion is possible only if the determinant of the stiffness moduli

$$
D = u_{ss}u_{vv} - u_{sv}^2 = \begin{vmatrix} u_{ss} & u_{vs} \\ u_{sv} & u_{vv} \end{vmatrix} \tag{G.15}
$$

is nonzero.

The matrix in equation G.14 satisfies the following relations:

$$
\begin{bmatrix} g_{TT} & g_{PT} \\ g_{TP} & g_{PP} \end{bmatrix} = \begin{bmatrix} \dfrac{u_{vv}}{D} & -\dfrac{u_{sv}}{D} \\[2ex] -\dfrac{u_{sv}}{D} & \dfrac{u_{vv}}{D} \end{bmatrix} \tag{G.16}
$$

$$
= \begin{bmatrix} -\left(\dfrac{\partial s}{\partial T}\right)_P & \left(\dfrac{\partial s}{\partial P}\right)_T \\[2ex] -\left(\dfrac{\partial v}{\partial T}\right)_P & \left(\dfrac{\partial v}{\partial P}\right)_T \end{bmatrix} = \begin{bmatrix} c_{P/T} & \alpha \\ \alpha & v\kappa_T \end{bmatrix} \tag{G.17}
$$

and

$$g_{TT} = \frac{\partial^2 g}{\partial T^2}, \quad g_{PT} = g_{TP} = \frac{\partial^2 g}{\partial P\, \partial T}, \quad g_{PP} = \frac{\partial^2 g}{\partial P^2} \quad \text{(G.18)}$$

in which g is the molar Gibbs potential G/N. The fully inverted matrix in equation G.14 is called the *compliance matrix*, and the matrix elements are called *compliance coefficients*.

The general result is clear. If equation G.15 is partially inverted, so that the variables that appear on the right are the natural variables of some thermodynamic potential, the associated matrix elements are the second derivatives of that potential.

It is a straightforward matter to write the general counterparts of the foregoing equations. Consider the quadratic form

$$d^2 u = \frac{1}{2} \sum_0^{t-1} u_{jk}\, dx_j\, dx_k \quad \text{(G.19)}$$

The stiffness matrix is

$$
\begin{bmatrix}
u_{00} & u_{10} & u_{20} \cdots & u_{t-1,0} \\
u_{01} & & & \cdots \\
\cdot & & & \cdot \\
\cdot & & & \cdot \\
\cdot & & & \cdot \\
u_{0,t-1} & & & u_{t-1,t-1}
\end{bmatrix}
=
\begin{bmatrix}
\dfrac{\partial P_0}{\partial x_0} & \dfrac{\partial P_0}{\partial x_1} \cdots & \dfrac{\partial P_0}{\partial x_{t-1}} \\[2mm]
\dfrac{\partial P_1}{\partial x_0} & & \cdots \\[2mm]
\cdot & & \cdot \\
\cdot & & \cdot \\
\cdot & & \cdot \\
\dfrac{\partial P_{t-1}}{\partial x_0} & & \dfrac{\partial P_{t-1}}{\partial x_{t-1}}
\end{bmatrix}
\quad \text{(G.20)}
$$

The stiffness matrix relates the "force vector" to the "displacement vector."

$$
[dP_0, dP_1 \cdots dP_{t-1}] =
\begin{bmatrix}
u_{00} & u_{10} \cdots \\
u_{10} & \\
\cdot & \\
\cdot & \\
\cdot &
\end{bmatrix}
\begin{bmatrix}
dx_0 \\
dx_1 \\
\cdot \\
\cdot \\
dx_{t-1}
\end{bmatrix}
\quad \text{(G.21)}
$$

The foregoing equation can be partially inverted. We consider the inversion in which the first s forces are made independent variables in place of the corresponding s displacements.

$$[-dx_0, -dx_1 \cdots -dx_{s-1} \cdots dP_{t-1}] = \begin{bmatrix} \psi_{00}^{s-1} & \psi_{10}^{s-1} \cdots \\ & \psi_{01}^{s-1} \\ & \cdot \\ & \cdot \\ & \cdot \\ & \cdot \\ & \cdot \\ & \cdot \\ & \cdot \end{bmatrix} \begin{bmatrix} dP_0 \\ dP_1 \\ \cdot \\ \cdot \\ dP_{s-1} \\ dx_s \\ \cdot \\ \cdot \\ dx_{t-1} \end{bmatrix} \quad (G.22)$$

The matrix element ψ_{jk}^{s-1} is

$$\psi_{jk}^{s-1} = \begin{cases} \dfrac{\partial^2 \psi^{s-1}}{\partial P_j\, \partial P_k} = -\dfrac{\partial x_k}{\partial P_j} = -\dfrac{\partial x_j}{\partial P_k} & \text{if} \quad j < s \quad \text{and} \quad k < s \\[2ex] \dfrac{\partial^2 \psi^{s-1}}{\partial P_j\, \partial x_k} = \dfrac{\partial P_k}{\partial P_j} = -\dfrac{\partial x_j}{\partial x_k} & \text{if} \quad j < s \quad \text{and} \quad k \geqslant s \\[2ex] \dfrac{\partial^2 \psi^{s-1}}{\partial x_j\, \partial x_k} = \dfrac{\partial P_j}{\partial x_k} = \dfrac{\partial P_k}{\partial x_j} & \text{if} \quad j \geqslant s \quad \text{and} \quad k \geqslant s \quad (G.23) \end{cases}$$

in which ψ^{s-1} is the Legendre transform of u with respect to $P_0, P_1 \cdots P_{s-1}$:

$$\psi^{s-1} = u - \sum_0^{s-1} P_k x_k \quad (G.24)$$

The matrix elements ψ_{jk}^{s-1} can be written in terms of the matrix elements u_{jk} by straightforward algebraic manipulation, inverting equation G.21 to the form G.22. We consider one particular matrix element; the element ψ_{ss}^{s-1}. From equation G.23 we note that this element is $(\partial P_s/\partial x_s)_{P_0 \cdots P_{s-1}, x_{s+1} \cdots x_{t-1}}$. We therefore put $dP_0 = dP_1 = \cdots = dP_{s-1} = x_{s+1} \cdots = dx_{t-1} = 0$ in equation G.21, and we write out the first $s + 1$ equations explicitly.

$$0 = u_{00}\, dx_0 + u_{10}\, dx_1 + \cdots + u_{s0}\, dx_s$$
$$0 = u_{01}\, dx_0 + u_{11}\, dx_1 + \cdots + u_{s1}\, dx_s$$
$$0 = u_{0,s-1}\, dx_0 + u_{1,s-1}\, dx_1 + \cdots + u_{s,s-1}\, dx_s \qquad (G.25)$$
$$dP_s = u_{0s}\, dx_0 + \qquad\qquad\quad + u_{ss}\, dx_s$$

Solving this set of equations for dx_s gives

$$dx_s = \frac{D_{s-1}}{D_s} dP_s \qquad (dP_0 = \cdots = dP_{s-1} = dx_{s+1} = \cdots = dx_{t-1} = 0)$$

(G.26)

or

$$\psi_{ss}^{s-1} = \frac{D_s}{D_{s-1}}$$

(G.27)

The notation D_k stands for the principal minor of the stiffness matrix, with $k + 1$ rows and columns:

$$D_k = \begin{vmatrix} u_{00} & u_{10} \cdots u_{1k} \\ u_{01} & \cdot \\ \cdot & \cdot \\ \cdot & \cdot \\ \cdot & \cdot \\ u_{0k} & u_{kk} \end{vmatrix}$$

(G.28)

The stability criteria (equation 8.68) are

$$\psi_{ss}^{s-1} > 0 \qquad \text{for all } s$$

(G.29)

so that, in terms of the principal minors of the stiffness matrix,

$$D_s > 0 \qquad \text{for all } s$$

(G.30)

Actually the condition that all the principal minors of a matrix be positive in order that the matrix correspond to a positive definite form is a standard algebraic theorem. Had we invoked that theorem, equation G.30 would have implied equation G.29, providing an alternative proof of our stability criteria.

Finally we note that

$$\psi_{11}^0 \psi_{22}^1 \psi_{33}^2 \cdots \psi_{tt}^{t-1} = \frac{D_1}{1} \frac{D_2}{D_1} \frac{D_3}{D_2} \cdots \frac{D_{t-1}}{D_{t-z}} \frac{D_t}{D_{t-1}} = D$$

(G.31)

in which $D_t \equiv D$ is the determinant of the full stiffness matrix. That is, the product of all the coefficients in equation 8.66 (or, rather, of their reciprocals) is equal to the determinant of the stiffness matrix. Since each of the coefficients must be positive and nonzero for a stable system, the determinant D must also be positive and nonzero.

Bibliography of General References

General Texts

P. S. Epstein, *Textbook of Thermodynamics*, Wiley, 1937.
An excellent textbook on the physical principles of classical thermodynamics.

J. W. Gibbs, *The Collected Works of J. Willard Gibbs*, Volume I, Thermodynamics, Yale University Press, 1948.
This is the great pioneering work in thermodynamics. Gibbs not only invented modern thermodynamics but succeeded in the incredible feat of anticipating, explicitly or implicitly, almost every subsequent development. His exposition is not known for its clarity.

E. A. Guggenheim, *Thermodynamics*, North Holland Publishing Company, 1949.
An authoritative treatment of contemporary physical and physical-chemical aspects of thermodynamics.

A. B. Pippard, *The Elements of Classical Thermodynamics*, Cambridge University Press, 1957.
An outstanding book, strongly oriented to principles rather than to applications. Emphasizes physical rather than chemical or engineering aspects.

M. W. Zemansky, *Heat and Thermodynamics*, McGraw-Hill, 1951.
This is the classical introductory text in English. It contains full and excellent treatments of thermometry, physical and engineering applications, and a wealth of references to thermodynamic properties of many specific systems and materials.

The Historical Development of Thermodynamics

S. C. Brown, "The Caloric Theory of Heat", *Am. J. Phys.* **18**, 367 (1950).
P. S. Epstein, *Textbook of Thermodynamics*, Wiley, 1937. (Section 11).
D. Roller, *The Early Development of the Concepts of Temperature and Heat*, Harvard University Press, 1950.

Temperature Standards and Scales

H. C. Wolfe, *Temperature, Its Measurement and Control in Science and Industry*, Volume 2, Reinhold, 1955.
Consists of the papers presented at the Third Symposium on Temperature, Washington D.C., October 1954, and contains several papers on temperature scales.

R. E. Wilson and R. D. Arnold, "Thermometry and Pyrometry," Chapter 5.3 in *Handbook of Physics*, edited by Condon and Odishaw, McGraw-Hill, 1958.
A convenient brief summary.

The Use of Jacobians and Other Schemes of Formula Reduction

N. Shaw, *Phil. Trans. Roy. Soc. London*, **Ser. A, 234,** 299 (1935).
Describes use of Jacobians.

D. E. Christie, *Am. J. Phys.* **25,** 486 (1957).
Contains several alternative forms of the mnemonic square and various references.

The Principle of Le Châtelier–Braun

L. Landau and E. Lifshitz, *Statistical Physics*, Oxford University Press, 1938, First Edition, Section 37.

Critical Points and Second-Order Phase Transitions

L. Tisza, "On the General Theory of Phase Transitions", Chapter 1 in *Phase Transformations in Solids*, edited by Smoluchowski, Mayer, and Weyl, Wiley, 1951.

O. K. Rice, *Critical Phenomena of Thermodynamics and Physics of Matter*, Princeton University Press, 1955.

The Nernst Postulate

W. Nernst, *Die theoretischen und experimentellen Grundlagen des Neuen Wärmetheorems*, Knappe, Halle, 1918.

M. Planck, *Treatise on Thermodynamics*, Dover, 1945.
This is a translation from the seventh German edition.

The "Unattainability of Zero Temperature"

E. A. Guggenheim, *Thermodynamics*, North Holland Publishing Company, 1949. Section 4.68.

Chemical Thermodynamics

K. G. Denbigh, *Principles of Chemical Equilibrium*, Cambridge University Press, 1955.

F. W. MacDougall, *Thermodynamics and Chemistry*, Wiley, 1939.

I. Prigogine and R. Defay, *Chemical Thermodynamics*, Longmans, 1954.

Elasticity

A. E. H. Love, *Mathematical Theory of Elasticity*, Dover, 1944.
This is probably the most widely known text on elasticity theory.

I. S. Sokolnikoff, *Mathematical Theory of Elasticity*, McGraw-Hill, 1956.

T. W. Ting and J. C. M. Li, *Phys. Rev.* **106,** 1165 (1957).
A collection of thermodynamic formulas and a description of Jacobian methods.

Magnetism

L. F. Bates, *Modern Magnetism*, Cambridge University Press, 1939.
R. M. Bozorth, *Ferromagnetism*, Van Nostrand, 1951.

Thermodynamic Fluctuations

A. Einstein, *Ann. phys.* 33, 1275 (1910).
R. F. Greene and H. B. Callen, *Phys. Rev.* 83, 1231 (1951).

Irreversible Thermodynamics

S. R. DeGroot, *Thermodynamics of Irreversible Processes*, North Holland Publishing Company, 1951.
A compendium and critique of applications of the Onsager reciprocity theorem.
I. Prigogine, *Introduction to Thermodynamics of Irreversible Processes*, M. Thomas, 1955.
An elementary treatment of the principles of the Onsager theorem and of the principle of minimum dissipation of entropy.

Thermoelectric and Thermomagnetic Effects

Lord Kelvin (Sir. W. Thomson), *Collected Papers I*, pp. 232–291, Cambridge, 1882.
The original discussion of the thermoelectric effects. This paper is particularly interesting for the clarity of Kelvin's understanding of the lack of rigor in his suggestive argument; a caution abandoned by his scientific heirs for almost a full century.
H. B. Callen, *Phys. Rev.* 73, 1349 (1948); also "Electrochemical Constants," National Bureau of Standards circular 524, August 1953.
P. Mazur and I. Prigogine, *J. phys. radium* 12, 616 (1951).
S. R. DeGroot, *Thermodynamics of Irreversible Processes*, North Holland Publishing Company, 1951.

Index